GET OFF THE DIET-GO-ROUND. GET ON WITH YOUR L...

START WHERE YOU ARE WEIGHT LOSS

SHELLI JOHNSON

START WHERE YOU ARE WEIGHT LOSS

For information:
startwhereyouareweightloss.com

Copyright Notice and Disclaimers

Author photo Copyright © 2019 Charisma Howard, A Brew & You

Cover and book design by Alpha Doll Media, LLC

First Paperback Print Edition

Published by Alpha Doll Media, LLC (the "Publisher").

ISBN: 978-1-948103-81-7

Also available now

SELF-HELP BOOKS

Start Where You Are Weight Loss Playbook
Start Where You Are Weight Loss Manifesto
Start Where You Are Weight Loss Freedom Commandments
Baby Step Your Way to a Life You Love: Encourage Yourself
Baby Step Your Way to a Life You Love: Forgive Yourself
Baby Step Your Way to a Life You Love: Heal Your Burned-Out Self
Baby Step Your Way to a Life You Love: Overcome Fear
Baby Step Your Way to a Life You Love: Crush Self-Doubt
Baby Step Your Way to a Life You Love: Get Out of Your Own Way
Baby Step Your Way to a Life You Love: Become Yourself
Baby Step Your Way to a Life You Love: Let Go

ADULT COLORING BOOKS

Color Your Way to a Life You Love: Encourage Yourself
Color Your Way to a Life You Love: Forgive Yourself
Color Your Way to a Life You Love: Heal Your Burned-Out Self
Color Your Way to a Life You Love: Overcome Fear
Color Your Way to a Life You Love: Crush Self-Doubt
Color Your Way to a Life You Love: Get Out of Your Own Way
Color Your Way to a Life You Love: Become Yourself
Color Your Way to a Life You Love: Let Go

NOVELS

Small as a Mustard Seed

CHILDREN'S BOOKS

Leave Me Alone

Dedication

This book is dedicated to
everyone who has ever thought or
still thinks that it's too late for them . . .

It's not too late. You're still here.
You're still breathing. There's still time.
You can turn this thing around.
So take a deep breath,
pick yourself up,
dust yourself off,
and just start where you are.

Don't Scare or Overwhelm Yourself

I know this book may seem intimidating by its sheer size and by what it's asking you to do. Don't be scared. Don't be overwhelmed. Don't let any anxiety rise in you about how you're going to make it through, how long it may take, how much work (play!) it may be, or anything else regarding this book that you may be anxious about right now.

This book is meant to be read and acted upon slowly over the length of your weight-loss journey. It's not meant to be finished in a week, a month, or even a year. It's going to take some time to get to where you want to be. Take that time to learn some things about yourself with this book. Learn what you really need, what you honestly want, what deeply matters to you. Learn why you abuse food. Learn what you need to do to best take care of yourself so that you can stop the food-abuse cycle and move forward in a straight line to create a body and a life that you love.

Do yourself a kindness and be patient with yourself, especially if you don't feel ready or willing to face this book and its contents right now at this very moment in your life. That's okay. For one, this book will still be here when you are ready for it. (Take heart: I've always been a big believer that books find you when you are ready for them.) And second, you have permission, always, to go as slowly as you need to go so that you don't scare and/or overwhelm yourself.

Every day, you just take a deep breath and start where you are.

Companion Playbook

This book has a companion book, *Start Where You Are Weight Loss Playbook*, which was designed to give you opportunities to answer probing questions, explore your innermost thoughts and feelings, chart your progress and successes, along with other encouraging activities, all in one convenient place. Please note: the companion book is specifically structured as a journal to complement this book. Complete instructions and explanations can be found in this main book, *Start Where You Are Weight Loss*.

Start Where You Are Weight Loss Playbook (ISBN: 978-1-948103-83-1)

Memoir Disclaimer

This book has sections that are memoir. Each of those sections were from separate events in my life that occurred decades ago. The memoir sections are stories from my childhood but do not comprise the whole of my childhood. They are my memories, and I've done my best to make each one honest to what happened as I remember it. Others may remember these events differently than I do, and I recognize that.

It is not my intention to turn any person into a villain nor to hurt any of the people involved. My intent is to show you how I was wounded because all of us, at some point, have been wounded by someone or something. And as you'll come to learn, wounds are a part of the reason you abuse food.

The people involved are no longer the same people they used to be years ago. Neither am I. They learned and grew from those experiences, and because of that, became better people. I did the same. What I've come to learn is that people who have been wounded (especially when they are children) tend to wound others if they don't do something to break the cycle. In the case of my parents, they were both wounded terribly as children and, in turn, wounded me in a similar way. Forgiveness matters, for others and also for yourself. So does realizing that none of us is completely good or completely bad. What matters most is acknowledging that all of us—you, me, everybody—make mistakes.

I did my best to recall events, characteristics, ages, dialogue, among other narrative elements. Some events were compressed and some dialogue was recreated. While the main point is there in each section, I may have gotten some of the details wrong. For this reason, I consider the memoir sections to be works of creative nonfiction. Tobias Wolff once said that "memory has its own story to tell." In that spirit, I've written the story as truthfully to my memory as possible.

Contents

Quotes for the Journey

Life don't often ask your permission first, that's true.
And sometimes you find yourself wandering
around in the dark.

It's real likely that you might stumble across
somebody else's path out there in the dimness.
You might even follow it for a time, trying
to get your bearings, and that's okay.

But in the end, you got find your own path in this world.
Ain't nobody that can do it for you.

Because if you keep on following in somebody else's footsteps,
you ain't ever gonna learn who you are,
you ain't ever gonna learn who you could become.

—Ned Horner

Be Brave: Those Who Are Brave Are Free

It is not the critic who counts; not the man who points out how the strong man stumbles, or where the doer of deeds could have done them better. The credit belongs to the man who is actually in the arena, whose face is marred by dust and sweat and blood; who strives valiantly; who errs, who comes short again and again, because there is no effort without error and shortcoming; but who does actually strive to do the deeds; who knows great enthusiasms, the great devotions; who spends himself in a worthy cause; who at the best knows in the end the triumph of high achievement, and who at the worst, if he fails, at least fails while daring greatly, so that his place shall never be with those cold and timid souls who neither know victory nor defeat.[1]

—Theodore Roosevelt

The meaning of life is to find your gift. The purpose of life is to give it away.

—Pablo Picasso

PREFACE

START WHERE YOU ARE

OR

**All is takes to begin a journey
is a single step
in the direction you want to go.**

Preface

**"The only person you are destined to be is the person you decide to become."
—Ralph Waldo Emerson**

I STAND IN a dark bedroom, leaning against the windowsill. There's a Marlboro pinched between my index and middle fingers, the tip glowing red and smoke curling around my wrist then catching on the breeze and rising above the eaves. It's so quiet, I can hear the soft crackle of the cigarette paper as it burns. The shutters are open and the sky is black satin and the stars click on one by one. Sparkling to take your breath away. Make you believe, even if it's just for a little while.

There is a God.

There is.

Please.

There has to be.

Please.

Wind rushes past and flaps the sheets still hanging on the line. It's late summer and the air is still warm enough for sweat to bloom on my forehead and underneath my arms. It bumps down my back and pools against the elastic of my (big, much too big) underwear. Honeysuckle rides that wind. So does the smell of the neighbor's algae-covered pond and exhaust from a diesel engine. My skin feels tight, stretched, my whole body swelled like a water blister. I take a long pull of the cigarette then hold my breath, feeling the smoke burn in my lungs. I feel numb and sort of safe and not so alone. Nothing can hurt me, not right now. I don't have to be on edge, eyes darting, watching all the angles, muscles taut, ready to bolt. Bats swoop above the driveway, dark shadows against the darkness. Two people walk down the road. I hear them talking, but their voices aren't loud enough to make out what they're saying. I fade back behind the window frame, hiding in the shadows, waiting for them to pass. I take another long drag of that Marlboro as the constellations slowly appear—Orion, The Seven Sisters, The Big Dipper. Follow the two stars at the end of the Dipper's bowl to the North Star. Polaris. Supposed to be able to guide you home. Maybe that's where God is. Ratholed on the North Star. Maybe hiding too.

I don't pray much. I don't know exactly what I'm supposed to do. Get on my knees? Clasp my hands together? Bow my head? Close my eyes? Does God listen better if you do those things? Does God listen at all? The couple has passed by and the night has gone mostly quiet again. I step back into the window and lean against the frame then take another long pull, smoking the cigarette nearly down to the nub. The North Star blazes, the brightest thing in the sky.

"Please," I say to it. "Please make me skinny."

I smack the crumpled pack against the meat of my thumb. The plastic film crinkles as I tap out a fresh cigarette. I light it with the one I'm now smoking. Then I crush the used butt against the windowsill, drop it onto the iron grate in the driveway below, then brush at the ash and soot with the flat of my palm and wipe it onto my jeans. I watch the sky and smoke and wait. I smoke that cigarette all the way down to the filter, use it to light another, then stub the spent one out.

"Please," I say.

And when there's no answer, I say, "I'll do anything."

And later, I say, "Whatever you want."

And when that third cigarette is smoked nearly to my fingertips, I say, "Anything. No restrictions."

And finally, staring at the sliver of moon high on the horizon, I say, "Really. Anything. I mean it."

The leaves rustle. The sheets flap. Twigs snap. A dog lopes down the street. It stops in front of the house, raises its snout, sniffs the air. It stands there for a long time, one soft ear cocked, ghostly in the faint moonlight. The silence is as heavy as the night. The quiet presses against my throat and chest and lungs. It just weighs too much. I cup a hand at the base of my throat, feel the pounding heartbeat in my neck. I whisper, "Please." It comes out hoarse, choked.

The dog barks twice then trots off toward the neighbor's yard. It trips the motion sensor and a floodlight winks on. The dog stands stock-still in the beam, tan with a white patch on its chest, a mutt the size of a Collie. It skitters away into the shadows, vanishing into the dark. A little while later, the floodlight winks off. I tap out another cigarette, roll it unlit between my fingers. Even the feel of it is calming. Maybe I'm not doing it right. Kneel and make myself small? Fling my hands above my head and tip my face to the ceiling and wail some passionately-felt words? Smack my palm to my heaving chest and sputter out a choked plea for deliverance? Steeple my fingers and dip my chin to my chest until my fingernails make tiny half-moon impressions in the center of my forehead then whisper a prayer? Promise something? Bargain? Strike a deal?

The word deal sets off something in me, flaring with all the intensity of a match set to flash paper. But what do I have to offer?

The answer pops into my mind so suddenly that my head rocks backward in surprise: my soul.

And then on the heels of that: if God won't help, maybe the devil will.

Is there really a devil? How do you talk to Satan? Is it like praying? I don't know. There's no one to ask. More stars click on, one by one by one, until the domed sky looks like it's been flecked by so much paint spatter. The breeze kicks up again and strengthens into a wind. Something (a stray leaf? a discarded wrapper? a forgotten scarf?) sets the floodlight next door blazing again. You can see my size 20 jeans hanging on the clothesline. Ditto on the XXL sweatshirts. All the better to hide you with, my dear. Heat flushes my face. My scalp starts to prickle. There's no hiding with those clothes out on display. Any passerby could stop and stare, could point and laugh. The wind soughs through the maples on the low hill sloping away from the house and makes my enormous clothes flutter like flags. The floodlight winks off again.

There's snoring down the hallway. Someone else cries out briefly in their sleep. There's the creak of a floorboard in the hallway. I startle, bobbling the unlit cigarette, dropping it onto the carpet between my bare feet where it bounces once then rolls to a stop against the baseboard. I breathe shallowly and for a little while, I don't breathe at all. I cock my head, listening hard. I wait, heart thumping wildly inside my rib cage. What I need to do must be done in secret. That much, I know for sure. I take in tiny sips of air. Listen. Listen. But there are no other sounds of movement. Nothing but the clock on my dresser ticking. The face glows green, the white hands luminescent. It's 12:42. My heart rises into my throat, lodging there, a hot wet mass.

If I do this thing, there's no going back, is there?

I lean down, pluck the cigarette from the floor, then light it. I take a long drag, pulling all that smoke deep down into my lungs, holding it there until my chest feels like a seam stretched and ready to burst.

What if it doesn't work at all? Or if it only works for a little while? What if I get skinny, hit that magic goal weight, and then, like usual, within a few days start gaining it all back again? Do I still have to honor the deal?

Again, I don't know. There's no one to ask. But what other choice is there? Back down in fear and stay fat? Make the deal and take my chances? I thump the cigarette against the window frame. Ash drifts down and sprinkles the bushes beside the house. Some of it catches on the wind and lands on the grass near the ditch. I look up at the sky, the North Star drawing my eye then the sliver of moon, and blow out a long stream of smoke that vanishes into the night.

"Okay," I whisper. "Satan? Devil? What do I call you? Will you help me? Will you make me skinny?"

It occurs to me that the devil wouldn't be up in the heavens.

I turn into the room. Shadowy corners. The closet door slightly ajar. Deep dark underneath the bed. If the devil is anywhere, he's there, tucked in the creepy places, lurking with the other monsters. And so that's where I face.

"If you're there," I say, "I want . . ."

I am trembling. The tremor starts in my hands and works its way up my arms, my neck, my head. My stomach flips and tumbles. Are you really doing this? Are you sure? Is this what you want? Yes. Yes. And yes. I want to be thin.

"I want to trade," I say. "My soul to be skinny. You can have it if you make me thin."

The cigarette smolders. My heart hammers. My hands shake.

Nothing else changes. Nothing dark breaks away from the shadows, materializes into some demon form, all muscle and bone and burning red eyes. Nothing comes for me.

"Did you hear me?"

No claws grasping at my ankles from under the bed.

"I said you can have my soul, just make me skinny."

No deep whispered voices.

"Please."

No swirling black ghouls or gnashing teeth or horned beasts tipping their heads back and howling. No movement at all. Nothing.

Did it work?

The words are out. I said them. I can't snatch them back even if I wanted to. Which I don't. Maybe it'll work. God hasn't done anything even after years of haphazard, whispered, desperate prayers. Maybe the devil is the answer. Maybe Lucifer has the power to melt this fat off me and keep it off. The tradeoff is worth it. I don't care anymore. I said whatever, anything. I meant it.

I am seventeen years old.

At my largest, I weighed 304 pounds and wore a size 26. As of this writing, I weigh 128 pounds and wear a size 0-2. I've been within twenty pounds (because I fluctuate and that's okay) of that weight for more than seven years now. A diet/food program/lifestyle or whatever you want to call it isn't worth your time, effort, and/or money if it doesn't have a track record of the participants actually being able to keep the weight off permanently. If what you're doing to lose weight doesn't have a proven track record then you're a hamster on a wheel, working really hard and, at the end, getting nowhere.

I'm around 260 pounds (because after that, I wouldn't let anyone take my picture).

I've done nearly every major diet program that you've seen advertised on television. I've sent away for questionable diets you find in the back of magazines. I have, at different points in my life and because someone told me it would work, stopped eating: sugar, white flour, fats, meat, processed foods, and/or anything that tasted halfway decent. I have weighed and measured what I ate down to the ounce. I have special-ordered food at restaurants with so many specifics that the waiter nearly threw his hands into the air in exasperation. I have spent hundreds if not thousands of hours going to weight-loss related meetings. I have spent thousands of dollars on prepackaged foods and consumed nothing but diet shakes and, at one point, ate nothing but lettuce, rice cakes, and water for over a month. I have exercised to exhaustion and purged with my index finger crammed down my throat and let the scale decide my self-worth and made myself completely crazy. At many times, I was so desperate to be thin that I was willing to give up just about anything and to try just about everything, no matter the cost to my physical and mental health. Because, to me, being skinny equaled being loved, equaled acceptance, equaled belonging, equaled worthiness. And desperate people tend to make hasty (read: bad) choices. Diet companies know that, too.

I'm roughly 130 pounds and wear a size 2.

Now, I'm thin. I've had no bariatric surgery. I didn't starve to get there. I don't take diet pills or diet supplements other than a few vitamins. I do exercise but not like a maniac. I eat whatever I want as long as I'm not allergic to it. I no longer have a raging eating disorder. I am no longer afraid of food. I no longer live trapped in a body that doesn't feel like me. I am finally (finally!) comfortable in my own skin. I don't live in fear that the weight is going to come back and I won't know what to do about it. I don't live in confusion and desperation and frustration and panic and humiliation and shame. Food is no longer the focus of my life. I got free. Your life can be that way too.

Just imagine what we—all of us—could all be doing with our lives, following our own dreams and reaching our own goals, cultivating our own passions, making both our inner and outer worlds a more blissful and peaceful place, if we weren't running in circles (I call it the diet-go-round) chasing a number on the scale, catching the goal weight, only to have it slip away so the chase begins again. I spent decades trapped in that circle, around and around and around I went, never moving forward to create the life I really wanted. So if that's what you're looking for, to get out of that cycle now and start moving forward in a straight line toward your future, then I invite you to read on.

The Reason Why

"They thought they could bury us, they did not know we were seeds."
—Mexican Proverb

THE UPPERCLASSMEN AT school make a semicircle around their lockers. I am not far away, working my way toward a classroom. One of them, popular, stocky, a football player wearing a jersey, turns and looks at me. He says, "Here comes bubble butt." Heads in the hallway turn like deer in a herd sensing danger, first to the boy then to me. No one says a thing. I stop. I go still. My face burns. I look left, lockers; right, more lockers. There's nowhere to hide. Laughter peals from the group.

"Thunder thighs," another one of them says.

"That ass ought to have a sticker that says WIDE LOAD."

The boy next to him makes the beeping noise of a truck in reverse as I take a single step back.

"A big blue cow."

"She gets any wider she might not fit down the hall."

"Man, that's fucking ugly. One fugly pig."

"Fugly? She's pretty from the neck up."

"Pretty?" one of them says. His face scrunches up like he's tasted something sour then he spits a bubbling wad of saliva onto the hallway floor. "I'd do my dog before I'd do her."

More laughter washes over me. Teenagers bustle around me, bump into me, hurry to class before the bell rings again. I stand stock still with my books clamped to my chest, staring at that handful of boys. All those insults feel like so many shiny straight pins stuck right in my heart. But I also know better than to cry. I can feel the tears, welling up, ready to spill over, and I blink and blink and blink.

The bell rings. Lockers slam. The boys, still laughing, move away down the hall.

I rush away from the classroom where I'm supposed to have history and scurry to the girls' bathroom. I lock myself in a stall in the back where I squat down, balancing on the balls of my feet with my back pressed against the tile wall. I read the declarations scrawled in black marker—Julie loves Ron, Go Knights, Edmonson sucks, when all else fails x = 3. The mesh-covered wall clock ticks and the sink closest to the door drips as I stuff my brown-bagged lunch (sandwich, potato chips, apple, bite-sized chocolate bar) into my mouth and wait for my breathing to slow and my face to cool and the tears to dissolve so when I unbolt the door I can face myself in the mirror.

I am fifteen years old.

REASONS TO NOT WRITE THIS BOOK

I've been a target by bullies (total strangers, school peers, work colleagues, people I thought were my friends, and even some relatives) because of my weight for far too many years and I'm not interested in opening myself up for that kind of hurt anymore. I have zero interest in being the center of attention in a way that diminishes and/or humiliates me.

There are countless (tens of thousands? hundreds of thousands? millions?) of weight-loss books out in the world. Does there really need to be another?

REASONS TO WRITE THIS BOOK

FDA-approved diet pills, which desperate people will buy and consume, that have side effects including: heart disease, hallucinations, depression, thoughts of suicide, stroke, cancer, even death, among others (as if cancer and death aren't bad enough). In much smaller print, the kind very few people bother reading, the drugs often state: 1. the drug needs to be combined with a healthy diet and exercise, and 2. less than 50% of the test subjects taking the drug lost 5% or more of their body weight (which effectively means that taking that drug gives you just a coin-toss chance of losing 5% of your body weight while you're risking your health and even your life taking it).[1]

Advertisements for bariatric centers that say stomach surgery is your best (and some that say only) bet to overcome obesity. Here's what they don't reveal in the ads: It's major surgery under anesthesia, with all the risks that involves, including complications, infection, and even death. According to my family doctor, possible side effects also include: gallstones, nausea, vomiting, constipation, blood clots, among others. He also said that the average weight loss is roughly 60% of the excess weight (so not all the weight you want to get rid of). Long-term success rates vary wildly depending on which study you read. Again, my family doctor said that roughly 1/3 of people who undergo bariatric surgery have *regained all their weight and then some* within five years (and he added that the percentage is likely much higher than that because 33% doesn't include the people who don't report back to their doctors for follow-ups because they're ashamed they regained the weight). He also said that it usually takes people roughly two years to lose 60% of the weight they want to (so not the quick fix some people think it is).[2]

The skin-care company, Dove, did some research into women, beauty, and self-esteem. *The Dove Global Beauty and Confidence Report* done in 2016 showed that 85% of women and 79% of girls will say *no* to activities they might otherwise want to do—such as joining a club or attending family events—because of low body esteem. The report clearly shows the effect a woman's relationship with her body has on a woman's ability to fully realize her own potential. Moreover, the report revealed that 70% of girls won't assert themselves if they are uncomfortable about they way they look, while 87% of women will refuse to eat and/or engage in other behaviors that risk their health because of low body esteem.[3] There's no getting away from yourself. Your body is the only thing you'll always and forever be stuck with. So better to make peace with it.

Overweight and obesity means having an excess of fat tissue that can cause health problems.[4] The National Center for Health Statistics (part of the Centers for Disease Control and Prevention) states that in 2015-2016, nearly 40% of American adults and 18.5% of children aged 2–19 years were obese. Obese is defined as a Body Mass Index (BMI equals height to weight ratio) of 30 or more.[5] The latest figures from Centers for Disease Control and Prevention also show that another 33% of adults are overweight (BMI of 25-29.9). The CDC estimates that 75% of the population in the United States will likely be overweight or obese by 2020 if the upward trend continues. Both the CDC and the National Institute of Health are calling obesity an epidemic in the United States.[6]

Obesity is not good for your overall long-term health. According to the Centers for Disease Control and Prevention, obesity has a direct causal link to cardiovascular disease, stroke, type 2 diabetes, and certain types of cancer. It can also be a factor in gallstones, stress incontinence, sleep apnea, and osteoarthritis. The CDC also states that obesity is a major contributor to many of the leading causes of preventable, premature death.[7]

The World Health Organization (WHO) states that in 2016, there were nearly 2 billion overweight people worldwide, with 650 million of those people considered obese. The number of people who are obese has increased almost 300% between 1975 and 2016. Obesity is considered a worldwide epidemic and one of the most critical public health crises the world currently faces. Obesity is also preventable.[8] If the upward trend of obesity continues, the World Obesity Federation estimates there will be 2.7 billion overweight adults worldwide, 1 billion obese adults and another 177 million severely obese adults by 2025.[9]

The vast majority of people who go on diets of any kind *regain most if not all their weight* within five years. Again, studies vary wildly depending on which one you read with failure rates from 40-99% after two years.[10] What most studies agreed upon is that maintaining a weight loss required indefinite adherence to some kind of food, exercise, and behavioral change program.[11] Weight loss is a 70-billion-dollar industry[12] and yet, nearly every study I came across seemed to agree that only a small percentage of people actually kept the weight off for more than five years. Based on what I've read and also witnessed firsthand, I'd argue that science says dieting doesn't work long-term, at least not for the majority of people.

♥

At my heaviest, I had a BMI of nearly 45, which got me labeled in one medical chart as morbidly obese. Over the years, I've lost and gained and lost and gained (and lost again!) hundreds if not thousands of pounds. Just so you know, researchers at The Endocrine Society reported that losing weight over and over again (basically yo-yo dieting) can result in an increased risk of death.[13]

♥

Hope is also in short supply, especially if you've tried and tried and tried and failed and failed and failed. A study done by *The Journal of the American Medical Association* states that fewer Americans than ever before are embarking on diets because of repeated failed attempts even as obesity rates are rising.[14]

♥

And finally: a fifteen-year-old overweight girl who wouldn't look me in the eyes when she spoke to me, who seemed embarrassed by her body and ashamed of who she was as she tried to hide herself behind her friend. I knew exactly what she felt like in that moment. I was her a long time ago. And all I could think was: *She's fifteen. She's got her whole life ahead of her. What if she spends it feeling like that? What if she spends it going in circles with her weight because no one will help her?*

♥

So reasons to write this book won.

I'm not a doctor or a psychiatrist or a nutritionist or a life coach. The particular expertise and training I have came from living and experiencing obesity and freedom from it firsthand. I wrote this book hoping to save you some time and money, yes, but also (and more damaging) the feelings of insanity and shame and careening out of control and self-blame and what-is-it-that's-wrong-with-me-there-must-be-something-wrong-with-me-why-does-no-diet-work-for-me.

My weight-loss journey started with a single question: *if it's not about food, then what is it?* Finding the answer to that question is what saved me and eventually became this book. The steps you'll find within these pages come from things I've learned after years of self-exploration, self-reflection, psychological counseling, various types of therapeutic experiential work, a myriad of self-help techniques, research from books and other sources, attending workshops and seminars, and a process of experimenting with each of those modalities to find out what worked and what didn't.

Just so you know: there are no testimonials in this book. Not one. This book details what worked for me. This is the first time I'm sharing it with pretty much anyone, even my friends. As a rule, I don't talk about my struggles with weight. But I felt called to write this book (more on that later), to figure out what I did that finally worked and to write it down in easy-to-understand steps, and after a long while of fighting against that call, I finally said *yes.* I've done what I can to show you a path out of being overweight and/or abusing food, and just to be clear: *it's my path.* Like the quote at the beginning of this book says, you can start following a path to help you find your way, but eventually you have to forge your own path. So think of this book more as a guide, some helpful suggestions and some friendly encouragement pointing you in the right direction, and not a hard-and-set bunch of rules you need to follow. What works for me may not work for you, and that's okay. You find what works for you and you do that. You take this guide and you make it your own.

The working title of this book was *(W)hole.* When the calling to write it came, that title is what popped into my head. This popped into my head too: *There's a hole inside you that needs filled. Food won't do it. So you need to find what will so you can be whole.* According to the dictionary, *whole* means: 1. in an undamaged state; 2. healthy; 3. something that is complete in itself.[15] And that encompassed everything this book aimed to convey. The title got changed, however, because by the time I got finished writing it, I realized how little it was about weight-loss strategies and how much it was about fixing everything else that's wrong with your life. I also realized that what I had always needed most was to be able to stop wishing I was somewhere in the past or in the future, to quit beating myself up for my mistakes, to cease waiting for something that I hoped was coming, and instead to just take a deep breath, to show myself a little kindness, and to start right where I was.

It's not an exaggeration to say this book healed me, especially in ways I didn't expect. The act of writing it made me stop and think about why I was doing what I was doing. It made me clarify what I really wanted from my life. It made me take a good hard look at the choices I was making that were leading me down a path that was taking me deeper into the shadows, a path that I just didn't want to be on. Writing this book made me finally realize some things about myself that I wouldn't have learned any other way. You don't have to write a book. You will, however, have to do some self-exploration. You will have to be completely honest with yourself. You will have to make some choices that are likely to throw you clean out of your comfort zone (no worries, though, because you'll have company: I'm right out there with you). You will have to practice self-compassion and be kind, gentle, and patient with yourself. You will have to forgive yourself as many times as it takes and give yourself unlimited tries. You will have to keep going no matter how much you want to quit. (Note: the wanting to quit is fueled by fear, even if it doesn't feel like fear in that moment.) And sometimes you will quit; and you'll have to learn that you can always start again, right where you are.

This book asked a lot of me. It asked me to be honest in a way that I usually avoid. It called for me to invite you into the vulnerable places in my life. It asked me to offer healing to strangers. I've done my best to show you a path out of being overweight and/or abusing food. I hope you'll choose to take a deep breath and step onto that path with me. And while we're there, you remember that you're on a journey to forge a path, your own journey and your own path, that will lead you out of the dimness and into the light. This book is here to hold your hand for as long as you need it to, and when you're ready to let this book go, you'll realize how strong and tenacious and intelligent and courageous and determined you are and always were. And you'll realize that you've always had all the answers you ever needed right there inside you, just waiting for you to listen. And you'll realize, too, that you've always been more than capable of saving your own life.

Shelli

November 3, 2017
3:33 PM

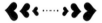

Things you'll need, how to read this book, and notes on nutrition information and repetition

"If not now, then when?"
—Hillel The Elder

I AM AT the doctor's office. There's a scale in the corner of the exam room. I stand on the black rubber pad, shifting my weight from one sock to the other, looking from the white wall to the yellowed linoleum that's curling away from the baseboard to the water stain in the ceiling in the shape of a mushroom, anywhere but at those etched numbers.

The nurse makes a face, all scrunched up, as she adjusts the black slider at the top from one hundred pounds to one hundred fifty. She shakes her head and clucks her tongue and makes a kind of unh-unh-unh sound. She looks from me to Mother then back to the scale.

Go away, I think. Go away. Go away. Go away.

But the nurse doesn't go away. Instead, she shifts the other slider, the one that counts single pounds, higher and higher. It stops at twelve. One hundred and sixty-two pounds. The nurse scrunches her face again.

"Lord have mercy," she says under her breath.

She scribbles the number on the chart, leaves the chart on the desk, then vanishes from the room, shutting the door behind herself.

I sit on the exam table in a threadbare blue gown with white piping. I fiddle with the hem, wadding the material between my palms then letting it go, wadding the material again then letting it go. My clothes are in a pile on the chair, my sneakers underneath it. Mother sits on the other chair. She reads a Better Homes & Gardens magazine. My thighs spread beneath the gown. It's a children's gown and not big enough. Cold air from the ceiling vent spills onto my bare back. I shrug my shoulders, hunching into myself, and smooth the gown over my thighs, trying to hide myself.

The doctor enters in a flurry, white coat swishing. He smiles at me then leafs through the chart. He says, "Your daughter is not at a healthy weight. She's a big girl, too big for her age."

My face gets hot. I curl over my lap, looking down at my socks, the bottoms dark with dirt. I wad the gown in my fists again, scrunching it tight. The material is stretched over my belly. There are rolls of fat. One. Two. Three.

Go away, I think. Go away. Go away. Go away.

But the doctor does not heed my thoughts. Instead, he checks my eyes and ears, my throat as I say "Aaaahhh," my heartbeat, my lungs, my reflexes. Then he asks, "Everything all right at home?"

I look at Mother.

Mother stiffens. She forces a little smile.

I nod at the doctor and say, "Uh-huh."

I am thirteen years old.

SUPPLIES

A JOURNAL

You'll need a journal (fancy or not, your choice) so you can write down your innermost thoughts. Write as much or as little as you like. If the act of writing scares you, then by all means start slow and just write a little bit at a time. There's no judgment here. No need to impress or prove or do anything but be yourself and let your own voice find its way onto the page. One other note: be sure to label each activity you're writing about because you may refer back to them during a later activity. You can also use the companion journal designed specifically to go with this book: *Start Where You Are Weight Loss Playbook* (ISBN: 978-1-948103-83-1).

NO PERFECTION NEEDED

Do yourself a kindness and make a mistake in your journal early on. Scribble on some of the pages. Spill your favorite beverage on the cover. Rip one of the corners off. Make your journal imperfect so that you'll feel free to be your real, honest self inside the pages. Being real, not being perfect, is what's going to heal you and set you free.

BE HONEST

I'd recommend that you don't show your answers inside your journal to anyone. Keep them to yourself for right now until you make it all the way through this book. Why? Honesty with yourself is what's going to heal you and help you grow. You won't be completely honest if you're worried about someone reading your answers. In fact, what you're likely to do is tweak your responses, edit them, or scratch them out entirely if you're worried about how others might perceive you. So be kind to yourself and let the work you're about to do be just for you for the time being or for as long as you need.

BE WILLING & OPEN

The first step to change is to be open and willing to it. You picked up this book because you're struggling in this area of your life. If you want things to be different, well, both you & those things are going to have to change. So be open to experiencing something new & be willing to do the effort to get there.

GIVE YOURSELF PERMISSION

It's hugely important to give yourself permission (whether that's verbally or written) to: do the suggestions in this book, have/be/do/say/believe whatever you need to so that you can heal yourself, give yourself unlimited tries as many times as it takes, believe in your own worth and value, and choose to create a life you love because you matter. Whenever you feel like you need someone else's permission to make a choice about your life, you just give that permission to yourself. The only permission you ever need to live your own life is your own.

YOU'RE ON A JOURNEY

It doesn't matter how old you are, how many times you've tried, or how far there is left to go. It's never too late to be the person you want to be. It's okay if you don't know things yet. You're on a journey and you'll figure it out as you go. This book is designed to help you do just that.

BEGIN YOUR DAY WITH THIS BOOK

If at all possible, read a little (don't overwhelm yourself) of this book daily and do what it suggests shortly after you wake up. That way, you'll be able to focus on yourself (because you're absolutely worth the time to do that) before your day gets away from you. Find a quiet place. Relax and reflect.

IT'S A PRACTICE & A PROCESS

There's no doing this perfectly, and that's okay. You strive for progress. You do the best you can. So show yourself some patience and kindness because self-compassion is what you most need to heal yourself. You will make mistakes, there's just no way around it. Don't ever use any mistake as a reason to give up on yourself. Just circle back around and start again. And know this: every mistake is simply a brand new chance to do it better the next time.

AND FINALLY . . .

Remember (not just for this book but for all of life): you get out what you put in. So make yourself a priority in your own life because: 1. you're absolutely worth the effort and 2. no one else can do it for you. And one last suggestion good both for this book and for all of life: be brave and move beyond your fear, that's where freedom lies.

HOW TO READ THIS BOOK

This book is not meant to be read fast. It's meant to be read slowly over your weight-loss journey so that you can experiment with the concepts, learn some things about yourself, figure out what works for you and what doesn't, and cherry pick to create a lifestyle and a body that suits you, so that when you no longer need this book to help guide you, you will have a strong and stable foundation on which to live the rest of your life.

A NOTE ON NUTRITION INFORMATION

There is very little nutrition information in this book. It occurred to me that I do know a lot about nutrition from all the decades I spent dieting. However, I am not teaching about nutrition as it's my firm belief that long-term weight loss has very little to do with food choices and mostly to do with changing and healing your mindset. With all that said, if you'd like to learn about nutrition, there are many free resources available to you, including a United States Government website: www.nutrition.gov

A NOTE ON REPETITION

I realize that I repeat myself in some places in this book. That's deliberate. I considered consolidating but then chose against it because 1. you'll likely be reading this book slowly over time and may not remember everything you've read previously, and 2. the concepts are important enough to bear being said more than once. Repetition, it's been scientifically proven, will help you learn and remember. So if you read something and it strikes you as familiar, as if you've heard it before, pay attention because it's important that you take that repeated concept to heart.

Some guidance for the journey

"The wound is the place where the light enters you."
—Jalaluddin Rumi

ONE MINUTE, I am dressing up dolls on the floor of my bedroom, hair in pigtails, wearing a red jumper with spaghetti straps over the shoulders and elastic around the bottoms of the shorts, listening to the neighbor boys splash in the pond. The next, I am tucking myself into the back of the closet, crouching in the dimness, the accordion doors mostly closed and a thin sliver of light coming through the gap, landing like a blade on my hand.

Dresses hang above my head, hems at my chest. A plastic shoe holder is propped against the wall to my left: my mother's black spiked heels and brown flats and a glittery pair of pumps that shimmer in the light. I sit, pull my legs up, wreathe my arms around my shins, and tuck my chin into the gap between my knees. The boys whoop and holler in the pond beyond the trees, their voices carrying through the open window. The television drones downstairs, some high-decibel commercial for toilet paper. Two teddy bears and a stuffed rabbit with a pink polka-dot bow tie sit in the far corner, black eyes staring. A bright-pink Easter basket sits beside them, green shreds of plastic grass spilling over the sides and a yellow paper daisy, crushed and sad-looking, wired onto the handle. I finger the ruffled edge of my socks, the white gone dingy and the tiny purple flowers faded to gray from *so many washings. I tell myself not to. The carpet is hard and scratchy. My heart beats hard. Don't, Shelli. The air's gone stuffy and thick. My breath is hot against my bare shins. Don't, I mean it. I pick at the pale nail polish on my thumb and watch powder-blue flakes dot the light-colored carpet.*

I slide that basket toward myself. I make a ring around my feet with the candy: dozens of speckled malted milk balls, maybe a hundred jelly beans, two full packages of marshmallow chicks, a solid chocolate bunny as big as my forearm with its ears already eaten off.

Don't.

Don't.

It's not too late yet.

The volume on the day gets turned down to the point that the only things I hear are the crinkling of the wrappers, the click of my jaw as I chew, the soft sound my throat makes as I swallow. Soon, I pick through the basket grass, searching, but all the candy is gone. So I tip my face toward the closet ceiling and yank on the hem of a lemon-colored sundress until it comes loose from the hanger. I crush all the wrappers and tuck them in the corner, where they unfurl bit by bit, then wad the dress into a ball and drop it on top.

When I open the closet doors, I squint and raise a hand against the sudden light. The noise level rises again. The boys are splashing. A radio plays some country song. The horses across the street whinny then gallop the length of the split-rail fence. There's the hum of a low conversation coming from the neighbor's house beyond the trees then a loud snort followed by a peal of laughter. I sit cross-legged underneath the opened window. A breeze blows in and the curtain brushes against me. I feel calm. Safe. Numb. I make the stuffed bear talk, his deep voice telling me that I'm not alone, that everything is okay.

I smooth a plastic doll's blonde hair, slip a frilly pink dress over her narrow body, then snap on tiny pink shoes. The ruffle on the canopy bed flutters as the doll and the bear have tea, chatting in a friendly way. The sudden tight panic in my chest (you don't belong) and the real fear in the pit of my stomach (no one wants you) are smudges now, like words quickly erased from a blackboard with the palm of a hand, not gone but blurred.

I am nine years old.

BREATHE, JUST BREATHE

Here's what I know for sure: breathing deep matters. The simple act of deep breathing will calm you, help you focus, connect your mind to your body, bring you back to the present moment, and help you center your thoughts.*

So do this:
1. Take a slow, deep breath in through your nose.
2. Hold it for three seconds.
3. Let it out slowly through your mouth with an audible sound.
4. Then pull your shoulders down away from your ears and let yourself relax.
5. Now massage your temples and the back of your neck.
6. Repeat five times.
7. Repeat deep breathing often, especially when you find yourself panicked, afraid, anxious, or any other emotion that makes you want to abuse food for relief.

*For the science behind why deep breathing is so important, see *Oh, Some Science (Part Two)* in Chapter Four.

NOW DO A QUICK EXERCISE

1. Write your age now.
2. Then write the age you were when you started dieting.
3. Subtract.
4. That's how long you've been on the diet-go-round.
5. Breathe deep. It's all gonna be okay.
6. Now before you read any further, answer this honestly: *Do I want to keep spinning on the diet-go-round or would I like to jump off?*

THEN LISTEN FOR YOUR VOICE OF WISDOM

Your voice of wisdom, also known as your intuition, is that still, small voice inside your mind that knows what you most want to have/be/do/say at any given moment. It also includes your body, how it feels/reacts in any given situation. Your intuition will guide you and get you to where you most want to be if you'll just listen to it and do what it says. Your voice of wisdom is the one that's kind, nurturing, and supportive. It will *never* tear you down or berate you. It will *always* strengthen you, encourage you, and help you grow, even if what it's telling you that you need to do to move forward in your life scares you. Know this: listening to, being guided by, trusting in, and taking action based on your intuition is a process and a practice; the more you do it, the easier and the better at it you will be. Start today.

So do this:
1. Trust yourself. You've been with yourself all these years. You *really* do know what's best for you.
2. Then ask questions about your life and look inward for guidance, listening for your intuition to give you the answers.
3. Be open and take those answers as they come (so no overthinking and/or editing).
4. Trust your intuition and do what it tells you to do even if that scares you.
5. Eventually, you'll learn to distinguish your voice of wisdom from all the other voices clamoring for your attention. When that happens, you'll realize that all the answers you need to fix your life truly are inside of you.

AND BE HONEST

Honesty with yourself is what's going to heal you and help you grow. *Complete* honesty with yourself means that you can no longer refuse to believe the truth and/or tweak your responses because you don't want to face the facts. Just to be clear: you don't have to tell the whole detailed truth to anyone else; you do, however, have to tell the whole, full, and unedited truth to yourself. So be honest with yourself throughout this entire process and ever after, even (and especially) if that truth hurts.

THEN ANSWER A SINGLE QUESTION

That raging and insatiable hunger you feel, the one that makes you feel crazed and out of control, the one that makes you abuse food and also the one that no food ever seems enough to sate, that's caused by the hole (or wound) inside you that you're trying to fill with food. The wound is the something (or somethings) that you feel/think/believe is (or are) lacking in you.

So do this:
1. Be alone for at least fifteen minutes.
2. Get still and quiet.
3. Listen for your intuition for the answer(s) to this: *What is that wound for me?*

That's the most important question you can ask. In fact, it's the only question you should be asking right now because it's likely the root cause of your abusing food. And as you've probably already come to realize: there's no fullness in the face of that hole; all there will ever be, if that wound goes unhealed, is a vast and unending emptiness that needs filling. *Food will never heal that wound.* Never. This book is designed to help you figure out what will.

AND ALWAYS (ALWAYS, ALWAYS) GIVE YOURSELF PERMISSION

The only permission you ever need to have a life that's fulfilling to you is your own. If you're in a holding pattern waiting for someone to tell you it's okay to be thin and/or to stop abusing food, okay to be yourself, okay to risk, okay to love yourself and take care of yourself, okay to believe that you're fabulous as-is, okay to take all the steps necessary to have the body/life you want, okay to [fill in the blank], do yourself a kindness and stop *right now*.

It's likely that you refuse to give yourself permission because you don't yet trust yourself. Permission can also be about risk management: maybe you think getting permission from someone else will somehow lessen your responsibility for your own life. Or maybe you use not getting someone else's permission as an excuse not to even try. Or maybe you want someone else to be in authority (and so shoulder the blame) if things don't work out like you'd hoped. But when you wait around for permission from others, your power goes right into the hands of whomever it is you're hoping will validate you. And it's the powerlessness that's got you abusing food and/or other substances/behaviors to numb yourself.

So you give yourself permission in whatever way is best for you—write it down, look in the mirror and tell yourself, set a daily reminder on your favorite electronic device, whatever you need to do to release yourself from waiting around—to do the work you need to do, to take excellent care of yourself, to meet your own needs, to fulfill your own wants, and to get the weight off and/or to stop abusing food so that you can comfortably live in a body that feels like you. Your own permission is *always* sufficient because wanting something for your life is reason enough.

THEN TAKE THESE FREEDOM COMMANDMENTS TO HEART

- You will let go, *right now*, of doing any of this perfectly.
- You will take the pressure off and cut yourself some slack and not beat yourself up.
- You will not measure your self-worth by how much you weigh, how many mistakes you make, how much money you earn, how many friends you have, and any other transient measurement (because all of that— *all of it*—changes).
- You will start believing in yourself and believing in possibility.
- You will stop listening to what everyone else tells you that you should do and start listening to your own intuition.
- You will stop waiting for your life to begin when you weigh a certain amount and/or wear a certain size and instead you will start enjoying your life *today*.
- You will be kind, gentle, and patient with yourself.
- You will not compare yourself and your life to anyone else's.
- You will take excellent care of yourself and put yourself at the top of your to-do list.
- You will forgive yourself for your mistakes and failures.
- You will stop judging and labeling yourself.
- You will realize that you can't ever go back, so you will go forward instead.
- You will not act on how you feel at the moment but on what you know to be true.
- You will put your blinders on and take the next right step and stop looking at the obstacles to overcome and the reasons why not.
- You will not give up.

NOW TELL YOURSELF YOU ARE ENOUGH AS-IS

You may not have everything you want or need, but you, as an individual, are lacking nothing. I know it's quite likely you don't believe that, but it's true.

So do this:
1. Open your mind to the possibility that this statement is true: *I am enough as-is.*
2. Say it aloud right now: *I am enough as-is.*
3. Find a mirror and look yourself in the eyes and say it again: *I am enough as-is.* Repeat often.

You'll come to believe it as you work through this book, and then your life will change in amazing ways. You really are whole and complete right now. You don't need anything or anyone to fill you up. The only thing that's needed is to get you to believe that.

AND KNOW THAT THERE MAY BE SOME PAIN

As you work through parts of this book, you may find that some of it is probably going to hurt emotionally. Some of it may hurt worse than any physical pain you've ever experienced. Some of it may hurt so bad that you'll wish you could do anything (including die) rather than have to go through it. But you'll be okay. This too shall pass. Everything really shall be well. In the end, it will. And if it's not okay, well, then you simply haven't reached the end yet.

You're going to have to feel whatever it is that's hurting you because you can't think your way out of a feeling. You just have to feel it without abusing food (or anything other substance/behavior) to dull the pain. And I know you can get through it. You are stronger than you know, I assure you that you are.

So do this:
1. Breathe deep.
2. Sit with yourself and let yourself feel the pain.
3. Always remember that the wound is where the light enters you, which means the wound that hurts you so badly in any particular moment will turn into goodness somehow. (Oh yes, it will. I don't know how, but I do know that at some point in your life it will.)
4. Encourage yourself and tell yourself words that you most need to hear to reassure yourself.

5. Let the feeling(s) pass through you (because they will pass) so that you can move on.

THEN LISTEN TO YOUR OWN SELF AND YOUR OWN BODY

A long time ago, I found myself kneeling on the chipped tile of the bathroom in my tiny apartment, catching the edge of my reflection in the porcelain base of the toilet. I'd already thrown up my dinner. My throat felt raw and painful. My face was hot and red. Sweat beaded along my hairline and cut tracks down my cheeks and dropped off my jawline, making ovals in the weave of my sweatshirt. Chunks of partially-digested food ringed the bowl and floated in the murky water. The only thing different about that particular evening was this: I curled over my lap and rested my forehead against the cool rim and I said a single word, meant as a prayer to a force that I wasn't even sure was there.

That word: "Help."

And the answer came in the form of a book that someone would give to me later that very same evening about a no-sugar and no-flour diet where you weigh and measure everything. That book is what first lit a path at the beginning of my journey (because I didn't know everything that I know now about why I was using food in a way it was never intended to be used). That book helped me break the binge-purge-starve cycle I was trapped in. I needed the narrow focus (all about the food, nothing about the emotions) and rigidity (a strict program with no deviations) that particular food plan offered at that time in my life. It made me feel like I had some control. It was a life preserver that I clung to. I made it my focus instead of anything else in my life.

But eventually that diet, too, became a prison. Food became my constant and sole focus: weighing and measuring, keeping a food diary, constantly looking at the clock to make sure I ate only when I was supposed to. All that rigidity (only so many ounces, only so many times a day, certain foods off-limits, spending hours of my life reading ingredient panels to make sure sugar/flour weren't listed, bringing my pre-portioned sugarless/flourless food with me wherever I went, charting my weight, and on and on the list goes) was not in any way freedom, not for me.

I got skinny, yes.

But I was still terrified of food.

I was afraid of deviating even an ounce from the allotted portions. I was afraid of going out and not having my own foods with me or forgetting my food scale to weigh what I was going to eat or going to restaurants where I couldn't control if what I got served was honest-to-goodness truly sugar/flour free. I was afraid of going to parties where there would be a buffet full of off-limit foods and/or lots of people offering me off-limit foods and/or watching others eat off-limit foods while I had to stand there and smile and eat my small apple. I was afraid of eating even the slightest bit of "forbidden" food, because I'd read (and so wholly believed) that sugar and flour were a "trigger" like a gun. Pull the trigger and that bullet lets loose and there's no going back, baby. Well, in the same way, I believed: eat some sugar/flour and that cycle gets activated and there's me careening out of control again.

Plus, as a person, I was still unfulfilled.

In the end, food still had all the power and I felt like I had none. I also felt like something about me was Wrong (with a capital W: *Just WHAT is the matter with me?*) because I simply couldn't eat the same foods as everyone else. That feeling kept me separated and apart; it destroyed my sense of belonging and normalcy. And, as it turns out, a sense of belonging and normalcy is exactly what I needed to help myself heal (more on that later).

So finally at the end of my rope, I stopped listening to everyone else and started listening to my own self and my own body. And that's when I finally found the answer that worked for me. And you need to do the same—listen to your own self and your own body and find the answer(s) and the path that works for you.

TAKE NOTE: what I suggest in this book is about ***eating whatever you want when you're hungry and stopping when you're comfortably full***. This book is <u>**NOT**</u> about eating a no-sugar and no-flour diet. I only mention it because you may be feeling crazed, overwhelmed, unable to stop eating and/or abusing food, unable to tell when you're actually hungry/full. In the beginning, cutting sugar and flour out of your diet will likely curb, if not stop entirely, the crazy-making behavior you're having around food. It might be a good place for you to start if you're struggling with feeling out of control, bingeing, purging, compulsive eating, and/or abusing food in any other way. But please hear me: you do **NOT** have to do a no-sugar and no-flour plan, you just might **CHOOSE** to while you start working through this book.

If you go that route, I would caution you to pay close attention to your body and especially to your mental state (how you're feeling and reacting, especially if you're starting to feel like you've traded one set of prison blues for another). You can do the no-sugar and no-flour plan for as long or as short as you want/need to (a couple of days, a week, a month, or whatever time you choose—just don't make yourself crazy by telling yourself you're stuck doing it; ***you're not stuck and you're not powerless, you get to choose when you start and when you stop***). And then, once you feel a little calmer around food, you can transition into the program that I describe in this book in Chapter Two: eating whatever you want when you're hungry and stopping when you're comfortably full.

And always remember: whatever you do is simply *your choice*. You do whatever works best for you. It's also quite possible that you're just done with any restrictive-eating options entirely and you just want to eat what you want, and that'll work just fine too. I no longer believe that any foods, especially ones containing sugar and flour, are an automatic trigger. I believe, having lived it, that *it's what you believe both about food and about the state of your life that's the trigger*. And what you believe about food and the state of your life is what this book aims to heal. So give yourself permission (oh yes, you can!) to listen to your own self and your own body, to be flexible and open, to cut yourself some slack and practice progress not perfection, and to be willing to simply change your mind.

THEN CHERRY PICK

For this book (and all of life really), take what works for you and leave the rest. Give yourself permission to do that. You need a diet plan, lifestyle change, food schedule/program, way of eating, or whatever you want to call it that works for *you*, and you alone. Period.

Don't get trapped in other people's rules, dogma, or what works for them, and that includes mine. That will just get you stuck and make you bitter/angry/resentful (*but it worked for them, why doesn't it work for me* or *why are they so special* or *why do they get to have what I don't have*). As you read through this book and do the exercises, try each of the suggestions at least once. Do the best you can. Take what works for *you* and tailor a lifestyle that meets *your* particular wants and needs. Feel free to change whatever you need to change so that you can create a way of being in the world that suits you. That's the only way you're ever going to stick long-term with whatever it is you're doing, be it weight loss or something else, at least that's been true for me.

THEN TAKE TO HEART (REALLY TAKE TO HEART) THAT FOOD IS FUEL FOR YOUR BODY SO YOU CAN THRIVE

Food gives your body the energy it needs to help you achieve what you most want for your life. It gives you nourishment so you can strive to become the person you most want to be. It can heal what ails your physical body so that you are free to pursue what matters deeply to you.

Food is fuel for your body, and that's all it is.

Because you're reading this book, I'm assuming that you've used food in a way that's not strictly as fuel to keep you healthy and strong. Just know this: food is not a way to numb your emotional state, a fixer of your problems, a means to give yourself courage, or any other reason you may use food in a way it was never intended. Food is an object. It is a thing that goes where you tell it. It has no emotions or emotional component at all. The only emotional attachments food has are the ones you give it.

Food will not make your pain go away forever, comfort you long-term, mirror back a person who is worthy, be your friend when no one else is around, or give you what is missing in your life. Food will not conquer your fears nor provide a permanent escape. It will not give you encouragement, a belief in yourself, permission, or approval. Food will not meet any of your emotional needs at all. Food has no power but what you give it. Food can nourish you. Food can be enjoyable. But food will never make you, as a person, whole.

I'm saying this again because it's that important, so please take it to heart: food is fuel for your body, and that's all it is.

AND TAKE TO HEART (REALLY TAKE TO HEART) THAT FOOD WILL NOT FIX IT

Whatever is wrong, whatever you're currently feeling, whatever you wish was different, whatever mistakes you made, whatever you did or failed to do, whatever someone else did or failed to do to/for you, whatever your unrealized hopes/passions/goals/dreams are, whatever anyone else thinks of you, whatever you think of yourself, *food will not fix it*. None of it. Ever. So before you start abusing food to make it (whatever *it* is for you) go away, just remind yourself that food will not fix it.

So do this:
1. Tell yourself out loud that food will not fix it. Holler it if you have to. (Yes, it is important to say it aloud. There's a neurological reason for that, which I'll explain in Chapter Two.)
2. Say this: *Food will not fix it. Food will not fix it. Food will not fix it.*
3. Tell that to yourself over and over and make it your mantra. (And yes, it's always mine. I *still* to this day have to remind myself of this.)
4. Say it long enough and you'll: stop abusing food, change the neural pathway in your brain that's made a habit out of trying to fix your problems with food (more on that later), and free yourself from the diet-go-round.

AND TAKE TO HEART (REALLY TAKE TO HEART) THAT NO ONE IS COMING TO FIX IT

Fixing your life is nobody else's job but yours. You know what feels broken in you. You do. If you get still and quiet and listen to your own self, to your own body, you'll know what's ailing you. And if you stay still and quiet and you listen for your intuition, the answers will be right there and you'll know how to fix it.

If you ask for advice from others, they will point you in a direction, sure, but that might be the direction that they, themselves, need to go, and not the direction that will heal you. No one else can fix your life the way you need it fixed for two reasons: 1. you're the only one who knows *exactly* what it is that you need (which is the reason you always need to cherry pick a lifestyle that works for you and not blindly follow what works for someone else), and 2. you got yourself into this mess so you need to be the one to get yourself out (because if you don't, if someone somehow manages to help do it for you, you'll take no ownership of the outcome and no pride in the work and, likely in short order, you will be right back where you started in the same or maybe even a worse mess as before).

I know all of us would like someone to come swooping in and fix everything. Some guru who could give us the magic pill to make the weight just slide right off or give us an iron-clad guarantee that we'll be thin no matter what or do the work that's needed to shed the weight for us. But, sadly, you can't lose weight by proxy. You can't live your life by proxy either. You will not save your own life by majority vote; you have to save it by only one vote, your own. The sooner you stop waiting for someone to come along and fix what's wrong and make it all better, the sooner you can get on with living your life on your terms.

AND TAKE TO HEART (REALLY, REALLY TAKE TO HEART) THAT YOU CAN TRUST YOURSELF AND YOU CAN SAVE YOURSELF

Be willing to believe that all the answers you need really are tucked inside of you (because they are). All you need to do is learn to trust yourself (which we'll be talking about in Chapter Three), then start listening to your own wisdom. Be open to the truth that you must save yourself (which we'll be discussing just how to do in Chapters Six and Seven).

THEN GIVE YOURSELF A PRIZE

I'm a fan of getting rewarded for a job well done. Who doesn't like a prize? Science backs me up, too: your brain fills with dopamine (which is biochemical that makes you feel good) whenever you get a reward, even if you're the one giving it to yourself.[1]

So with that in mind, celebrate *every time* you complete an exercise, do something hard, step out of your comfort zone, tell the truth to yourself and/or others, make yourself a priority in your own life, lose a pound, reach a goal, and on the list goes. Don't skimp on this one. You get a prize. *Every. Single. Time.*

Prizes can be big if you want them to be (just make sure your budget allows, so you don't add more stress to your life). Prizes can also be small and free. A bubble bath with candles. A long walk. An hour to sit on the couch and watch TV, guilt-free. Dancing to your favorite music. Picking a bouquet of wildflowers. Whatever will make you feel nourished and encouraged and supported, with the exception of food. Food is fuel for your body, and that's the only thing it is. Anything that you really want—other than food or a substance/behavior that you abuse—is a prize.

AND FINALLY ...

1. Take a deep breath in through your nose.
2. Hold it for three seconds.
3. Let it out slowly through your mouth with an audible sound.
4. Pull your shoulders down away from your ears and let yourself relax.
5. Now massage your temples and the back of your neck.
6. Remember to repeat this often, *especially* when you find yourself panicked, afraid, anxious, nervous, sad, angry, frustrated, disappointed, and/or any other emotion that makes you want to run to food for relief.
7. Now, turn the page and start where you are.

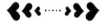

CHAPTER ONE

YOU ARE NOT ALONE

OR

At least one other
person has been where
you are . . . me.

Chapter One

**"Out beyond ideas of wrong-doing and right-doing,
there is a field. I'll meet you there."
—Jalaluddin Rumi**

THE MIRROR ON *the back of the bedroom door isn't wide enough for me to see all of myself at once. Naked, I spin in a circle like the ballerina in a music box. I angle my body, frown at each sliver of reflection. A belly that pooches out. Thick thighs that rub together. I pinch my inner thigh so hard I wince. I frown. I slap my behind, watch it jiggle. I frown again. Red indents at the waistband of my underwear. I snap the elastic. I frown for a third time. Two stretch marks snake up along my hip. I pinch a roll of fat hard enough to leave red marks. I give another frown. Double chin. Round face with cheeks that make me think of the gerbil at school, the way it looks when it gets done hoarding its food. Sad eyes behind oversized glasses. I frown so hard that the muscles of my face hurt.*

Out loud, I say: "Fat."

Then I say, "Ugly."

I twirl again, pinching here and there, frowning.

After I spin in a complete circle, meeting my eyes once again, I say, "You are fat and ugly."
I say it over and over: fat, ugly, fat, ugly, fatuglyfatuglyfatuglyfatugly.
It's the first time I turn on myself, chipping away at my own self-esteem.
I am eleven years old.

KNOW WHAT YOU'RE SIGNING UP FOR

I'm a big believer that you should be fully informed and understand what you're getting into before you agree to it. I wouldn't ever want you to think you'd gotten a bait-and-switch. I don't want you feeling like you were lured in by one thing (weight loss!) and then you got something else (how to fix the rest of your life!). This book will address both because it's my firm belief, having lived through it, that weight issues and food abuse are just symptoms of a bigger problem. That bigger problem is namely all the stuff that you believe is wrong with you and/or your life.

There are solutions in this book, both for the weight/food issues and for the life challenges. I just want you to be clear about what you're headed into so there are no surprises later on: you're going to have to look at your life as a whole and not just deal with the food part of it. Trying to just deal with the food part separate from everything else won't work; I know because I've tried. And if all you want is someone to tell you how to fix the food and skip all the rest: 1. this is not the book for you, and 2. I'd argue that not dealing with the underlying cause is the reason that you stay on the diet-go-round and find it difficult to stop abusing food and/or to keep the weight off.

SOME THINGS YOU NEED TO CONSIDER BEFORE YOU EVEN GET STARTED

CHECK YOUR MOTIVATION

Approval really is an inside job. You are doing all this work *for you*. You are getting the weight off *for you*. You are keeping it off *for you*. Period. I know you've heard that before. You're probably thinking/saying to yourself:

I am doing it for me. But are you really? Have you had any of these kinds of thoughts when you consider losing the weight (a partial list):

- I'll show them.
- He/She will come back, care about me more, and/or finally love me.
- They'll like me better.
- He/She wants me to.
- Look how jealous/regretful they'll be.

If those kind of thoughts (ones where *you* aren't the front-and-center reason) are rattling around in your head, then you're not doing all this work solely for you. And if your motivation is someone else, in the end all your efforts won't work. Here's why:

- At some point, you'll get to a hard place where it takes some fortitude to get through and that person may not be around or may not support you or may even, sad but true, try to sabotage your efforts because they want to keep you small and non-threatening and the same. And if these kinds of people are your reason for getting rid of the weight, you will end up abusing food again because either 1. you think you have no one in your corner rooting for you, or 2. you just want to make others more comfortable and/or less threatened around you. You need to build a strong and sturdy foundation in your life, one that won't get shattered when someone leaves or doesn't agree with your own assessment of yourself or rallies against the choices you're making or the behaviors you're doing. That strong and sturdy foundation is you.
- Or maybe you get to your goal weight and the person you were doing it for doesn't react the way you thought, wanted, and/or hoped they would. There are two perils in this situation if your motivation is someone else: 1. you are confined by someone else's wants, needs, wishes, fears, limitations, and on the list goes, and 2. if/when the relationship crashes and burns, you and your goals will go down in flames along with it. You will end up feeling rudderless and adrift, bitter and resentful, angry or maybe sad, and most likely suckered (but I did all this *for you*!). You'll likely feel crushed and give up. Then you'll blame them for your failure, which will leave you powerless. And finally, because you feel like you've been defeated, you'll start abusing food once again to numb the pain.
- Or because people are fallible. They make mistakes. They don't live up to your expectations. They steal your joy or stab you where it hurts the most. They push your most painful buttons or betray you or refuse to love you back. You need a rock you can stand on. The good news is that you have a rock: yourself. You are strong and courageous and gifted and talented and amazing and worthwhile and completely capable

of shedding the weight and living the life you want. Whether you believe it or not, you are. I believe that about you. Even if you don't yet trust yourself, you can trust me that all those things are true about you.

You don't need someone else to tell you who you are and what you want. You've lived with yourself all these years; you know yourself better than anyone. So before you read any further, choose *right now* to do this *for you and you alone.* Choose to do all this work because being comfortable in your own body matters deeply *to you.* And choose to do it *for you* every single day, *especially on the challenging days.* Choose to do this for you because you're worth the effort. You can trust me on that, too.

BLAME WILL NOT HELP YOU

It's really easy to blame somebody else for the way your life turned out, I get that. Takes the responsibility off you and puts it squarely on the shoulders of someone else. You can easily wind up stabbing your finger at someone else in blame, and that (I can tell you without a doubt) will stick you fast and keep you stuck for as long as that finger is jabbed in someone else's direction. Blame takes your power away, and you don't ever want to give away your power. Your power is the only thing, along with your body, that you ever truly have. Blame gives all the power to whomever's fault you think it is. You put your life on hold, waiting for them to fix it. In the meantime, you don't move forward with your own life. But what if they never admit to what they did? What if they never make amends? What if they never come to fix what's wrong? Well, if you keep blaming them, then you're stuck until they do. That's not an empowered position for you; that's not a position you want to be in at all. I know because I did it for years.

Let me start off by saying that The American Medical Association,[1] World Health Organization,[2] and World Obesity Federation[3] have all declared obesity to be a disease in its own right. Here's what I believe having lived it: *overweight and obesity are not a disease, they are a choice.* That said, for a long time I blamed others as the reason I overate or my metabolism for the reason I could never seem to get/keep the pounds off or "my disease" of overeating/obesity for why I was so overweight. So I resigned myself to living in a body that didn't feel like me. But here's the truth: I chose to overeat and abuse food because I wanted to numb myself. I felt sad, frustrated, angry, hopeless, scared, unworthy, trapped, and/or some other emotion that I just didn't want to feel. Blame was much easier than looking at myself and my choices as the problem. Here are two other truths, I say kindly: 1. unless someone is force-feeding you, you are one hundred percent responsible for what you eat, and 2. unless you have an underlying medical condition *diagnosed by a medical doctor*, you are fully responsible for your weight. You're the one choosing what you're putting in your body and how much and when. So, I say this kindly too: choose better.

Until you take full responsibility for your own life and for your own choices, you will not be likely to succeed at getting and/or keeping the weight off, you will not be likely to succeed at ceasing to abuse food. The simple fact is: *you are the boss of you.* So be the kind of boss that you'd love to have: one who is supportive, affirming, gives you the time and space you need to breathe and get the work done, but one who also knows when to give you a gentle kick in the behind to motivate you when you've stalled.

And yes, I know that sometimes other people really are to blame for things that have happened to you. But remember this: no matter what they did or didn't do, there was a lesson in it for you. You got a lesson in that person's character, they have showed you who they are *so whatever you do* believe them the very first time. Learn your lesson, take it to heart and remember it, so the next time you run into a person like that, you will know to stand up and roar, enforce your own boundaries and defend yourself, then get the heck away from them.

So if you're blaming someone or something else for where you are in your life, if you're making excuses for why you are the way you are, you're going to have to stop, I say gently, *right now.* Don't waste any more of your life trapped in blame. Know this: the only way to get your power back is to take it. So take it back.

SELF-PITY IS A SHEER CLIFF INTO A BLACK ABYSS

It's entirely up to you whether or not you want to fall off that self-pity cliff. It's a deep drop. The abyss is dark. Cold. Lonely. Pitted with landmines and traps. It's hard to get out of once you're in it. There's nothing good or helpful for you there. You will wander around lost, bitter, resentful, and angry. I'm aware that some horrible things may have happened to you. Things that were under your control but that you botched terribly. Things that were completely out of your control and were forced upon you anyway. Things done to you by others. Things you allowed not fully knowing the consequences you'd be getting. Things you chose out of fear or desperation or loneliness or longing or a myriad of other reasons. Things that changed the trajectory of your life and who you could've been forever. But, sadly, you can't go back and fix any of that. Not ever.

I'm also aware that it's not fun or even comfortable to be where you are right now. I've been there. I know. But sitting around feeling sorry for yourself (*isn't this awful, how terrible it is to be me, I'm stuck and can't get out, no one will help me,* and on the list goes) won't get you out of it. The first step that will is action. *You* need to take action, make a plan, and take steps forward to get yourself out of the mess you're in (just how to do that is coming up soon). You got yourself in by abusing food, you can get yourself out. Oh yes, you can. You have it inside you to do it; I know you do. You are absolutely capable, of that there's no doubt. So the question you need to ask yourself is: *Do I want to?*

YOU'LL HAVE TO INTERRUPT THE PATTERN SO YOU CAN GROW

Most people, myself included, don't like change. You probably don't like it because you're afraid of what's going to happen once you change. Uncertainty is scary, I get it. But doing the same or similar things over and over have gotten you to where you are today. And if you don't like where you are, you're going to have to do things differently. You're going to have to stop doing and thinking some things that are probably habits, which means they might be a challenge to break. You're going to have to start doing and thinking new things, which will likely frighten you because that will shove you out of your comfort zone. You may, at times, feel like you're in free fall without a safety net. You're most likely going to be kicking and screaming and throwing a tantrum at some point (yes, my hand is raised) because you aren't going to be happy about it at all.

It's true that you've got some patterns in your life. With food, certainly. And likely with what you believe about weight loss. And possibly with the role of exercise in weight loss and what exercise is supposed to look like. But you've also got patterns with how you approach relationships and the way you see the world and what you believe about yourself and what you think you're capable of and on this list goes. All those patterns keep you going in circles, too. You don't move forward because instead you choose to remain in (what you believe is the safety of) the pattern of the diet-go-round, or staying in toxic relationships, or maybe going to a job you despise day after day, or possibly chasing after the approval of others, and on this list goes, too. Imagine how powerful you'd be if you'd simply interrupt the pattern and break free of the circle, allowing yourself to move forward to where you most want to be.

So, *right now*, be willing to change. Just be open to the possibility of doing things differently, to thinking things differently, to seeing your life in a new light. *Be willing to be okay with uncertainty*. Be willing to relax into the space between where you are now and where you most want to be; be willing to let that space motivate you instead of scare you. Be willing to let yourself be a beginner again so you can take the pressure off and just learn as you go. Be willing to try new things. If you'll just be willing and open, you'll come to find out that you are absolutely capable of creating the life and body you most want to have.

IT'S LIKELY GOING TO TAKE LONGER THAN YOU THINK

I know everybody wants a quick fix. I have yet, in all my decades of dieting, ever found a quick fix that actually worked long-term. If I were you, I'd be very wary of any diet that makes wild promises (Drop 10 pounds the first week! Drop 30 pounds in a month!). You may think that's what you want. Trust me, you don't. Why? Because when the weight (and then some) inevitably comes back, you'll feel: like a failure, that there's something wrong with you, depressed, frustrated, anxious, embarrassed, humiliated, ashamed, and on the negative list goes.

For one, those diets are likely to be really unhealthy for you. For another, they are typically not sustainable long-term (meaning the rest of your life). Plus, they don't deal with the root cause of why you're abusing food (which has nothing to do with food, by the way), and so the odds of you keeping the weight off afterward are truly not in your favor. Fourth, if you lose weight really quickly, you'll likely end up with lots of extra skin sagging everywhere (depending on how much weight you lose), which you'll either have to live with or have surgery to remove. And finally, what's the point of putting forth all that effort and/or spending all that money if you can't maintain the weight loss?

It will be easier and healthier for you (both physically and mentally) to find some kind of peace with food that works for you long-term even if it takes some time to get to the end result. So prepare yourself to be in this for the long-haul. It may take months or a year or more, depending on how much weight you want to lose, your own physiology, your choices, and the like. It took me two years to reach my goal. Yes, *two years*. But the great news is that I don't ever have to go through it again. Better two years and done then another couple of decades (or more) on the diet-go-round.

You are in your body until your life is over. You're already in it for the long-haul. You are worth having patience and not giving up on yourself. Now you just have remind yourself of those things, daily if necessary.

SOME LIES YOU'LL HAVE TO STOP BELIEVING (A PARTIAL LIST)

If someone tells you a lie long enough or with enough authority, you're bound to believe it. That someone might even be you. If you hear something repeated over and over or even just once but with an "expert" behind it, you're bound to take it for the honest-to-goodness truth. But hear me: no matter how many times it's repeated or how forcefully it's said, a lie is still a lie; nothing will ever turn a lie into the truth. Even if you want to believe the lie, it's still a lie. So another question you need to be asking yourself is: *What lies do I believe?*

Until you recognize the lies that you believe, you can't do anything to combat them. And how do you combat a lie? You tell yourself the truth, of course, over and over, as many times as it takes to change your thinking/beliefs. Your brain thinks what you tell it to. And your thinking is what drives all of your behavior. We'll get into the science shortly, but for now, know this: you're unlikely to get the weight off and keep it off until you confront and change the lies that are holding you hostage.

What follows is a partial list of my own lies. Keep in mind: you may have other lies that you believe, *so make your own list and be honest with yourself.* And finally, each lie has a mantra that combats it, which you'll need to repeat (*repeat, repeat*) to yourself whenever that lie pops into your head. If that mantra doesn't work for you, for whatever reason, then make a mantra for yourself that does.

- Losing weight or maintaining weight loss is hard & gets harder with age and/or nothing is harder than breaking food abuse.
- You have to live this way.
- You are not worth the effort and/or you don't have what it takes.
- Loneliness will break you.
- Your life is not your own and/or your life is a dress rehearsal.
- You're being selfish.
- This is who you are (& always will be).
- You are damaged goods.
- You don't belong unless you're someone else.
- You cannot control what you think/believe.

LOSING WEIGHT OR MAINTAINING WEIGHT LOSS IS HARD AND GETS HARDER WITH AGE AND/OR NOTHING IS HARDER THAN BREAKING FOOD ABUSE

It's quite likely that you've bought into the idea that weight loss and/or maintenance is an excruciatingly difficult process. Or maybe you believe that, because you have no choice but to eat if you want to live, breaking the crazy-making behavior with food is the hardest thing you'll ever have to do. Or maybe you've believed the lie, because likely every diet you've been on tells you this, that you cannot eat what you want. Or the lie that if you want to lose weight, you can *only* eat "healthy" foods the vast majority of the time with maybe a cheat day thrown in once a week. Or that you should weigh and measure your food so you know exactly how many calories you are consuming. Or that some foods are just completely forbidden for you to eat at all. Or that you must keep a food journal and write it all down so you can track your eating.

I'm sure you've also heard the lie that you need to exercise a lot. Or that cardio is what you need to do to burn fat. Or that your heart rate needs to be in a certain zone for the majority of the time you're exercising. And the lie that if you've got a slow metabolism, well, you're out of luck. Or the odds of you actually succeeding are stacked against you; that only a lucky special few (the chosen ones?) have what it takes to get the weight off and keep it off. And if you're over thirty-five years old, you've probably taken to heart that your odds of successful weight loss have decreased exponentially because of your age.

Advertisements bombard you with all those ideas. So do your friends, colleagues, family members, and on the list goes. Sadly, some medical professionals will tell you those same things. Look, I'm here to tell you that I used to believe all that, too. I bought into those lies because someone in authority, someone whom I thought knew more than I did, said they were true. And for that reason alone, I didn't question; I just took what they said to be the truth. I'm also here to tell you that none of the lies I just mentioned, in my experience, are true. None of them.

Here's what is true: you will *always* live out what you believe. Your weight loss journey will be as hard or as easy as you want it to be based on what you choose to believe.

So a mantra for you to take to heart: *I live out what I believe, so I will choose beliefs that help me.*

YOU HAVE TO LIVE THIS WAY

If someone told you that you're just destined to be overweight, that abusing food and/or being overweight runs in the family, that you're big-boned, that you're weak-willed and don't have the fortitude to keep the weight off, or any such thing, listen to me right now and very carefully . . . THEY WERE WRONG. If you're telling yourself those same things, well I say kindly, you're wrong too.

Nobody is destined to be overweight/obese and/or to abuse food. Nobody.

The only thing that believing you have to live this way does is make you lose hope. And losing hope is the quickest way from where you are now to diving head first into numbing substances/behaviors. Why try if there's no hope? Why move forward only to fail? Why step out and do anything if it's just not going to work out? Why give any effort at all if it's not going to make any difference in the end? There's no hope to be found inside the belief that you have to live this way. It's like a black hole in space that sucks anything and everything into itself. There's no light to be had in believing that you're stuck and there are no choices left to you.

Beliefs are just thoughts that you've repeated over and over and over again to the point where you don't have to think about them anymore. Lucky for you that you get to choose what you're going to think and believe. So stop choosing to believe that you have to live any certain way. You don't have to live overweight. You don't have to live abusing food and numbing yourself and just trying to survive through the days. You don't have to live in pain and suffering. You don't have to live in despair. You don't now and you never did. Instead, you can choose to think about and believe in your ability to change and grow and thrive.

Another new mantra to take to heart: *My beliefs are not by chance, they are by choice, so I will choose to believe differently.*

YOU ARE NOT WORTH THE EFFORT AND/OR YOU DON'T HAVE WHAT IT TAKES

Part of the problem you're having, most likely, is that you don't believe in your own worth and value. Maybe you believe that you don't matter much at all. And so, because you believe you don't matter, you also believe that what you say and do doesn't matter much either. Those are all lies that you picked up somewhere along the way, I assure you. But until you stop believing them, those lies will be truths to you. Here's what's real: your worth and value are innate. You were born with them and no one—hear me, *no one*—can *ever* take them away from you. And because you have intrinsic worth and value, you matter. And because you matter, your life story matters and what you have to say matters and what you do matters. That's what you need to be telling yourself, over and over as many times as it takes until those words become the story that you believe about yourself and your life.

Willpower isn't the problem. It wasn't my issue, and I doubt it's yours. I tried. And tried. And tried. And tried. I had times when I got skinny, but nothing ever lasted long-term. And within months, maybe even a year, I'd be back to where I started or, more often, heavier. Because none of those diets, not a single one, ever dealt with the root cause, which was the (figurative) hole/wound inside me that made me feel/think/believe something about me as a human being was lacking/missing/wrong. And, as you probably already know, until you yank something out by the roots, it keeps growing no matter how hard you might try to stop it. You have a hole/wound inside you too. And once you find out what the root cause of your hole/wound is, once you take steps to fill that hole/wound in a healthy way (more on that soon), you'll see that you do indeed have what it takes. You'll come to understand that you had what it takes all along.

So do this:
1. Starting *right now*, you treat yourself like the worthy and valuable person you are. You treat yourself with kindness and respect, always, *even if you don't feel like it.*

2. So, *right now* and not when you lose X amount of pounds, you take excellent care of yourself and do n things for you and speak strengthening words to yourself and think thoughts that build you up.
3. You stop hiding yourself and you start enjoying your life *right now*.
4. Know this: if you act that way long enough, your feelings will catch up and your beliefs will change, I assure you they will.
5. Then do yourself a kindness and make a list of all your accomplishments, no matter how big or small.
6. Read that list aloud, tack it up where you can see it, and let that list strengthen you.

Play this mantra in a loop inside your head: *I have worth and value because I am alive. I have everything I need inside me to create a life I love.*

LONELINESS WILL BREAK YOU

Loneliness is a feeling; it cannot break you. It can be tough, sure. Loneliness may hit your self-esteem and your self-worth, especially if you equate how many relationships you have to how valuable and worthwhile you are. Loneliness often leads to thoughts of: what's wrong with me, why does no one want me around, why doesn't anyone like me, why don't I belong. That line of thinking tends to spiral into abusing numbing substances/behaviors because you are giving the power over your well-being to someone else. Trust me on this: you never want your self-esteem and self-worth to be in someone else's hands. Ever.

Being alone with yourself can also be daunting because feelings you may have been avoiding and/or suppressing tend to come up. You don't like feeling them and so you do your best to avoid being alone at any cost. But feelings can't hurt you; only your reaction to them can. Numbing/avoiding/denying your feelings all have consequences to your mental and physical health. A feeling only has the power that you give it. And loneliness is just a feeling. Maybe a sucky, difficult feeling but still just a feeling. All you have to do is sit with it, *really feel it*, then let it pass (which we'll be discussing shortly).

To be alone and not lonely comes from being okay with yourself and not looking for others to validate you. Here's the truth: people come into your life and then they leave. The only constant will be you. And here's another truth (even if you don't quite believe it yet): you are whole as you are, alone, not doing any particular thing or being any particular way, and you don't ever need anything or anyone else to make you complete. You may believe that you do and that's a belief that you can change (simply by choosing to believe something different).

A mantra to repeat until it becomes what you believe: *Loneliness is just a feeling and feelings pass. I am whole as I am.*

YOUR LIFE IS NOT YOUR OWN AND/OR YOUR LIFE IS A DRESS REHEARSAL

First, there is only one life in this world that you can truly save: that's your own. Your life is not your dad's expectations or your mom's hopes. It's not what your grandmother wants for you or what your grandfather wishes you would do. It doesn't belong to your best friend, who maybe you're afraid to let go of, or the person you'll date who will shatter your heart. It's your life, and when all is said and done, you'll be the only one responsible for your own happiness. Remember that every time you make a choice.

And second, your life is happening *right now* and you're likely missing it. Look, there's just not that kind of time. I know you believe there is or else you wouldn't be in a holding pattern in your life, waiting and waiting. Maybe you think you'll get to it this afternoon, or start fresh tomorrow morning, or for sure next Monday, or without a doubt January first of next year. Or maybe you're waiting for the next big milestone to happen or to lose ten/twenty/fifty pounds and so you're not enjoying your life *right now*. Or maybe you're putting your life on hold until you get a sign from above or an absolute sure thing or an unwavering belief in who you are and/or what you're supposed to be doing. In the end, it all comes down to a belief that you have an infinite amount of time. And as we all know, you don't. Intellectually, you understand that, I'm sure. But emotionally, well, maybe you don't want to face it or you don't believe your life will end anytime soon. But, I tell you kindly, there are no absolute guarantees.

And abusing food and/or any substance/behavior is putting your life on hold. Every time you choose to abuse food or another substance/behavior over yourself and your well-being, you put yourself in a holding pattern. All the time you spend looking in a mirror and pinching your thighs and berating your appearance and calling yourself names and spiraling in circles on the diet-go-round is just a distraction to keep you in perpetual waiting. Waiting for your life to get better. Waiting for you to feel good about yourself. Waiting for your real life to begin. Here's something, I say gently, that you need to fully understand: *this is your real life. Right now.* And your life won't get better by wishing; it'll get better with work. And you won't feel good about yourself by chance; you'll feel good about yourself by choice.

Putting your life on hold also drains you of any power you might have. You say *no* to opportunities and you wait. You hold out for the future and miss the present. You shame yourself and beat yourself up and keep your own self small, which only serves to distract you from the work you need to be doing to make your life what you want it to be. You likely choose the diet-go-round day after day after day to keep yourself from moving forward toward what you most want (your hopes, passions, goals, and dreams), because at the core, no matter how it manifests itself, putting your life on hold all stems from fear.

Simple, ordinary fear.

Imagine how powerful you'd be if you'd focus on moving forward instead of focusing on waiting.

So do this:

1. Go somewhere alone then get still and quiet.
2. Ask questions about your life like: *Why am I putting my life on hold? What do I hope to gain by waiting? Who will I upset by claiming authority over my own life? What am I afraid will happen if I move forward?*
3. Then listen to your intuition for the answers. Write down the first things that come to you (so no overthinking and/or editing).

You need to discover, truly, the reasons behind your choice(s) to put your life on hold and keep yourself powerless. And then you need to start living and enjoying your life *right now*, this very moment (yes, that's a choice, too).

Then make this your new mantra: *My life belongs to me and me alone, I get to choose how I want to live it. I am responsible for saving my own life.*

YOU'RE BEING SELFISH

I'm going to guess, because you're reading this book, that you're unfulfilled with who, what, and/or where you are at this moment. You likely aren't where you wanted or envisioned yourself to be at this point in your life. Right now, at this particular time, you aren't in the body that you most want. You also may not have the things (career, education, family, and on it goes) that you want to have. You're possibly in some emotional pain about that. And it's the pain that you're trying to numb by abusing food. The underlying cause of that particular pain is likely an unwillingness to accept your life as it is, right now at this moment.

It's also entirely possible that your motivation has been someone or something other than yourself and your own well-being. You may have elderly parents or needy kids or a demanding significant other or your own business or stresses at school or a to-do list as long as my leg. Maybe you've been putting all those other people/things in front of yourself for a long time, maybe even for as long as you can remember. Maybe you believe it's your duty to keep yourself low on the priority list. Maybe someone in authority or someone you loved called you selfish and, because you don't want to be perceived as selfish (because who would?), you have put the wants and needs of other people/things before yourself. Maybe you've come to the point where you've completely fallen off your own to-do list so your needs and wants get sacrificed because you believe it'd be selfish to do otherwise.

It's also possible, I say kindly, that you have other motives entirely. Maybe you're trying to gain something. Perhaps you think that putting everyone and everything ahead of yourself, and thus playing the part of the martyr, will make you look good in other people's eyes. Maybe you want them to like you and you think that providing for their wants/needs *at the expense of your own* is the way to do that. Or maybe you're looking for some kind of sympathy. In the end though, you'll end up living in a body you don't like and having a life you don't want because you'd rather be unfulfilled than perceived as selfish (and yes, that's a choice).

I'm here to tell you that taking excellent care of yourself is not selfish at all. Not even a little bit. In fact, putting yourself first on your daily to-do list is the most responsible thing you can do. Seriously, answer me this: why should you live overweight (which takes a toll on your physical health) and unfulfilled (which takes a toll on your mental health) just to please someone (anyone) else? The answer: you shouldn't, *ever*. To shed the weight, *you must put yourself and your well-being first every single day*. Period. That's non-negotiable.

Hear me on this: there's no guilt in that whatsoever. Absolutely none. So do not feel guilty, ever, about making yourself number one on your priority list. It really is true that you can't take excellent care of others if you don't take excellent care of yourself first.

So another mantra to live by: *Taking excellent care of myself is the healthiest thing I can do.*

THIS IS WHO YOU ARE (AND ALWAYS WILL BE)

You are not who other people say you are. You are not the labels and the judgments and the slights and the slurs meant to cut you down and keep you small that you may have heard said about yourself.

The only person you are is the one you decide to be.

If you don't much like and/or believe in yourself, you end up looking to others to tell you who you are. There are perils to doing this. First, you are putting the power over your life in someone else's hands (which is a terrible predicament to put yourself in). Second, you will not think for yourself, listen to your own intuition, forge your own path, and make decisions based on your own wants/needs; instead you'll end up living your life by committee and/or majority vote. You will never become who you are meant to be if you follow along instead of leading your own way. And third, you will not be true to yourself and who you know yourself to be, thus betraying yourself; and it's the self-betrayal that will have you abusing food faster than anything.

Another problem that comes into play is that you end up valuing other people's opinions about you over your own. Maybe some misguided person taught you through their words and/or actions that what others thought about you and/or life in general was more important than what you thought about yourself or life. And so maybe you've come to believe that others must know more than you do about how to live in the world, must know you better than you know yourself. That belief disempowers you: it puts the power over your life into the hands of whomever it is you're listening to about who/what you should be and about how you should live your life.

You are who *you* believe you are. You get to choose who you are and who you want to be. You get to decide how you look at life and what you want to believe. It's your choice and yours alone. You can reinvent yourself, as many times as it takes, until you discover just who you truly are at your core, what matters deeply to you, and how to create a life that best fits you. In the end, it all comes down to you giving up being someone else so that you can become yourself.

Another mantra for you to take to heart: *The only person I am is the one I decide to be, and the only opinion that matters about my life is my own.*

YOU ARE DAMAGED GOODS

You may have been told by others that you're damaged goods, that there's something broken about you that's just beyond repair. And if you believe you are damaged goods (unfixable, unwanted), you will live that out in your life. But here's something you need to keep in mind: those people who have said that you're broken, won't amount to anything, have nothing to offer, are less than, are undeserving, and on the list goes, are the people who themselves are hurt and feel unworthy and want some way to lessen their own pain. The way those people choose to do that is to take all their own feelings of brokenness and dump them right onto you. But those feelings don't belong to you. They never did. They aren't about you. They never were. You need to and must reject any words/thoughts/beliefs, coming from others and/or from yourself, that you are not whole as you are right now (and yes, that's your choice).

You might believe that something about you is amiss, that something inside you got shattered at some point and you haven't been able to put it back right since. You may let whatever you did or was done to you fester, rolling it over in your memory and replaying it, wondering what you should've/could've/would've done to make it better or different. And in that way, that little cocklebur of pain that got lodged inside you when whatever it was first happened grows and grows until it becomes a belief that you somehow deserved what you got because you are damaged goods. You may tell yourself that something deep down inside you is just Not Right. And you may also have convinced yourself that if you could just fix that Not Right part of you, you'd have more and better relationships, you'd be happier and more fulfilled, you wouldn't be afraid so much, you'd have a richer and fuller life, you'd no longer be struggling with food, and on the list goes.

While you may feel/think/believe/say you are broken or damaged, here's the truth: you are not broken, you are not damaged goods. So you're not in need of fixing. You have quirks and preferences and personality traits. You may be a little peculiar and different than everybody else. You may have some ailments or congenital health problems. You may have been abused or traumatized or assaulted or wounded. You may struggle with mental health issues. You may just not like to be around people. None of that means you are broken. None of that means you are damaged goods. The essence of you, who you are deep down at the core, is healthy and whole. It is shiny and new, not even a single scratch. The essence of you is unblemished and unbroken and undamaged. That's the part of you that belongs to you and you alone. That's the part of you that no one else can touch. The strong and resilient and persevering part. The part that will always be there no matter what may happen in your life. And that's the part of you that matters the most. It's the wellspring of who you are. It's where everything flows from. And, I assure you, the essence of you is neither broken nor damaged.

So repeat this new mantra until it becomes the main point of the story you tell about your life: *The essence of me, who I am deep down, is healthy and whole.*

YOU DON'T BELONG UNLESS YOU'RE SOMEONE ELSE

One of the most basic needs a person has is to be part of a group, to build relationships and have a sense of belonging.[4] So it's completely natural for you to want to fit in. But forcing that connection at any cost just fuels numbing behavior. Losing yourself—what you value, what matters to you, who you are at the core—just so you don't have to be the odd person out is an act of self-betrayal that will destroy your trust in yourself and decimate your self-esteem. It will chip away at you until you end up just a husk of who you once were.

Then the cycle starts: you're in emotional pain from pretending to be someone else and from believing that you're not likable as yourself so you abuse food or some other substance/behavior to numb the pain/suffering so you can keep on being someone you're not, which keeps causing pain, which keeps you heading for the refrigerator/pantry. Conforming, like dieting, is a vicious circle, and you will keep going around and around until you decide you've had enough and jump off.

Real connection, where you truly see someone and they truly see you, only comes from honesty. Meaningful connection only happens when you're vulnerable and you risk and you let people experience the real you. True connection is when you show up and say, "Well, this is me. This is what I've got. This is what I can do. This is who I am. Take it or leave it." The people who stay—the ones who take you as-is—those are the ones who are worth your time. Those are the only ones with whom you will find that real connection you're searching for.

Popularity is really a pointless endeavor. Numbers are fleeting. Rankings change all the time. The person(s) you might be chasing—the people for whom you are changing your beliefs, lifestyle, morals, values, personality, and/or anything else about yourself just to appease them—will likely leave your life as soon as you can no longer keep up the facade. And trust me on this: at some point you won't be able to keep playing the role of someone you're not. The sheer exhaustion and emotional strain of keeping up appearances will wear you down, the real you will be exposed, and those people you are chasing will leave. Then, when that happens, you'll be angry, bitter, and/or resentful at them. You're also likely to be angry, bitter, and/or resentful at yourself for having wasted so much time and energy attempting to be someone else in what ended up (*and will always end up*) being a futile quest.

So choose to show up as yourself. You are only powerful when you go out into the world as-is. Some people won't like the real you, both people you just meet and people you may have known a long time. That's their choice and that's okay. *It's not your job to convince them.* You want genuine connection (yes, you do!) so just take your awesome self and move on. Let the people who like you as-is gravitate toward you; those are the only people you want in your life anyway.

And keep this as your mantra: *The only way to free myself is to be myself.*

YOU CANNOT CONTROL WHAT YOU THINK/BELIEVE

Negative thoughts and beliefs (which, again, are just thoughts you've repeated to yourself) can easily and quickly spiral out of control if you let them. Here's how: one negative thought/belief pops into your mind. You choose not to put a stop to it right then and there. Another one comes after it. Then another and another. You choose not to stop any of those either. And, I say kindly, it is a choice. *Your choice.* It's your head after all; you're the one in control of either accepting or rejecting any thought inside it. And yes, you can reject any thought you choose to. (*Nope, not helpful. No, not true. Naw, not buying into that.* You get the idea.) Those negative thoughts are like a Mack truck coming at you while you're standing on the double yellow line in the middle of the road right in its path. If you don't do something—dodge to the right or the left, call for help, even go sprinting in the opposite direction—those thoughts will come barreling down and flatten you.

When you let the negative thoughts spiral out of control, when you choose to focus on them and believe them, you'll end up in the deep dark, trapped in a strange landscape, trying desperately to find your way out. The longer you stay there, the harder it'll be to find your way back to a good place or even just back to the place where you started. Those negative thoughts build on one another like an avalanche, pushing you away from where you want to be, burying you, crushing you, leaving you feeling pressed and tight and suffocated. And then in the end, if you let the onslaught of negative thoughts go on for too long, there'll be an overwhelming feeling of helplessness and hopelessness. And it's those last feelings, the ones where you're convinced that you're not in charge of your own life anymore, that'll have you running to abuse food for numbness, solace, avoidance, and/or relief.

Letting the negative thoughts spiral out of control is also a distraction. It's a way to avoid something you don't want to deal with (for instance: taking responsibility for your own happiness, moving forward in your own life, overcoming your fears, [insert what you're avoiding here]). If you're busy falling into a bottomless pit of negative thoughts, you don't have to do anything to push through and face whatever it is you need to face. The death spiral of negative thoughts also changes your focus. Instead of keeping your eyes on creating the life you want, your gaze falls down into the bottomless pit along with you. It really is true that whatever you focus on grows. So if you focus on those negative thoughts, well, those are what will grow (and grow and grow and grow).

So do this:

1. Challenge the thoughts and beliefs that come into your head (oh yes, you can!), especially the ones that you are continually repeating to yourself and/or the ones that are holding you back.
2. For *each* thought, ask: *Is this thought/belief honestly true? Does it serve me? Is it helping me or harming me to think/believe this?*
3. Then choose (yes, it's a choice) to reject any thoughts and beliefs that don't encourage you, nurture you, and/or help you grow and move forward.

Your new mantra: *All I have to do to change my life is to change my mind.*

SOME THINGS YOU'LL HAVE TO START DOING

- Tell the truth.
- Make weight loss a journey you're on by yourself.
- Decide right now what you'll do when obstacles come.
- Decide right now what you'll do when the temptation to quit comes.
- Commit to being true to yourself.

TELL THE TRUTH

Honesty with yourself is paramount to your healing, like we talked about earlier. What's also necessary for your healing is being honest with others. You've got to tell the truth about how you really think and feel, even if that's uncomfortable for you to do. The truth about who you really are, even if your voice shakes when you do it. The truth about what you want out of your life, even if admitting that makes your body tremble when you say it out loud.

This one is hard sometimes, especially if you've been lying to yourself or to others for a long time. You might not even think you're lying, but have you ever said/thought any of the following (a partial list):

- It's not as bad as … (when it really is a bad situation)
- It'll be okay if… (when it doesn't feel okay to you at all)
- I don't want to do this but… (when you really don't want to do whatever it is but are now talking yourself into why you should)
- I do want to do this but… (when you really do want to do whatever it is but are now talking yourself into why you shouldn't)
- Uh-huh, yeah, sure, I'm fine… (when you're really not)
- I don't really want that… (when you really do).
- I do really want that… (when you really don't).

You might think those are small white lies, just harmless little fibs, but they're damaging to you as a person. Every lie, no matter the size or severity, whittles away at you, digging a little deeper that hole inside you, the one that you're trying to fill by abusing food. That's especially true of the lies you tell to yourself.

It's going to take some courage and emotional strength to find your voice, stand up for yourself, speak the truth, and let the chips fall where they may. But remember: you have it in you. You are strong, courageous, tenacious, and determined to fix your own life. Oh yes, you are or you wouldn't still be reading this book.

MAKE WEIGHT LOSS A JOURNEY YOU'RE ON BY YOURSELF

The fastest way to make yourself overwhelmed and stressed is to make your weight-loss goal about beating someone else. Do yourself a kindness and don't do that. There will always be someone thinner than you or shedding the weight faster than you. So you pick a goal (number on the scale, clothes size, how you feel in your body, whatever works for you) that you want to reach because that goal deeply matters to *you*.

When I first started my journey, I felt very much like I was standing at the bottom of a huge mountain, looking up at the peak (my goal weight), and thinking: *there's no way*. Some days you, too, may feel like you're climbing a mountain. That's okay because it's your own mountain, and that mountain is only as steep and rocky as you make it. You get to decide. So think easy and winding path to the top of a hill in the summertime, not straight up and icy and full of chasms like to the peak of Mount Everest. The other thing to keep in mind is that there's nobody else on your mountain/hill with you, so there's no rush to the top, no competition, no need to worry or fear. You'll get to the summit when you get there, and that's okay.

You've heard that old phrase: slow and steady wins the race. That's true. Show yourself some compassion. Be kind, gentle, and patient with yourself. You keep moving forward/upward. You keep your eyes on the blue skies of your own goal. That's how you'll get there. One small step after another. It truly (and I do mean *truly*) does not matter how slowly you go as long as you don't stop.

And remember: while you're on that mountain/hill by yourself, you're still not alone. I was once there. Lots of other people are climbing their own mountains/hills. The people who are succeeding long-term are the ones who are doing it for themselves and who value themselves enough to not give up. So you make your own goal. Then you reach it for you because you're worth the time and effort it's going to take to get there.

DECIDE RIGHT NOW WHAT YOU'LL DO WHEN OBSTACLES COME

You will face obstacles. This is true in life, period (whether you're on a weight-loss journey or not). It's not a matter of *if* but of *when*. There's no getting around it. You need to fully understand that going in. Eventually, you're going to get hit with some uncomfortable things. You need to mentally prepare yourself *now* so you don't get blindsided and derailed, so you don't turn back to abusing food to cope. You need to decide what's more important to you: either taking care of yourself and having the life you want and reaching your own goal(s) or numbing yourself against whatever it is that blocks your way. So choose, *right now*. Keep in mind: obstacles in life are inevitable; defeat, however, is optional.

Below is a partial list of the obstacles I faced over the past nine years (while losing the weight & also maintaining that weight loss):

- Almost all my friends left my life at roughly the same time.
- My dad dying and all the things that were left unresolved and unspoken.
- A loved one with a mental illness, whom I took care for over a year even as insults and hatred and rage were hurled my way.
- Another loved one with a life-threatening illness, whom I took care of for ten months.
- A betrayal by a loved one that completely broke my trust.
- A massive attack of self-doubt, which led to a crisis of faith.
- Writing, which had been a haven, became a torture.
- Clinical depression.
- A sudden and unexpected loss of my entire source of income.

- A car accident that wasn't my fault, which left me in often-debilitating pain every day for well over a year and took away, in an instant, my ability to do nearly everything that I enjoyed and that fulfilled me.

Yes, some of those derailed me. In more than one case, I ran back to abusing food because I didn't want to feel the emotional and/or physical pain. Every time I turned to food for comfort, I gained weight in short order (in two instances, nearly twenty pounds) before I stopped, sat back, and looked around. The only thing overeating was doing was making me overweight again. *Numbing myself by abusing food wasn't actually fixing anything.* My friends were still gone. Words to my dad were still left unsaid. The broken trust was still broken. The page was still blank. The nerve pain was still there.

In that moment, I made a choice. Taking care of myself and reaching my own goals, I decided, were more important than any of those obstacles. Period. All I did was make a choice. You can (and need to) make the same choice, too.

DECIDE RIGHT NOW WHAT YOU'LL DO WHEN THE TEMPTATION TO QUIT COMES

You have to decide, *right now before you even begin*, what you're going to do when the temptation to quit comes. Because it will. It, too, is not a matter of *if* but of *when*.

So will you believe, *right now and always*, that you have worth and value and that you matter? Will you commit to yourself, *right now and always*, to keep going, to not give up on yourself, to keep moving forward regardless of how long it takes? Will you hold to that commitment even if progress seems slow/nonexistent or on the rough days when everything seems to be going wrong or on the weeks when the scale goes up even though you're fairly certain you did everything you were supposed to?

Will you choose, *right now before you even begin*, that when challenges get thrown at you and uncomfortable feelings rise up and not-so-pleasant stuff comes at you fast that you'll keep going in the face of all that? That means you'll have to sit with whatever you're feeling, regardless of how painful it may be, without numbing yourself. You'll have to let yourself feel, raw and unchecked, whatever those feelings are until they pass. That also means you'll have to take steps to fix whatever's wrong in your life, regardless of how scared you are or how overwhelming that might seem. You'll have to start believing that you are so much stronger than you give yourself credit for. And finally, that means you won't be able to keep abusing food as a crutch to get you through. You'll have to take to heart that food will never fix whatever is wrong; it might numb you or comfort you, yes, but food will never fix anything.

So choose, *right now before you even begin*, when the temptation to quit comes that you won't go running back to the way you've always done things (bingeing, overeating, starving, purging, exercising like crazy, and/or some diet that gave you faster but temporary results). None of those things worked, mind you; if anything had, you wouldn't still be searching for an answer. In the end, there really are only two choices: 1. keep going until you reach the goal you set for yourself or 2. quit. Decide *right now before you even begin*: which one will you choose?

COMMIT TO BEING TRUE TO YOURSELF

The difference between *impossible* and *I'm possible* is simple: it's commitment.

The commitment you're making is to yourself. You're giving yourself your word. You need to treat that like a commitment that you'd make to anyone. (And if you don't keep your commitments to others, well I say kindly, that's a character issue that you need to work on.) You must have integrity with your own self. *Self-trust is paramount to your success*. It's vital because you are the only person you can ever one hundred percent count on to be there for you. And the only way you'll ever learn to trust yourself completely is by keeping your word to yourself, over and over again, every single time. You are worth the commitment you're making to yourself, I assure you of that.

It turns out that the answer to permanent weight loss really is as simple and as easy as you want to make it. It all comes down to committing to yourself and not giving up on yourself. That's it. So you need to decide, *right now before you even begin*, that you're committed *to your own healing*, that *regardless of what comes up* you're going to see this weight-loss journey through, that you're going to reach your goal(s) *no matter how long it takes* because that goal(s) matters deeply to you.

And know this too: if you're not keeping your commitments to yourself, you are not being true to yourself and you are, in fact, betraying yourself. If you think that being betrayed by someone you love is painful and debilitating, it absolutely pales in comparison to betraying your own self. No matter what, you can't outrun yourself. There's nowhere you can go and nothing you can do to get away from that hurt. The only thing left at that point is to either: 1. forgive yourself and begin again or 2. numb the pain with your drug of choice, food. Sadly, many people (at one time, myself included) don't choose to forgive themselves and start over; instead, they abuse food.

Not keeping your word to yourself is not the only way you are not true to yourself. What follows is a partial list of other ways you may betray yourself:

- Not defending your own boundaries and saying *yes* when all you want to do is holler *no*.

- Talking to or about yourself in a way that diminishes you instead of spurs you to change (like judging, labeling, shaming, and/or beating yourself up).
- Utterly ignoring your own intuition, or worse, flying in the face of it by doing the exact opposite of what your voice of wisdom is saying.
- Letting other people's opinions of you and your life be more important to you than your own.
- Looking to others to validate you and your decisions, especially if you won't move forward until they do.
- Making compromises that cause you to feel less than and powerless.
- Staying in bad relationships, including romantic ones and friendships and even with people related to you, for far too long, especially when you *know* it's time to leave.
- Allowing others or even yourself to treat you badly and/or disrespectfully.
- Letting other people and/or things determine your self-worth.
- Actively trying to be someone you are not.

The motivation behind self-betrayal usually comes down to shame. Shame, according to the dictionary, is a painful emotion of humiliation or disgrace.[5] Shame makes you believe you're not worth anything. If you don't believe you're worth anything, you won't think twice about betraying yourself. But shame can be overcome. We'll be talking about how in Chapter Three.

For your healing, know that there are really only two choices when you're faced with a decision to be true to yourself: 1. have your own back always or 2. turn your back on yourself. Decide now: which one will you choose?

OH, SOME SCIENCE

So I'll do my best not to make the science parts a snooze. You should read them anyway even if they are because it's important for you to understand how your body works and how you can best help yourself heal. Keep in mind for all the science sections: this is my layman's understanding, so for a more in-depth explanation, you should take the time to do your own research.

Let's start off by talking about your brain. Your brain does some 400 billion (yes, billion with a *b*) actions *per second*.[6] It's busy. So it's always looking for a way to streamline and make things more efficient. When you do or think something over and over, you're actually forming and strengthening neural pathways that make your brain cells communicate more efficiently.[7] Those pathways make it easier for your brain to know what to do the next time when the same or a similar situation comes up. In essence, your brain no longer expends effort to analyze and decide, it just follows that well-worn neural pathway to automatically tell you how to act/react. (It's sort of like walking the same stretch of grass over and over, eventually you'll flatten it down and make an easier-to-walk dirt path.) That's how habits, both good and bad, get formed. You tend to respond in the same way (reacting the same way, thinking the same kinds of thoughts, turning to a substance like food to numb yourself instead of dealing with your feelings, choosing to not take good care of yourself, and the like) because the repetition of those behaviors are now a neural pathway worn in your brain.

All is not lost, though. Your brain has something called neuroplasticity, which means it can change and new paths can be formed.[8] Why does that matter? It means that you don't ever have to be stuck in habits that aren't helping you. It means you don't have to respond by automatically doing and thinking the same things. *You get to choose.* You can change your thinking and your behavior to create a new path, a healthier path that gets you to where you want to be. Yes, it's going to take some work on your part; it is your brain and yours alone after all. The great news is that it really doesn't have to take all that long. Researchers at University College London have shown that it takes an average of 66 days (depending on the person, not quite three weeks on the short end and nearly nine months on the long end) to form a new neural pathway.[9] So on average, it takes just two short months of changing your thinking (for instance, believing in your own worth and value *daily*) and behavior (for example, treating yourself with kindness and respect *daily*) for you to form a brand new neural pathway in your brain, which in turn will completely change your life in the direction you want it to go.

You are worth taking those couple of months to become the person you want to be.

So do this:
1. Mark your calendar for at least 66 days from today.
2. Then write an answer to these: *What do I want/need to think about myself and/or the task at hand to get to where I most want to be? What behaviors do I want/need to stop/start doing to get to where I most want to be?*
3. Then start today: think at least one of those thoughts you want/need to think & do at least one of those behaviors you want/need to do that will help you heal and move you forward to where you most want to be.
4. Repeat *every day*, that same thought(s) and that same behavior(s) that will serve you and not harm you.
5. If you do those two things *daily* over an extended period of time, you'll come to find you've created a new habit(s), one(s) that will serve to heal you and help you grow.

THIS IS A PRACTICE AND A PROCESS

First and foremost, cherry pick from the information you've read, figure out what works for you, then do that. Second, know that eventually, at some point, you will make a mistake. You're human. It's okay. You don't have to do *any* of this perfectly. You couldn't even if you tried really hard. So do the best you can and don't give up on yourself. When you screw up (no matter what it is: overeating or bingeing or purging or starving or gaining weight or running back to things that didn't work before or [insert your mistake here]), you just forgive yourself and start again right where you are, as many times as it takes.

There is *no limit* to the number of tries you get. *So don't beat yourself up. Don't use any mistake as an excuse to quit. Just forgive yourself and start again.* It's a practice and like anything you practice, you'll get better and better at it over time. It's also a process to discover for yourself who you really are, what you really want, and what works for you and what doesn't.

So keep this as your mantra as you move forward: *every mistake is simply a brand new chance to do it better the next time.*

CHAPTER TWO

LISTEN TO YOUR BODY

OR

What looks/feels/sounds like crazy probably is.

Chapter Two

"The summit is for the ego. The journey is for the soul."
—Unknown

FATHER WATCHES ME as I eat. I keep my eyes on my plate, but I can feel his stare. It bores into the top of my head. It raises the hairs on the back of my neck, flushes my cheeks. I start to shake, first in my hands. They are tiny almost imperceptible tremors that no one can see. But I can feel them. I clamp down my stomach muscles, make my body go rigid. I grip the fork tighter. I try to force my body to be still. Sweat trickles down the sides of my face. It runs from my temple, past my ear, toward my jaw. Does Father see it? I hope he doesn't. Father doesn't like weakness. He doesn't like it at all. You want something to cry about? I'll give you something to cry about. The shaking travels up my arms, into my shoulders, across my chest, toward my neck, jaw, head. I clench my teeth so hard that I give myself a headache. I lean hard on a single word: stop. Stop. Stop. Stop. But the shaking doesn't stop. My whole body quakes like a leaf in a windstorm.

I cut a piece of chicken. My hands tremble. The knife wobbles, scraping against the plate. That stare bores into me. I chew and chew. Please stop looking at me. I swallow. The meat is a hot lump in my throat. I take another tiny bite. I don't know how to hide the tremors. So I stop lifting the fork. Instead, I push the food around with the tines. I dip my mouth toward the plate. I take miniature, infrequent bites. Then I set the fork and knife down on my napkin. The knife leaves a smear of grease on the white paper. I rest my hands in my lap and curl the fingers against my thighs and press down until the shaking stops.

Father says, "Aren't you going to eat?"

"I'm not hungry."

"Good for you to eat less. No daughter of mine is going to be fat."

I look at my lap. Blood rushes to my face until it's so hot that I feel like I've been set on fire. My thighs spread across the chair. I press my fingernails into my jeans. Hard. Then harder. Then harder still. When I draw them away, there are half-moon indents in the denim fabric. Don't look at him. Don't look at Mother or Brother. Don't raise your eyes at all.

His words echo in my head: no daughter of mine is going to be fat . . . no daughter of mine . . . fat . . . no daughter of mine. I pick at my shirt, pinch the flesh underneath it. I am already fat. So whose daughter am I?

Later that night, Father and I sit together in the dark. The kitchen light is on, spilling out the sliding glass door, falling in a long rectangle onto the deck. We are quiet underneath the hemlock except for the sound of my smacking lips as I chew gum. Above us, the stars click on slowly. I raise a finger, connecting the pinpricks of light. Cassiopeia. Pegasus. Little Dipper. My index finger lingers on the North Star, which is my favorite. A star to guide the lost home. Then I use that same finger to bob the lemon wedge in my drink. One of the seeds slips from the pulp and drifts slowly to the bottom. I tap the side of the foggy glass with my fingernail then use the pad to make two dots for eyes and a long curved slash for a smile. Thunder rumbles far off. I tip my head toward the sound.

"We've got time," Father says.

A raccoon knocks over the metal garbage can near the garage. It lopes through the beam of the motion light then back into the shadowy woods. The can lid rolls through the grass for a short while, wobbles, then falls over. The neighbor to the west swings back his screen door, squawking on its hinges, and hollers for the dog. The neighbor to the east rides a lawn tractor around his yard. Why is he doing that, I think, this late at night? Headlights from that tractor arc across the slatted fence at regular intervals.

"Crazy man," Father says.

I don't mind though. I love the smell of fresh-cut grass.

Babies in a bird's nest above us chitter as the mother darts off into the night. I work a wad of Big League Chew in my mouth then blow a pink bubble that pops over my nose and chin. Father says, "You want a taste of brandy?"

"Okay."

He fishes the lemon from my glass and sets it on the table. The ice clinks as he tosses the water over the railing. The cubes roll across the grass toward the woods. Father uncaps the brandy bottle, pours until the glass is a quarter full, then pushes the glass in front of me. "Try that."

I pluck out my gum and stick it to the side of the patio table. I take a small sip. The brandy is sweet. It spreads warm against the back of my throat, across my chest, through my belly. It tingles the hairs in my nose. I suddenly feel something I haven't felt in a long time: a dulling sensation, sort of numb and safe at the same time. I look at Father. I'm in my body. Right now, in the moment. Right here with him.

He's smiling at me, at the expression on my face. "Good, huh?"

I nod. "Can I have some more?"

Father glances at the house, the soft glow of the light above the sink, the kitchen still empty. He tips the bottle, filling my glass to a quarter full again. "Just don't tell your mom."

In the distance, the neighbor walks through the woods, the flashlight beam bouncing. He calls the dog again then once more. Father feels kind and welcoming right now, not big and scary. I want to reach out and touch his hand, but I'm afraid of how he'll react. Will he hold my fingers gently? Will he rear back and yell? Will he grab my arm and yank me up and haul me into the house, away from eyes that might see? He's smiling and friendly. Mellow, one of my classmates might say. Will he stay that way?

I want to tell him that I love him, but I'm afraid he won't say it back.

I am twelve years old.

SOME BEGINNING STEPS TO TAKE

TAKE A BREAK

You are probably exhausted.

You may have been on more diets than you can count with both hands. You've probably: memorized calorie counts, learned new food rules about what you can and can't eat, weighed/measured yourself and/or the food you're allowed to eat down to the ounce, beaten yourself up for not following said rules exactly, gone to whatever lengths each diet required no matter the toll it took on your body or mind, lived in utter desperation to get the weight off, compared yourself to other people who have gotten rid of the weight when you have not, spent time and energy hating skinny people, wrestled with starving/bingeing/purging, and the list goes on. Or maybe your feelings of exhaustion have little to do with dieting and more to do with life in general.

Whatever the case may be, getting some rest and taking short breaks will ultimately help you focus, make you more productive, and also, I'd argue, make you happier. So you take this opportunity to stop reading and take a break from all of it. Go lie down and take a nap. Or go to bed earlier and get some more sleep. Or go do something that makes you happy, something *you* really want to do, something that both fulfills you and doesn't involve eating. (And if you don't know what fulfills you other than food, no worries, because we'll be talking about that in Chapter Six. For now, just go do something *you*, not someone else, would like to do that doesn't have anything to do with food.) Stop stressing. Stop worrying. Stop pushing yourself and trying so hard. Stop beating yourself up. Take the focus off food and weight for a while.

Go enjoy your life, *right now*. Come back to this in a day or two: refreshed, revived, ready to dive in. See you in a little while. Stop reading, *right now*. I mean it.

TAKE THE PRESSURE OFF

Maybe you have an outside reason (an upcoming wedding or a reunion, for instance) to lose the weight. Maybe you have a significant other or family members hounding you. Or a doctor concerned about your health. Or people around you bullying you (also known as vampires—more on that in Chapter Five). Or a life coach, trainer, and/or someone else you don't want to disappoint. Or a job that won't hire you unless you weigh less. Or a perceived belief that everything in your life will be better once you finally drop the weight.

But here's the thing, all those outside influences are just adding more pressure to a situation that's already stressful enough. So you've got to take the pressure off yourself. For starters, like we talked about before, *make your own self and your own well-being the only reason you're shedding the weight*, which takes all those other people and events out of the equation. You're not doing it for them, you're doing it for you. And so they have no stake—none whatsoever—in how your weight-loss efforts turn out. And second, do yourself a kindness and look at this entire weight-loss journey (and your entire life as well) as if it's all just a big experiment. Experiments are all about trying new things and seeing what works and figuring it out. That way if you screw up (because at some point you will and that's okay), well, no worries, you just give it another shot and try again until you find something that does work. Or if you prefer, look at your journey and your life as a game. Games are about playing and having fun. If you lose, no big deal, just play again. Odds are, if you keep playing, you're bound to win at some point.

Lower the stakes. Let yourself make mistakes. Take away the deadlines and the time tables as to when you'll be finished. Let the only voice in your head be your own (cheering you on, of course). You'll find that you'll get to where you want to be much faster and you'll also find your life much easier and a lot more enjoyable if you'll ease up on the pressure and just relax into the journey.

PUT YOURSELF AT THE TOP OF YOUR TO-DO LIST

If you put all the important stuff onto your schedule first, there's little room left over for anything else. It's my guess (because for so many years, I did it too) that you, yourself, are not one of the important things on your own schedule. You squeeze yourself (your wants, needs, desires, passions, and/or goals) in where there's room. Sometimes, there is no room and so you're not on the schedule at all. Know this: *you and you alone are responsible for your own happiness.* And you won't find happiness and fulfillment or have the life you want by not prioritizing yourself. All you'll end up with, if you do that, is burnout. And you'll remain a burned-out husk of who you once were until you make yourself priority number one on your daily to-do list. Remember your mantra: *Taking excellent care of myself is the healthiest thing I can do.*

Know this too: *you are exchanging your life for the things you choose to do with your time.* I know family is important. So are friends and work and school and the list goes on. But you are important too.

So do this:
1. Write your daily to-do list.
2. Now put your name at the top of that list.
3. Then answer these: *Who am I living and doing and making choices for on a regular basis, is it me? Why don't I think I'm important enough to be number one on my own list of priorities? Why do I believe that my wants and needs matter less than others? When will I look at my life as my own and take responsibility for my own happiness?*
4. Now answer this: *Do I want more exhaustion or more fulfillment?*
5. And assuming you want more fulfillment, answer this: *What can I rearrange on my daily schedule to bring myself more fulfillment?*
6. Give yourself permission (oh yes, you can!) to put yourself at the very top, number one, of your to-do list *every day.*
7. Then do something (big or little) that fulfills you (again, activities that have nothing to do with eating) *every day.*

The easiest way to keep yourself at the top of your daily to-do list is to remember this: *No* is a complete sentence. *No.* You are allowed and need to have boundaries. In fact, the only way you are ever going to be healthy and free to be the person you want to be—to stop abusing food and get rid of the weight and live in a body that feels like you, to pursue those things that matter deeply to you, to come alive and have a life that excites you—is to recognize and protect your own boundaries. You will have to learn to say *no.* Then you must *stand by that decision.* You don't have to negotiate your refusal with anyone or explain yourself or give excuses as to why you can't. All you have to say is: *No.*

Keeping in mind that you are the top priority on your to-do list now, politely say *no* to anything that you don't want, need, and/or have time to do. You create the life you're living. So make and enforce your own boundaries until you create a life that is manageable and enjoyable for you.

So repeat after me: *No. No. No.*

And like anything you practice, saying *no* and prioritizing yourself gets easier over time.

TAKE EXCELLENT CARE OF YOURSELF

I know, because I used to do it to, that you probably don't value yourself highly. And when you don't value something, regardless of what it is, you don't take care of it. When it comes to yourself, that needs to change.

Physical Health

It's always in your best interests to see a medical doctor before you embark on making significant changes to your life and/or what you're eating. It's also in your best interests to see your physician and have a physical so you can work with your doctor to address any medical problems you may have and to make sure there's not a medical reason for your excess weight. There are medical conditions that can cause you to gain weight even if you are *honestly* not overeating. You need to make sure you're not battling your physiology. If you have preexisting health conditions, it's imperative that you're under a physician's care while changing your lifestyle and eating patterns, especially with regards to the foods you choose to eat and any medications you may take.

It's also in your best interests to make sure you're getting enough sleep. Your body needs time to rejuvenate and heal itself; it does that when you're resting. So don't skimp during the week and think you'll make up the sleep hours on the weekend because the restorative power of sleep doesn't work like that. Rearrange your schedule so you can get at least six hours or more a night. I know you're busy, but remember: you create the life you're living. Both you and your health are worth finding the time to rest.

So do this:
1. Answer this honestly: *What do I most need to do today to improve my physical health?*
2. Then give yourself permission and go do those things today (and every day).

Mental Health

Reducing stress matters. So make a space in your home filled with your favorite things where you'll love to go to help you relax. Having time to yourself matters too, both time to socialize with others and time to do things you enjoy. Finding something (big or small) that fulfills you, like we just talked about, then doing that *every day* will help heal you. Say *yes* to new things that interest you. Challenge yourself and learn something new. Visit a therapist, life coach, and/or personal trainer if you need someone objective to listen to you and to give you advice. Go for a walk outside every day (or if you can't walk and/or get outside, then open a window and feel the breeze) so you can be reminded that it's a big world and you're part of it, not at odds with it. Take steps to quit doing those things you dislike and instead find out what makes you feel alive, then go do that. (This topic is so important, all of Chapter Six is devoted to it.)

Also, it's entirely possible that you're suffering from anxiety/depression, which your physician will determine. Having suffered from panic attacks and been through clinical depression, I want you to know that you don't have to live in emotional distress and melancholy and despair. You just don't. There is a way out. You can be happy and thriving once again. The key is this: *you will have to take the first step and ask someone to help you.* I know from experience that it's easier and safer to avoid people, stay in bed with the shades pulled down, and yank the covers over your head. But that's existing, not living, and you will not be healed that way. You honestly do need to take action. So please tell *someone you trust* (lover, best friend, parent, preacher, and/or the like) that you're struggling with overwhelming stress/restlessness/sadness/hopelessness so you don't feel so alone. And please seek medical advice so you can get the help you need. You may need to take medicine and that's perfectly okay. Both anxiety and depression, according to my doctor, are linked to an imbalance of biochemicals (low levels of serotonin, for one) in your brain.[1] They are medical conditions, not a personal weakness/failure. Know this: there is no shame in having anxiety or depression. None at all. Not even a little bit. So ask for help.

Personal hygiene also matters for both your physical and mental health. I mention this because some people may not realize that personal hygiene matters enough that it will change how you view your life: it will help you believe, if you don't already, that you have value and are worth taking care of. That means bathing regularly, brushing your teeth and your hair, putting on lotions and creams for your skin, using deodorants, putting on perfume, and the list goes on. It also means getting dressed in fresh clothes (and not wearing the same sweatpants/pajamas you've had on for the last three days). How you treat yourself and how you dress really does have an effect on your mood/attitude not only toward others but also, more importantly, toward yourself. When you truly believe that you deserve to take care of yourself, you will change your entire outlook on yourself and your life for the better and you will absolutely move through the world in a much more positive and confident way. So you do whatever hygiene-type things you need to do for you that will make you feel cared for and nurtured and good about yourself.

So do this:
1. Answer this honestly: *What do I most need to do today to improve my mental health?*
2. Then give yourself permission and go do those things today (and every day).

Spiritual Well-Being

Your spiritual well-being is not about religion (although it can be). What I'm referring to here is a sense of connectedness to others and to the world around you and even to some force greater than yourself. It's the understanding that the same atoms and molecules that created the earth, the sun, the moon, and the stars are some of the very same atoms and molecules that can be found in your own body. This also encompasses a belief that life has meaning and that you have a purpose and a reason for being alive. It's a knowledge that you have gifts and talents that are unique to you and that are meant to be shared with the world. Your spiritual well-being also includes a deep belief that life is on your side, supporting you, and an equally deep trust in your intuition to guide you wherever you need to go.

So do this:
1. Answer this honestly: *What do I most need to do today to improve my spiritual well-being?*
2. Then give yourself permission and go do those things today (and every day).

MEET YOUR OWN NEEDS

Everyone has needs, you included. There are certain things that must be in your life for you to function in a healthy way. And if you are low on your priority list, then it's likely your own needs are not getting met. Always remember: no one is coming to fix it. If someone else isn't meeting your needs, then *you must do whatever is necessary to meet your own needs for yourself so you can be healthy and whole.*

In 1943, psychologist Abraham Maslow created what he called a hierarchy of needs that every person requires to be healthy and whole, or in his words, "to become more and more what one is."[2] Each need builds upon the next so if you don't meet the first one, you'll have a hard time meeting the second one, and so on. I realize this might be a bit of a snooze, but stick with me anyway because you'll learn why *making sure your own needs are met is of the utmost importance to your healing and your growth.*

These first four are what Maslow called "deficiency needs," which basically means if you don't meet them, your health will suffer.

1. **Physiological:** Food, water, sleep, and sex. If you don't meet these needs, you end up becoming obsessed with them to the exclusion of everything else.
2. **Safety:** Physical, financial, and psychological. If you don't have this need met, you move through the world in fear for your well-being, in fear of other people (that they'll hurt you) or maybe even yourself (that you can't take care of yourself), fear of sliding into utter ruin, fear that you might be losing your mind. And all that fear is no way to live.
3. **Belongingness:** Being part of a group, being included, having someone or a group to turn to when life gets challenging. If this need doesn't get met, you end up feeling: rejected, lonely, ostracized, excluded, and the like. If this need goes unmet for too long, you can slide into depression.
4. **Esteem:** Self-respect, the respect of those around you, the sense that you have a purpose in the world, the belief that you have unique gifts and talents, and the belief that you are capable and valuable. If this need isn't met, you stop believing in yourself and your abilities, then you stop taking charge of your own life, then you fade back into the shadows and let life just pass you by.

These next four are what Maslow called "growth needs," which basically means that meeting them will help you become more of who you want to be. Thing is, you can't even properly get to these growth needs until you fulfill, and keep fulfilling, all the deficiency needs we just talked about. Remember, each need must be met before you can successfully move on to the next.

5. **Cognitive:** Understanding the world you live in, being able to articulate your thoughts, mastering your surroundings. Meeting this need for yourself will grow your self-confidence: you will know who you are, and you will know your place in the larger world.
6. **Aesthetic:** Looking for and being able to appreciate the beauty in the world, enjoying the artistic endeavors of others, being creative yourself. Meeting this need brings self-fulfillment and happiness.

7. **Self-Actualization:** Seeing life as awe-inspiring, focusing on improving your circumstances instead of complaining about them, finding life so much more full of happiness than suffering. Meeting this need leads to inner peace.
8. **Transcendence:** Championing a cause that is greater than yourself. Meeting this need means that you've found your purpose in life.

So now that you've put yourself at the top of your to-do list and you've freed up some of your time by enforcing your own boundaries, now it's time to meet your own needs.

So do this:
1. Get still and quiet for a little while.
2. Listen for your intuition to guide you.
3. Then determine where on the hierarchy you currently fall, which of your needs in that category are not being met.
4. Now take action to meet those particular needs *today*.
5. Repeat, meeting your own needs from one level to the next, so that you can move forward and create a life that matters to you, a life you love.

THINGS YOU NEED TO KNOW THAT ARE THE CRUX OF EFFECTIVE AND PERMANENT WEIGHT LOSS

DON'T BE POSSESSIVE ABOUT FOOD

It's crucial that you don't take possession of food ("*my* food, *my* food plan"), food abuse ("*my* bulimia, *my* anorexia, *my* binge eating, *my* overeating"), a disease process ("*my* disease" if you are one who believes you have a disease), and on the list goes. Why? Because it's been my personal experience that taking possession of anything will psychologically make it yours; and when you believe something is yours, is part of your identity and what makes you the person you are, you'll have a much harder time changing that thing and/or entirely getting rid of that thing (or changing and/or getting rid of what you believe about that thing).

YOU ARE EATING TOO MUCH

I say this kindly: you need to admit to yourself that you are eating too much. I know you don't want to hear this. I never wanted to hear it either. I'm sure you'd rather hear that you have a slow metabolism or genes that make you overweight or a disease that causes you to overeat. Any reason is easier than taking responsibility for your life, I get that. Any excuse also lessens the shame that you may be feeling about struggling to lose weight. But if you haven't been diagnosed by a medical doctor with an underlying medical problem, then there are no other explanations or excuses. In the end, the only one responsible for your weight is you. And the short truth of it, when all is said and done, is this: *you are eating too much.*

I've done this lifestyle for over nine years now, and I eat probably about 1/3 of what I used to. I'm not starving. I don't feel deprived. I'm not making myself crazy over food. I eat whatever I want. And still, I'm eating a fraction of what I used to. So I can tell you without a doubt, and as gently and kindly as I can, that you are simply eating too much.

EAT WHEN YOU'RE HUNGRY

The only times you should eat are when you are hungry, and eventually the only times you'll even really think about food are when you feel hungry (yes, this is true). How do you know you're hungry? Your body will have a physiological reaction: your stomach will rumble and/or there'll be a kind of empty feeling in your belly. That means you're going to have to quit looking at a clock or to others to decide it's time to eat. That means you're going to have to start listening to your own body. You'll have to stop making food a balm for your emotional state and instead start making food simply fuel for your body.

Most likely you're reading this book because you're overweight. With that in mind, it's likely that you won't be very hungry at all in the beginning. Your body will be using up the fat tissue stored on your hips, thighs, buttocks, and/or belly before your stomach starts asking for food. That's as it should be, so don't panic. Be patient (which, believe me, I understand is the strong suit of almost no one) and wait for true physiological hunger to happen.

I know waiting is hard. I don't like it either. But if you don't wait, you're not giving your body time to use up the reserves of carbohydrates, fats, and proteins that are already stored in the tissues of your body. So practice patience. Patience is a tool that'll serve you well not only for weight loss but also for life in general. So be kind, gentle, and patient with yourself while you wait to be hungry. You'll also come to find out, once you learn to wait, that food actually tastes better—more delicious—when you're hungry because your taste buds are primed and ready (yes, this is true too).

EAT CALMLY

You will need to slow down when you eat. You are no longer going to be out of control, not thinking clearly, not paying attention to your body, stuffing food blindly into your mouth, wanting food to numb you, and/or hoping food will fill that hole/wound inside you when you eat. When you're in some kind of highly-emotional state, expecting food to do something it was never intended to do, you're not really tasting any of the food anyway. In that state, you tend to chew fast, swallow faster, then repeat. You don't savor or enjoy food because your taste buds are in your mouth not your stomach. So if you're an emotional train wreck, the best thing you can do for yourself is to calm yourself first before you eat.

Again, you will never be able to think your way out of a feeling. Your first reaction in the past has probably been to grab some food to calm/numb yourself. But instead, you need to interrupt that pattern so you can change the neural pathway in your brain, and to do that, you need to stay present in your body and feel whatever emotions are coming up in you.

So do this:
1. Take a breath and a pause.
2. Don't put anything in your mouth. Don't go running off to some other substance/behavior. Move away from the refrigerator, cupboard, drive-thru window, and/or wherever you have your stash of comfort foods. If you are in the midst of abusing food, take a breath and a pause (yes, you can, I say kindly; it's a choice) and step away.
3. Ask yourself **out loud in a calm, kind voice**: *"What's the matter, [insert your name]? What do you need?"* Speaking out loud activates a different part of your brain. When you're reacting, when you're just tearing through the pantry, eating whatever you can find in an effort to make the emotion go away, your amygdala (the emotional part of your brain) is in charge. Speaking out loud activates the neocortex (the rational part of your brain), which is responsible for problem solving and thinking, among other things.[3] It's been my personal experience that speaking aloud in a calm voice will interrupt the barrage of biochemicals coming from the amygdala. Speaking kindly to yourself in that moment when you feel out of control will help you to interpret the situation more logically and rationally, it will help you calm your body from high alert to a more normal state. If you find yourself unable to speak in a calm, kind voice, you can write your responses as writing will also activate the neocortex and slow the barrage of biochemicals.

4. Know this: the answers to those questions are never (*never, never*) about actual physiological hunger or food. The answer to the first one is always (*always, always*) about something you're feeling. The answer to the second one is what you must do for yourself to support yourself and meet your own needs.

5. Do yourself a kindness and go somewhere that you feel comfortable and safe, preferably by yourself so you don't have to concern yourself with the reactions of others, including that they may try to "help" you by getting you to stop feeling what you need to feel.

6. Now let yourself feel whatever it is that's coming up. Really feel it, however that looks for you. Cry. Scream. Pound your fist into the ground. Whatever you need to do to let that feeling come up and run its course. Because the feeling will run its course in a short while, and once it passes, you'll come to find out that the need to numb/avoid that feeling by abusing food will be gone.

7. And if you realize that you're still not calm after that, then find something else (that's not another numbing substance/behavior) to interrupt the pattern because what matters most is interrupting that pattern in your brain where you abuse food as a solution to your emotions and/or problems. So if you're still not calm, go outside and take your shoes off and shuffle around in the grass. Call a friend. Write in a journal. Go for a walk. Listen to music. Sing loudly and off-key if that's your thing. Dance like a fool if that'll make you feel better.

8. Then when the feeling passes, take a deep breath in through your nose, hold it for three seconds, then let it out slowly through your mouth with an audible sound. Pull your shoulders down away from your ears. Feel your body relax.

9. Then, once you're a bit calmer, take some time to address the origin of the feeling that caused you to want to abuse food. (The answer to the first question: *What's the matter?*) Walk it back from the present moment to whatever moment it was that triggered the emotion in you. You will find the moment you were triggered is what's really causing the problem. (An example from my own life: bingeing on cookies that, when I answered that first question and worked my way backward from that moment to its source, came down to me feeling less than and not good enough because I had been rejected.)

10. Then take some time to address exactly what (that is *not* food-related) will make you feel safe and comforted and supported in that moment. (The answer to the second question: *What do you need?*) Trust yourself to know. Befriend yourself, build your self-trust, and take action to do whatever it takes to meet that need(s) for yourself. (An example from my own life: during the cookie binge, when I answered that second question: what I needed, in that moment, was to befriend myself, take the pressure off myself, and go do something that nourished me.)

11. Then, *only when you're more relaxed and thinking rationally*, you choose your favorite foods, ones you have a craving for in that moment, and *you eat slowly* so you can savor the food.

EAT MINDFULLY

It's important that you pay attention to your body as you eat. Just like you got a cue from your body that you're hungry, well, you'll get a cue that you're full too. But you'll miss that cue if you're eating fast and not paying attention.

You'll be better served if you sit down at a table without distractions, especially early on while you're getting the hang of eating mindfully. That means no eating in your car or in front of the television or munching away at your work desk, and the like, at least not in the beginning. You'll also be better served if you eat your meals on a plate. That means no eating directly out of a jug or a bag or any other type of container. Why? Because when you're distracted and/or when you're feeding yourself hand-to-mouth like that, you're likely not paying any attention to your body. And until you learn your body's cues for fullness, you need to pay close attention to what your body is trying to tell you. What you most need is for your body to cue you in to the fact that it has had enough.

Your body will tell you when you're full, but you won't hear it unless you are listening. You are, without a doubt, capable of slowing down and eating mindfully and listening to the wisdom of your own body. That wisdom is not in some of us, *it's in all of us*. The only thing you have to do is pay attention and listen for it. If you'll just do that, you will come to the point where you stop eating because your body wants you to, not because your mind tells you that you ought to.

EAT WHATEVER YOU WANT

Best news ever: there's no food plan.

Although, I do understand that might be scary for you because it's quite likely you're accustomed to diets that tell you what to eat down to the ounce and/or when to eat down to the minute. Well, now you're going to have to start listening to your own self, listening to your own body, and choosing what's best for you. What exactly do you want to eat? What is your body craving? Something sweet? Salty? Crunchy? Or maybe protein? Dairy? Fruits? That's what you're going to be paying attention to.

Right now, you may believe that your body is craving nothing but sweets and junk food. It isn't. That's most likely your mind (your thoughts) craving those things nonstop. It's also likely that you think you crave only those things because you've been denying them to yourself. Eventually, as time goes on, you'll come to find out that your body does crave sugary and salty things. But maybe it also craves potassium and so you'll want bananas. Or maybe vitamin C and so you'll want citrus. Or maybe protein and so you'll want beans or meat. You'll find yourself eating all kinds of varied foods. It's just a matter of listening to what your body is telling you.

One caveat: avoid foods you're allergic to and/or that your physician has told you to remove from your diet; those foods are the only ones that are off-limits for you. Do yourself a kindness and don't let yourself obsess over those foods you can't have because they will become your focus (and remember: what you focus on grows, which means your obsession with off-limit foods will grow). There are plenty of other foods to choose from so simply choose other foods that will help you heal instead of harm you.

This too is a process and a practice so cut yourself some slack as you learn. You'll recognize your body's cravings over time. Once you start really listening to your body, you'll come to trust it and trust yourself in the process. Your body really does know what it needs and also what's best for you.

EAT EXACTLY WHAT YOU WANT

You know how you're going to still enjoy food and eating? You're going to eat *exactly* what you want.

This is particularly important to stop the crazy-making thinking/behavior that happens when you start denying yourself foods that you really like to eat. Again, what you focus on grows, so when you tell yourself that you can't have chocolate (or substitute whatever food you deny yourself), and you're good for a while, don't eat any chocolate, look how awesome and full of willpower you are, bulletproof you think, and then you have a really bad day and you slide right off the deep end and binge on chocolate, wolfing down an entire two-pound bag in one sitting because you've had an obsessive focus (consciously or subconsciously) on chocolate for days, weeks, and/or months. That kind of crazy-making thinking/behavior is what I'm talking about.

So how does this look in the real world?

Let's say your body is craving a donut (which you tell yourself is bad for you), but your mind says you should eat a salad (which you tell yourself is good for you). Do yourself a kindness and choose to eat the donut. Why? You'll be satisfied. You won't be thinking constantly about the donut. You won't be snacking/nibbling most of the day and eating too much of other foods you really don't want because you were sated with what you did want.

Maybe, you're thinking: *But I can't eat just one donut, I'll start and I'll eat the whole box.* Okay, a note on binge foods: you know what foods currently trigger a binge for you. Trust me on this: they won't always do that. But for right now, if eating a single donut (or whatever food acts as a binge trigger) is a problem for you, then hold off for a little while and pick something else you would like to eat instead. Avoiding foods that trigger binge behavior in you is not forever; please remind yourself of that as often as necessary so you're not obsessing over what you can't have. You can choose, whenever you need to and for as long as you need to, not to eat foods that trigger binges in you. *It's a choice.* Don't make yourself crazy with: *I can never have another [insert your binge food(s) here].* You *can* have another, yes, but only once you've calmed down about eating it. It's not a matter of can't; it's simply a matter of choosing not to have it *right now.*

And finally, if you're hungry but not able for some reason to get *exactly* what you want, well, eat something you like that's available. And if there's nothing you like available, well then you have choices: 1. go somewhere else that has something you'd like to eat or 2. eat just a little so your stomach will stop growling until you can get somewhere else that has something you'd like to eat or 3. wait to eat until you can get exactly what you want. If you're hungry and can't get to food at all, relax. Don't panic. You won't starve. Just eat as soon as you can. Eat mindfully when you do, and pay attention to your body cues of fullness. Honestly, there are no hard, set-in-stone rules here. Use your intellect, I say kindly, and make the choices that are best for you.

A suggestion that will help you: get "good/healthy foods" and "bad/unhealthy foods" out of your vocabulary. If you've been dieting for any length of time, you've likely got a mindset that you should only be eating "good/healthy foods" and you also have a mental list of what those foods are. You are limiting yourself with that list. So do yourself a kindness and get out of the mindset that certain foods are off-limits. Just so you know, you'll have to consciously tell yourself that there are no "good/bad" foods as many times as it takes until you believe it. Also, it may take a while to change your mindset, and that's okay; just keep going, your mind will catch up eventually.

EAT ONLY WHAT TASTES GOOD

Here's the truth: you're going to be eating a lot less volume and likely a lot less frequently.

If you want to enjoy eating (*and you should enjoy it*), then do yourself a kindness and make sure your meals taste delicious. If your food is overcooked, undercooked, too cold, mushy, stale, burnt, and/or in some way that's not the way you like it, then know this: *you don't have to settle.* Send it back if you're at a restaurant. Make it again if you're at home. Whatever you need to do to make it a pleasing experience for yourself. So pick foods your body is craving, make sure they're prepared just the way you like, and savor them. You're worth the effort to do that.

And again, this isn't a hard, set-in-stone rule either. If your food doesn't taste utterly delicious and you're hungry, you can choose to eat it anyway. Just don't go looking for something delicious to eat until you are hungry again.

DRINK WHEN YOU'RE THIRSTY

When you're thirsty, you need to drink not eat. When I was starving myself and hungry, I wanted my stomach to stop growling, to stop hurting, and so I drank any calorie-free liquid that would make that happen. When I was bingeing and thirsty, I would eat until the thirst went away. Neither one of those scenarios is listening to your body.

Some diets will tell you to drink eight glasses of water a day. I've found it's healthier and saner for me when there's no set amount of liquids I need to consume every day. If you're thirsty, drink. If you're not, don't.

I'm a big believer in water. Your body needs it. As an added bonus, water will also pack on exactly zero pounds. It's good for your overall health and in particular your brain (and we've already talked about how your brain is your biggest ally, which means it's in your best interests to keep your brain in optimal working condition). Science has shown that when the brain is more than 2% dehydrated, a person will experience problems with paying attention, thinking, and reaction times, among other detrimental effects.[4] So when you are thirsty between meals, drink water. You can also choose unsweetened tea or black coffee (in addition to but not as a substitute for water). The reasons why:

1. Ghrelin is a hormone produced and secreted by your stomach when it's empty. It's known as the "hunger hormone" because it increases when your stomach is empty (signaling you need to eat) and decreases as your stomach is stretched (as you consume a meal).[5] But drinking sweetened (with glucose, sucrose, and/or fructose, which are all different types of sugars that metabolize differently in the body) causes hunger signals to be initiated and fullness signals to be repressed.[6] What does that mean to you? First, it'll be harder for you to tell when you're truly physiologically hungry for food. Second, you'll likely consume more of a sweetened beverage than you need to feel satiated.

2. Artificial sweeteners have been found to be 200-7,000 times more sweet than natural sugars. These kinds of sweeteners, found in diet drinks, have been found to increase appetite and increase false hunger signals, according to a study in *The Yale Journal of Biology and Medicine*.[7] The study showed that consuming something sweet prior to eating a meal will cause overeating. It also showed that because they are so extremely sweet, artificial sweeteners will also increase cravings of and dependence on sugar. That means, because you're drinking artificially-sweetened beverages between meals, you are continually encouraging your own dependence on and cravings for sweetness and sugar. To add to all of that, the *YJBM* study showed that artificial sweeteners will cause you to seek food to satiate that sweetness craving even though you're not hungry. All that to say, drinking diet drinks between meals will also make it make it harder for you to tell when you're actually physiologically hungry.

Do yourself a kindness and save the sweetened drinks to go along with your meals so you can be mindful of your body's hunger cues. Hear me: I'm not saying you can't drink what you want to; I'm saying to drink sweetened beverages *only with your meals*. Once again, don't make yourself crazy with rigidity or any kind of hard, set-in-stone rules. Just know that if you choose to live this way, you'll be making it easier on yourself.

STOP WHEN YOU'RE COMFORTABLY FULL

You need to stop eating when you're *comfortably full* even if that means you've got several bites or half a bag or most of the food your plate left over. How do you know when you're comfortably full? You feel sated, not stuffed. You feel energized, not drained. You feel good, not guilty. Your taste buds will change and food will actually start to taste different, not as flavorful, when you are comfortably full.

Remember, you're the one in control. You're going to have to be the one to push the plate away and cover it with a napkin, take it over to the garbage can and dump it, wrap up the leftovers and stick them in the refrigerator for later, and/or get up and walk away from the food. Part of taking excellent care of yourself is deciding what you're going to put in or not put in your body. That choice is always yours.

GET RID OF THE ALL-OR-NOTHING THINKING

Some people, and I used to be one of them, believe that if you screw up (even just a little), that gives you the okay to keep screwing up a lot. For example: you meant to eat perfectly, wait until you're hungry, stop when you're full, today was the day you were for sure going to do it, you promised yourself, and then by breakfast you screwed up and ate WAY too much, so much that your stomach hurt and you had to unbutton your pants, and now you've decided to blow it for the rest of the day/week/year, you'll just start again fresh tomorrow or next Monday or January first of next year. This also includes the scale: well, you were on a perfect track, losing pounds every week, and now you've gained weight and blew it, so the heck with this, you're done trying, so you're just going to start abusing food again.

That's all-or-nothing thinking, *and it doesn't serve you at all.*

The first hint that something was wrong with that scenario is the word *perfect*. Look, you're going to make mistakes. You're going to screw up. There's no way around it simply for the fact that you're human. So, if you subscribe to all-or-nothing thinking, you're going to have to talk yourself down from the ledge each and every time you make a mistake. Instead, you need to learn to practice being kind, gentle, and patient with yourself.

Do yourself a kindness and stop taking all of this (weight loss, yourself, life in general) so seriously. All you need to do is remind yourself that it was just a mistake, no need to freak out, you'll just do better next time.

So do this:
1. Treat yourself with kindness after you've abused food in some way (in this example, by overeating).
2. Then speak words *out loud* (activating the rational, thinking part of your brain, remember) that you really need to hear to reassure yourself. (For example: *Okay, so I ate way past full. No worries. That's completely fixable. I'll just wait until I'm hungry to eat again and get myself right back on track.*)
3. Know this: it really is as simple as that.
4. Know this too: weight loss and the cessation of abusing food really is as easy as you want to make it. You don't have to spiral out of control. You don't have to punish yourself. You simply don't. You just have to change your mind.
5. So just choose to take the pressure off, cut yourself some slack, and simply do better the next time.

WHAT TO DO IF YOU JUST AREN'T SURE

And if you have no idea how to tell if you're hungry or how to stop when you're comfortably full because you just aren't picking up on your body's cues (yet!), here are some suggestions *to start with*:

- Eat three meals a day with four to six hours in between.
- Make up a plate with what you would normally eat then divide that into two halves. Eat one half. Either wrap up the other half to eat later or throw it away.
- Repeat *until you start feeling hunger and fullness on your own.*
- Eventually, you will feel hunger and fullness, then you can listen to your body cues and eat accordingly (regardless of the time of day).
- And when you screw up by eating when you're not hungry and/or not stopping when you're comfortably full, because at some point you will (again, there's no reason to ever believe you'll do any of this perfectly—I still make mistakes with it, too), all you have to do is simply wait until you're hungry again to eat. No beating yourself up. No giving up and abusing food again. Just wait until you're hungry then eat until you're comfortably full.

SOME OTHER SUGGESTIONS TO HELP YOU

- If you need to take medication with food (and there are no specific instructions with the medicine), choose to take it with something small, whatever the minimum you need to stop stomach upset. You don't need to eat an entire meal (unless your physician tells you otherwise). I mention this because I once used taking medication as an excuse to overeat.

- If you have a medical condition and you need to eat at various times during the day (for instance, because of low blood sugar) then you should absolutely follow the guidelines your physician has prescribed for you in addition to listening to your body cues. Again, you should absolutely tell your physician that you're doing this program and you should remain under a physician's care while you do this program.

- If you have a medical condition that requires a certain diet (for instance, gluten-free), then you should absolutely follow that diet within the boundaries of hunger and fullness.

- If your family is eating a meal together and you're not hungry, simply sit with your family, drink water or some unsweetened beverage if you're thirsty, and wait until you're hungry to eat. If mealtime with your family is a short time away and you're hungry, then just wait (you won't starve in the meantime). If mealtime with your family is not a short time away and you're hungry, then have a *small* snack/meal so you'll be hungry once again when family mealtime comes around. You'll get the hang of this as you practice, so don't worry.

- Don't ever think of yourself as the odd person out; you're just learning a new way of being in the world, one that works for you, so cut yourself some slack.

- If you're afraid of food, terrified of eating the wrong things, scared because you're sure you're going to gain weight, that fear will ease over time. Be kind, gentle, and patient with yourself *always*. You don't have to be afraid of food. You're the one in control. You're the one putting foods in your body. Food only has the power that you give it. So simply look at food as fuel for your body (because that's all it really is) to get you to where you most want to be. Set yourself free.

- If you're on a time schedule with breaks, say for work, ask for flexibility with those breaks so you can eat when you're hungry, especially in the beginning as you're learning this way of life. If flexibility is not possible, well, you can choose to eat a little less at an earlier meal (so your hunger is sated but also so you're not quite comfortably full) so you'll be hungry when your meal break at work comes around.

- If you only have a short amount of time to eat and you're hungry, then eat in that short amount of time. I've been on diets that claim you should take twenty minutes or more to eat your meal. That's great if you have the time. If you don't, well, eat in the time that you do have. Just be mindful when you're eating, eat as slowly as time allows, enjoy the taste, and stop when you're comfortably full. Again, the more you practice this, the easier it will get.

- Do yourself a kindness and don't sneak food. Sneaking food will make you feel shame and also like you're doing something wrong by eating. Eating what you want when you're hungry and stopping when you're comfortably full is a normal activity; there's nothing wrong or shameful about it. You do not have to hide the fact that you're eating.
- And if you find yourself trying to justify why you're eating when you're not hungry (*I deserve this because [insert your reason here]; I just want to be normal and eat like everybody else; I don't want to miss out*; and the like): 1. who are you justifying to? (see *Check Your Motivation* in Chapter One, then remember: you're not doing this for them, you're doing it for you), and 2. keep in mind that you are not hurting anyone but yourself.

SOME THINGS YOU'RE GOING TO HAVE TO START DOING

RELINQUISH YOUR MEMBERSHIP IN THE CLEAN-PLATE CLUB

You will be eating a lot less, that's just a fact. That means you're no longer going to be able to be a member of the clean-plate club, where you always finish everything served on your plate no matter what and which is also a terrible club to belong to anyway. So with that in mind, you'll have to:

- Serve yourself a lot less (which will make your life easier), or
- Be okay with eating leftovers, or
- Start throwing away food when you're comfortably full.

I've found, for me, that most of the time, what I really want is just a taste of things. I really don't want a whole bottle of root beer; I just want a couple sips. I don't want a whole candy bar; I just want a bite of chocolate. I don't want the whole container of fries; I just want a handful. You get the idea. So, that's what I eat. You may get served (or serve yourself) a big plate of food, but know this: just because it's on your plate does not mean you have to eat all of it.

If you do get served (or serve yourself) a big plate of food, choose the foods that you are craving and start with those first. That way, when you get comfortably full, you'll have eaten foods you really wanted. You can also eat just parts of foods—for instance, buttercream icing on a cake: I eat the icing, mostly leave the cake. You can eat a little bit of everything if you like; you don't have to finish off anything. Your plate does not have to be clean. And in case you've been told that you should clean your plate because others are starving, know this: no hungry/starving person will ever be helped by you eating everything on your plate.

If you find yourself sitting with other people and there's still food on your plate, but they aren't finished eating and you're struggling not to start nibbling to give yourself something to do, then signal to yourself that you're done by pushing your plate away, putting your silverware on top of it, then placing your napkin on top of that. You should also signal to your waiter/hostess that you're done, then either let them take the plate or get a to-go box and pack the leftovers away. Like everything you practice, being able to stop eating and not start up again when you're comfortably full gets easier as you go along.

A note of caution: you're probably going to run into people who'll get upset that you didn't eat everything on your plate (like your mom, or the person throwing the dinner party, or the person who paid for your meal, and on the list goes). They'll take your not finishing the meal personally. They'll make it about them. (And as we already discussed, you're not doing this for them, you're doing it for you.) You'll need to explain gently but firmly: yes, you're grateful, the food is delicious, but you're simply full. You'll likely have to tell them it's not about them, it's about you. Again, you need to know your boundaries and defend them. You need to take care of yourself. You need to say: *thank you, but no more, I'm full*. Hear me: you do not need to overeat just to be polite; that doesn't serve your best interests at all.

You also might believe that throwing away food (leftovers) is a waste of both good food and hard-earned money. It isn't. You may believe that the food matters more and/or is worth more than you. It doesn't and it's not. Food is fuel for your body, that's it. Anything else you believe about food comes from your mind. You give food the value it has in your life by what you believe about it. Know this: you can always (*always!*) change your mind so choose to think this instead: *I am worth more than whatever money it costs me to throw this food out*. Think that over and over until it becomes what you believe and so live out in your life. Now do yourself a kindness and make sure any leftovers taste good when you eat them later. If they aren't tasty and flavorful, choose to throw them away.

Finally, if you don't like leftovers and you'd prefer to eat freshly-prepared foods (which is perfectly fine), but you're using that as an excuse to keep eating way past full (*it tastes so good and it won't taste as good as a leftover so I have to finish it all now*), then you have two choices: 1. make and serve yourself a lot less or 2. be okay with throwing out the excess food.

I know these are issues for people because they were issues with me. Remember: you are worth more than whatever money it costs you to throw away that excess food. Don't choose to let your dislike of throwing out food and/or eating leftovers be the reason that you overeat. And as with everything else, throwing away excess food will get easier for you the more you practice it.

MOVE MORE (IF YOU'RE NOT ALREADY GETTING SOME EXERCISE)

You already know you need to get some exercise because nearly every diet on the planet tells you this. Most of them are telling you this because they want you to burn calories. I'm telling you this for two reasons: 1. to help you get more physically fit and stronger, and 2. to increase certain biochemical levels in your brain. Dopamine, endorphins, and serotonin are biochemicals that, when they're released in your body, make you feel good. Physical exercise causes your body to produce and release all these biochemicals.[8] So it follows that if you move more, you'll feel better, both about yourself and about life in general. This is especially important if you are depressed, sad, prone to negative thinking or negative self-talk, and the like. You need your hormones working for you, not against you. Help them out by doing your part and moving more.

You'll also need to get out of the mindset of exercising solely to burn calories. All that mindset tends to do is give you permission, either consciously or subconsciously, to eat way past full and/or abuse food. Well, you may tell yourself, you'll make up for what you did with food by staying a little extra at the gym. The problem with that thinking is that it stops you from paying attention to your body. Instead of listening for your body to cue you in to when it's hungry or comfortably full (your body telling you), you let your mind take over which is what has gotten you to the place where you find yourself today (you telling your body). So do yourself a kindness and get into the mindset of exercising to be strong physically and exercising to make yourself feel better mentally. You get into that mindset simply by repeatedly telling yourself those two things every time you exercise: *I'm exercising to be strong and feel better.*

You don't have to commit to a lengthy or strenuous routine. You just have to move more than you're moving now. *Anything* that gets your heart rate elevated is exercise.[9] Want to know the secret to being motivated to move more? Here it is: *the right exercise for you is the one that you'll do, so pick something you enjoy.* Start small and start slow so that you don't injure yourself. Go for a walk outside. Lift light hand weights. Take a beginner's yoga class. But, you say, I hate all exercise. Well, horseback riding counts as exercise. So does swimming. A paintball war, playing laser tag with your friends/kids, working a hula hoop, a water-balloon fight, cranking the radio and dancing across your living room: all of it exercise. My point is: do a little something more than you do now. You'll feel better about yourself, and you'll be building muscle mass and slowly sculpting your body.

Again, patience is your friend. If you *start small*, slow and easy with something you enjoy *and then build on it*, you're more likely to stick with it. And the only way to make a permanent life change is to stick with something until it becomes a habit (which on average takes some 66 consecutive days to build a new neural pathway in your brain, like we already talked about). Here's the thing: if you start out aiming for the big lofty goals, you will end up discouraged because you don't see enough progress. Then you'll feel defeated because it's been so long and your goal is still way too far away. Then you'll get hit with despair because you'll start thinking you're never ever going to get there. And then you'll quit. So *start small* and build on your exercise routine, a little bit more every time.

And remember: *no one is coming to fix it*. So you're going to have to be the one to push yourself to move more, especially on the days when maybe you just don't want to. That's why you need to start small and pick something you enjoy: you're less likely to make excuses as to why you can't and more likely to make the time to move more. That's also why it's important to remind yourself why you're moving more: to be strong and feel better; you're doing it *for you*. And even if self-motivation is not your strong suit, you still need to remember: you are fully responsible for your own happiness and for how your life turns out. So do yourself a kindness and just move more.

One last note: if you honestly and truly cannot move more (maybe for medical reasons), then you just listen to your body, eat when you're hungry and stop when you're comfortably full. In your case, the only difference is that you'll most likely be eating less often than someone who's moving more.

DISCOVER WHAT NONFOOD THINGS NOURISH YOU

All of us need things and activities that fulfill us and give us pleasure and make life worth living. Here's the problem: because you're reading this book, that thing for you has probably been food. You may even be thinking that if you take food away, there'd be nothing good left in your life at all. That's why you need to find out what other things and activities nourish you. And I assure you, there is something else, likely even more than one. Nourish means something that will build you up, help you grow, fulfill you, and make you feel good about yourself and about being alive. Nourish does not mean abusing some other activity (shopping, sex, watching television/internet, playing video games, and on the list goes) or substance (alcohol, drugs, inhaling chemicals, and on the list goes) in lieu of food, trying to numb or fill that hole in yourself.

It might be that someone along the way (or even your own self) told you that you shouldn't do what nourishes you: that you wouldn't be good at it or that it wouldn't be worth your time or that it wouldn't earn you a living or [insert that soul-crushing advice here]. Maybe you like to paint. Or write. Or bake. Or take photographs. Or work on car engines. Or skateboard. Whatever it is, you need to discover it for yourself. So how do you do that? Well, here's a quick lesson that worked for me:

1. **Pay attention.** Start small. Don't panic. Don't let all the *what-if's* and *what-could-be's* overwhelm you. Observe and pay attention to those things or activities that you respond to. If something grabs your attention, makes you stop and take a breath, makes you feel calm and relaxed, makes you feel like you're

finally home, and/or makes you feel like *this is what I'm supposed to be doing* when you do it, well that's most likely something that will nourish you.

2. **Narrow your focus.** For each thing or activity that catches your attention, ask: *What do **I** (not anybody else) love about this?* For instance, say photography nourishes you. Start with what kind of pictures *you* like to take (portraits, nature, objects, animals, etc.). Notice what color palette *you* gravitate toward when you shoot. Pay attention to how *you* like to light and frame shots. You've started with a narrow focus (just photography) and you've fine-tuned it to something specific & unique to *you*: what nourishes you most about that particular thing or activity.

3. **Trust yourself.** You responded to that thing or activity for a reason. Give it a try and see if it nourishes you. If it turns out that it's not as nourishing as you thought, that's okay. Learning about yourself is a life-long process. When Michelangelo created the statue of David, he said he sculpted the block of marble by chipping away everything that wasn't David until the only thing left was David. You can do the same. Find what nourishes you by trial and error. Chip away until you find the real you. Every error gets you closer to what nourishes you most.

One of the best things you will *ever* do for yourself is to find things and activities *other than food* that nourish you. You might have to do a little digging to discover them, but they are there. If you choose not to do this, you will inevitably keep turning back to abusing food, trying to fill that hole inside you. Take some hard-earned knowledge from me: that will never work so stop doing that to yourself. What will fill that hole are those nonfood things and activities that nourish you. (Again, this point is so important, all of Chapter Six is dedicated to it.)

UNDERSTAND THAT FOOD WILL NEVER —I REPEAT NEVER—PROTECT YOU FROM LIFE

Food will likely numb you, yes. It may comfort you, sure. It may even make you feel energized or euphoric or brave or unstoppable. You may think it's helping you brace yourself mentally or create a kind of protective wall around you physically. But your life is still happening. People, places, and things are still coming at you. Life will still always happen without asking your permission first; food will not make that fact any different. Your life, in whatever state it is in, will still be there after the food reaction wears off. And just so you know, if you're overeating processed carbohydrates (which I'd venture a guess that most binges tend to be), researchers have found that the food reaction (comfort/numbness/energized/etc.) usually wears off after only twenty minutes.[10] And when that happens, you'll realize that all abusing food has done for you is make you: 1. feel guilty and ashamed, and 2. hurt your body by adding to your size (bingeing) or damaging your tissues (purging and starving). Food will not actually have fixed anything at all, I assure you of that.

Whenever you are faced with something that makes you want to go running to abuse food, you—yes, you, I say kindly, because you are responsible for your own life—are going to have to tell yourself this:

FOOD WILL NOT FIX THIS.
FOOD WILL NOT FIX THIS.
FOOD WILL NOT FIX THIS.

You will need to say that *out loud* when you're on the verge of abusing food or even thinking about abusing food. You will have to say that over and over, as many times as it takes to stop yourself from abusing food. You will have to say that day after day after day until it becomes a new neural pathway in your brain so you believe it. And then you may still have to remind yourself (because even after nine years of living this way, I sometimes still have to remind myself, too). Those words—*food will not fix this*—are a refrain in my head now whenever I get hit with challenges or obstacles or feel overwhelmed or terrified or out of my comfort zone. It's much easier now to trust and believe those words than when I first started, true, and yet, I still on occasion have to tell myself that phrase out loud so I don't go scrambling for food when life gets rocky.

Food will not fix this.

Period.

It's a mantra I live my life by now. *Food will not fix this* needs to be your mantra, too.

BREAK YOUR BAD HABITS AND MAKE SOME GOOD ONES

Bad habits are familiar and safe and they let you stay right smack in the middle of your comfort zone. *But why would I ever want to leave my comfort zone*, you might ask, *because it's warm and cozy and my favorite slippers are there?* Well, as some wise person once said, nothing—including you—ever grows in a comfort zone. You will never realize everything you are so capable of by staying confined by and limited to a comfort zone of your own making. And for you to get to where you most want to be, to a way of being in the world that makes you excited and makes you feel alive, to a life that you love, you're going to have to grow into the person that you're meant to become.

Bad habits don't let you grow. Instead, they let you stick to your daily routine without much thought. Bad habits really do keep you from thinking. You don't stop to ponder anything. You don't ask the most important questions. *Do I really want to do this? Will it help me or hurt me? How could this be done differently or better? At this point in my life, is this still the best thing for me? Will this serve to get me to where I most want to be?* Instead, you just react the same way you've always reacted, which is what has gotten you to where you are today.

Bad habits also keep you doing the same things over and over again (like abusing food when life gets challenging or uncomfortable feelings come up). Again, you don't pause to see if there's a better way to handle the situation or even to just let yourself feel whatever feelings are arising in you; instead, you do whatever that bad habit of yours would have you do. But you won't ever get different results by doing the same thing. You won't ever get to where you want to be by doing things you already know don't work. (*But maybe they'll work next time!* you cry. Um, no, they won't.) Do yourself a kindness and don't be the person banging his/her head against a wall in frustration because something's not working while at the same time completely snubbing a new approach. Instead, be open and willing to change.

Habits all get formed the same way: repetition. This goes back to brain science and the neural pathways that we talked about in Chapter One. Your habits are simply shortcuts to make the work your brain has to do easier. All you need to do is create a new pathway, which you might tell yourself is really hard but doesn't have to be really hard at all (that's a habit too, by the way, believing that change has to be difficult). You create a new neural pathway simply by changing your thoughts and behaviors then repeating the change. That's it.

Some bad habits you may have (a partial list):

- Dealing with your problems/emotions by abusing food and/or other substances/behaviors.
- Eating when you're not hungry and/or eating way past comfortably full.
- Not paying attention to and listening to your own body (not just about food either).
- Doing things simply because that's the way you've always done them or that's the way others have always done them.
- Telling yourself a story about your life that isn't accurate or doesn't help you move on.
- Putting yourself low on your own priority list and not taking good care of yourself.
- Letting the scale determine your self-worth and happiness.
- Procrastinating or making excuses or rationalizing or assigning blame.
- Feeling sorry for yourself.
- Beating yourself up over your mistakes.

But you can turn all that around. (Oh yes, you surely can!) Changing your habits is under your control. Just start repeating thoughts and behaviors that help you instead. Repeat them long enough (66 days, remember) and they'll become your new habits.

Some good habits you can make (a partial list):

- Taking action (not with food) that will actually fix your problems or help you learn from them.
- Paying attention to your body, listening for cues, then waiting to eat until you're hungry and stopping when you're comfortably full.
- Deciding for yourself what kind of life you want, what works for you and what doesn't.
- Telling yourself a new story about yourself and your life, one that will help you move on and grow.
- Choosing yourself and your well-being over abusing food; treating yourself with kindness and compassion *always*, being your own cheerleader.
- Believing in your own worth and value regardless of what the scale or anyone else says.
- Taking the first step *now* even though you can't see the whole path to where you are going.
- Believing in yourself, that you have what it takes (because you most certainly do), and pressing on when you want to quit.
- Enforcing your own boundaries.
- Enjoying your life *now*.

You don't ever have to be stuck in a rut of thinking the same way and/or doing the same things. You just don't. It's not only me saying that. It's brain science and neuroplasticity telling you that. You can change your brain and make new pathways. You can create new habits and haul yourself up out of the pit you might've fallen in. You can move forward. (Oh yes, you can!) You just have to choose to do so.

SOME NOTES ON

SABOTAGING YOURSELF

So here's where we talk about what abusing food and/or being overweight are doing for you—or better yet, what you perceive they're doing for you. That's what psychologists called secondary gains.[11] You're getting (or perceive you're getting) some benefit by being overweight and/or abusing food. It's your job, *right now*, to figure out what that benefit is.

It's entirely possible (and likely) that you've previously gotten (or will get) to your goal weight or within pounds of your goal weight and then you sabotage yourself. You stop waiting for hunger. You eat way past comfortably full. You go back to not listening to your body at all and bingeing. Or purging. Or starving. You throw your hands in the air and quit and go running back to some diet you've done in the past with strict rules to follow (that didn't work, mind you) and let the vicious diet-go-round start up again.

In my experience, self-sabotage almost always has something to do with fear. It's about getting in your own way and stopping forward progress so you can minimize risk and not have to step out of your comfort zone. So ask yourself these: *What am I afraid, anxious, concerned is going to happen when I lose the weight and/or stop abusing food? What am I afraid, anxious, concerned I am going to have to do once I lose the weight and/or stop abusing food?* You absolutely MUST answer those questions because self-sabotage is part of that hole inside you, too. You need to heal it. If you don't, you'll find yourself in the same cycle your entire life (and not just with food either): reaching for what you want, so close that you can almost but not quite touch it, or maybe you can touch it and it's there in your hands, then *bam!*, you do something that knocks you clean out of the game and back into the safety of the bleachers.

You may think the excess weight and/or abusing food keeps you safe. All it does, though, is keep you from facing your fears. And it's the fears that you need to overcome. For me, the fears were these (a partial list):

- I was terrified about receiving sexual attention from men because I didn't know how or even believe I had the right to defend my boundaries and my body.
- I didn't want to stand out in a crowd, ever, and have people looking at me because I feared both their judgments and the possibility of them yelling slurs at me.
- I wanted people to like me and to let me belong and the skinnier I got, the more people (sorry to say, jealous women especially) didn't like me and didn't want me around.
- I didn't believe I deserved good things.
- I was terrified of change and letting go.
- I had a paralyzing fear of the unknown.
- I didn't want to reach for great things and challenge myself because I was terrified of failing and what I believed failing would say about me as a person.
- I was afraid of any kind of relationship because I trusted almost no one and all the excess weight gave me an excuse to avoid people.
- I was terrified of intimacy because I was equally terrified of rejection.
- Being overweight was the excuse that allowed me to stay deep in my comfort zone.

Secondary gains can include things like getting attention from others so you can feel valuable or not feel lonely, a sense of belonging from others who also suffer with abusing food, reinforcing your own limiting beliefs so you don't have to change, and the list goes on. Just know this: secondary gains are excuses, and you will never be empowered by making excuses.

So do this:
1. Go somewhere alone then get still and quiet. Be brave and sit with yourself.
2. Make a list of all the benefits you gain by being overweight and/or abusing food. *Be honest.*
3. Write down the mistakes you made when you were so close to what you wanted.
4. Then write down why you made those mistakes.
5. The answer to why will likely show you your fears.
6. Read all those answers and find the common thread running through them all. Write it down. That common thread is likely your biggest fear.
7. Take note of that biggest fear and keep reading because you'll soon learn how to overcome it (in Chapter Seven).

EATING DISORDERS

For those people who suffered or are currently suffering with anorexia, bulimia, and/or binge eating disorder, this process will work for you. I know it will because at different points in my life, over a span of more than twenty-five years, I suffered with all three. In each case, you're going to have to stop the out-of-control behavior and abusing food, both of which have become bad habits for you. In each case, you're going to have to wait until you're hungry to eat and stop when you're comfortably full.

For those with anorexia, you're going to have to eat more than you're eating now, and in your case, likely gain weight. For those with bulimia, you're going to have to keep the food down. For those with binge eating disorder, you're going to have to stop when you're *comfortably full* and *wait until you're hungry* to eat again. In every case: ***it's okay for you to be a healthy weight; you are so much more than a number on a scale.*** I can write those same words for pages and pages, even fill this whole book with them, but those words won't become truth for you, and so the story that you live out in your life, unless you're the one who believes them. So you need to be the one telling yourself those words, over and over, as many times as it takes to beat a new pathway in your brain. I assure you that if you say it and think it long enough—*it's okay for me to be a healthy weight, I am so much more than a number on a scale, I have so much more to offer than the smallness of abusing food, I refuse to be trapped in a cycle, I believe that food is fuel so I can thrive*—you'll come to believe it and then live it out in your life. And the most important thing to always remember and also repeat to yourself: you're not doing this for anyone else, you're doing this for you … to save your own life.

I know all of that is terrifying because food, for you, is about control. Maybe abusing food makes you feel like you have control over yourself and your emotional state, the direction of your life, and/or the events happening around/to you. But know this without a doubt: you are not free; it's the food that controls you. You may not believe that, but I assure you that if you're suffering with an eating disorder, that statement is true. You are not free to do as you wish because, in some way, your life revolves around abusing food. You are trapped in a cycle/circle and not moving forward in a straight line to where you want to be. You spend your time and exchange your life for counting calories or bingeing then vomiting or eating wildly instead of pursuing your hopes, passions, goals, and dreams. That is not you being in control; that is you enslaved to food.

The entire process described in this book is about changing your beliefs about your own worth so you can see yourself as the valuable person you are. This process is also about changing your thinking about food and its role in your life, not as a crutch or as a way to numb yourself or as a way to avoid fear but as a way to fuel your body so you can get busy doing those things that you love to do, those things that make you come alive. I can just about guarantee you that you do not love to suffer with an eating disorder and that being crazed around food does not make you feel alive. Even if you think you're getting some benefit from an eating disorder (secondary gains like we just talked about), I would still argue that keeping up with the demands of an eating disorder is neither something you love to do nor something that makes you feel excited to be alive. Part of the reason, too, that it's so important to stop abusing food is so that you will have the time, energy, and focus to find out what it is you really love to do and then go do it. This process is also about seeing your own courage, strength, resilience, intelligence, and perseverance and how those things don't come from numbers on a scale. And most importantly, this is about healing yourself so you can be healthy and whole.

One final note: you may need some professional help, and that's really okay. You don't have to go it alone. You just don't. Just so you know: I see a therapist, even now. She helps me, and that's reason enough to keep seeing her. Living your life with an eating disorder is not living. It's surviving. It's existing. It's just trying to make it through the day. It's not enjoying your life. It's not feeling passionate. It's not chasing your dreams. It's not finding your purpose and pursuing it. Instead, having an eating disorder is crazy-making and utter desperation and a swamping belief that you're never enough and a suffocating kind of fear, at least it was for me. So please, reach out to someone you trust (*trust* is key) and ask for help. You find whatever form works for you: one-on-one with a therapist, professional group therapy, a weekly support group with like-minded people, pastoral counseling, and/or whatever would help you most. You're worth the effort. You truly are. I believe that about you. Now you just need to believe it about yourself.

THE SCALE

It's in your best interests not to weigh yourself more than once a week. Why? Because your weight will fluctuate from day-to-day due to a variety of factors not under your control (water retention, for instance), and if you're the kind of person who freaks out when the scale goes up (and judges your self worth, shames yourself, uses it as an excuse to binge, beats yourself up, and/or decides just how good your day is going to be based on that number), you will just be making your life more difficult. Do yourself a kindness and don't do that.

It is, however, a good idea to weigh yourself once a week and write it down so you have a realistic idea of your progress. It's a good idea to not live in denial (about anything, really). But here's the thing you need to understand: you may not lose weight every week. In fact, it's entirely possible that you may gain on some weeks. Hear me: *that's entirely normal.* It doesn't mean what you're doing is not working. It doesn't mean you're failing. What you're looking for are the overall trends that your body goes through. You'll see patterns on how your particular body sheds the weight. Once you see the patterns, you'll be able to calm down and not freak out over the number on the scale.

Our bodies are all different. What happens for one person will most likely not be exactly what happens for you. There will be fluctuations in your weight, and *that's okay.* If you find your weight stagnant for too long (and you decide for yourself what is too long), then you need to take an *honest* look at how much you're eating. Are you genuinely waiting to be hungry? Are you truthfully stopping when you're comfortably full? Your first reaction will probably be: *of course I am.* But it could be, and I'm saying this as gently as I can, that you're still eating too much. I'm often shocked at how little I eat now (without feeling deprived, mind you) compared to how much I used to eat.

And again, if you've just had it up to here with scales and numbers and charting your weight, if you need a break from all that, then you don't weigh yourself at all for a little while. You just track your progress by how your clothes fit and how your body feels. One last thing: you need to remember (even if it's hard to do so) that your weight (like your age) is just a number; it has nothing (and I really do mean *nothing*) to do with your worth and value as a person. Character matters more than the number on the scale. So does morality. And ethics. And honesty. And kindness. And compassion. And generosity. And the list goes on. So keep that in mind.

ENCOURAGEMENT AND SUPPORT GROUPS

So we all need encouragement at some point. You. Me. Everybody. Obviously, it helps if you have someone in your life that can give you that encouragement, someone you can call when things get rough. But what do you do if you don't have someone like that?

Know this: you are capable of doing this process whether anyone helps you or not. You are strong, brave, courageous, tenacious, intelligent, and you have what it takes to see this thing through and save your own life. You may not believe that about you, but I know it's true. I didn't think I could do this by myself either, and then my support system suddenly vanished and it was just me. Alone. And that's when I learned that I am capable of meeting my own goals because they matter deeply to me, that I don't need anyone else's permission to live my life, and that no one is going to get me out of the mess I made but me. That's how I know you can do this, too.

If, however, you feel like you need a support group in order to thrive, then by all means seek one out. The most important thing is to find one that feels right to you. If you don't feel like you're being supported and nurtured, then keeping looking until you find a group that works for you. I'm an introvert, always have been. Big support groups don't work for me at all. I don't feel supported; I feel panicked. Too many people for me, which sends me right into fear mode, which makes me want to grab the nearest pint of ice cream. So now, I meet one-on-one with another woman who needs encouragement, too. It's a support group of two, which is what I need in my life. We have coffee and chat. No pressure. No panic. Perfect for me. You need to find out what's perfect for you and do that. And if you can't find an existing support system, then you must create one for yourself. Some diets (and people, too) will tell you that you'll do better with a big support group. But if you don't like big support groups, they can actually be a hindrance. It's okay if you don't want to be part of a big support group or part of any support group at all. I'm telling you that you don't need one to thrive. I'm proof of that. So don't get in the mindset that you do.

One other thing to keep in mind: I've also found that sometimes support groups turn competitive (and not just about weight loss and/or abusing food). You don't want that. I already said this but it bears repeating: you're not in competition with anyone here. It's just you, making and striving toward and meeting your own weight-loss goal(s)—that holds true with all of your other life goals, too. So keep yourself sane and don't worry about what anyone else is doing. There is bound to be someone who can do this better, faster, easier, and/or some other -er than you. That's okay. Let them do their thing. You do yours.

Whatever you choose to do, don't be afraid to ask for help or to ask for what you need. If you're scared but you feel like you don't want to do this weight-loss journey alone, then you're going to have to take a risk and

..... or help. The easiest way to minimize that risk is to ask for help from *someone you trust*. So do yourself a kindness and ask, because you are worth both the risk and the effort.

RECIPES

There's not a single recipe in this book. Not a one. That's deliberate. I don't need to tell you what to eat. Neither does anyone else. You need to decide for yourself what you want to eat. It's your body after all. You need to listen to your body and give it what it needs. Nobody else can do that for you either. You need to be in control of your own choices. *Always.*

If you'd really like some recipes and have a slow cooker, then you can grab some of my favorite recipes on my website at: shellijohnson.com/recipes. None of them were created with low-fat, low-carb, or calorie-conscious in mind. But, I dare say, they are all delicious. Feel free to eat any of them when you're hungry and just stop when you're comfortably full.

YOU HAVE EVERYTHING YOU NEED

Eat when you're hungry, stop when you're comfortably full. That's the secret. It's as simple and as easy as you want to make it.

So why is this book longer than two chapters? Because right now, you probably don't believe it's simple or easy, and I need to show you that it is. And also because you'll need to do some self-exploration: learning a few things about yourself and what you love, discovering some other things about why you do what you do, and taking action on yet other things to care for yourself so that you can keep the weight off permanently.

OH, SOME SCIENCE (PART ONE)

When you have an emotional reaction to some stimulus in your life, biochemicals (hormones, neurotransmitters, electrical impulses and the like) flood your body, causing an automatic physiological response (meaning what's happening in your body is not your choice). According to Jill Bolte Taylor in her book, *My Stroke of Insight*, that influx of chemicals only lasts briefly, leaving your system after less than ninety seconds. After that time is up, the chemicals disperse and the physiological reaction goes away. However, if you keep having an emotional reaction to the stimulus (resentment, anger, fear, anxiety, and the like), then the physiological reaction lingers.[12] At that point, it's the *thoughts about the stimulus and not the stimulus itself* that are causing the same physiological reaction (an influx of biochemicals and electrical impulses), playing on a loop, *starting anew every time you think about the stimulus*, time and time and time again, until you break the cycle. At that point, *it's your choice* whether to continue the cycle or to make it stop by changing and/or letting go of your thoughts about the stimulus.

What does that mean for you? Because you're reading this book, it means that you need to stop trying to break the physiological reaction with food. It also means that you need to sit with whatever psychological reaction you're having to a situation and not abuse food or some other substance/behavior to relieve your emotions. It means you need to fully feel, accept, and learn from whatever emotions are coming up for you, even if those emotions are incredibly uncomfortable (even if those emotions make you scream or cry or curl yourself into a ball or pound your fists against the wall). It also means you need to *stay in the present moment* and stop dredging up any history (also known as your personal backstory) that you're reminded of because of the stimulus (for instance: *this always happens to me, I'm always the one who can't ever do anything right, they were right when they said I'd never amount to anything*, and the like). You must stay in that uncomfortable moment, let yourself fully feel your emotions and learn about yourself from them, then choose to change and/or let go of your thoughts about the stimulus.

My guess is, because I did it for so many years too, that you have a hard time sitting with what you're feeling, that you haul up lots of history that the stimulus triggered in you, which in turn makes it incredibly hard to be inside your own body, that you feel swamped and suffocated by the emotions coupled with the history, that you'd rather abuse food and numb yourself than to deal with the anger, hurt, shame, fear, pain, and/or [insert the emotion you're avoiding here].

So to summarize, do this:
1. When you find yourself reacting to something that's happened, accept that whatever you're feeling is what you're feeling, and that's okay.
2. Stay in that uncomfortable moment and let yourself *fully* feel whatever emotions come up inside you.
3. Stay in the present moment without hauling up your history.
4. Learn about yourself.
5. When the emotion passes (because it will), change and/or let go of the thought(s) about the stimulus that triggered the emotion to begin with (so you don't keep causing a physiological reaction over and over again).

OH, SOME SCIENCE (PART TWO)

Peptides are molecules that carry information to and from the different systems of the body. Gherlin (like we talked about earlier) is a peptide hormone secreted by the stomach to tell you if you're hungry. Leptin is also a peptide hormone, but it's secreted mainly by fat cells and it tells you if you're full.[13] In addition, your pancreas releases a variety of different peptides, all dealing with your state of hunger or satiety.[14] All these various peptides carry information to your brain, specifically to the hypothalamus, which regulates feelings of hunger and fullness.[15]

When stimuli come into your brain, the thalamus regulates where the stimuli go. It sends the information both to the cortex (which processes thought and decision making) and the amygdala (the emotional, nonthinking part of your brain). If you're in a highly-emotional state, the amygdala senses danger in those incoming stimuli, and it will make an instant decision to react by starting the fight-or-flight response, completely subverting anything the cortex might want to do.[16] When the amygdala is flooded with distress biochemicals, it stops the connection to the prefrontal cortex (which is responsible for decision making).[17] The amygdala then signals the hypothalamus, whose primary job it is to keep the body and its systems stable, to activate the sympathetic nervous system, which is what reacts during times of stress (fight-or-flight) to give you the energy you need.[18]

All that to say, from my layman's understanding, the hypothalamus is being flooded with distress biochemicals by the amygdala during a fight-or-flight response. Any hunger/fullness messages coming into the hypothalamus during that state will basically: 1. not be prioritized in the deluge of other biochemicals being produced to get you ready for fight-or-flight and 2. never make it to the part of the brain where you can actually think about and decide what to do with them.

That's why you need to fully feel your emotions first and let them pass. You need to let go of any thoughts of the stimulus before you eat so you don't keep triggering a physiological response. You need to break the cycle so you can calm down and bring your body back into balance. Then once you've calmed down, you can listen to your body and you'll be able to pay attention to the cues to know if you're actually physiologically hungry. And if you are, that's when you let yourself eat.

THIS IS A PRACTICE AND A PROCESS

Always figure out what works for you and do that. And while you're figuring it out, you will at some point screw up. You'll eat too much. You'll go on a binge. You'll fall back into calorie counting, starving, excessive exercise, and/or some restrictive diet mentality because that feels safer and familiar. You'll do something that will make you feel like throwing in the towel and giving up and going back to your old habits and ways. Don't give up. Don't go backward. Just stop and take a deep breath. Know that you're going to make mistakes just like everyone else. Hear me: *there's no doing this perfectly, so don't make yourself crazy trying*. You do the best you can. You keep moving forward. And always remember this: every mistake is simply a brand new chance to do it better the next time.

CHAPTER THREE

TRUST YOURSELF

OR

How to unlock your inner phenomenal.

Chapter Three

"Self-trust is the first secret of success."
—Ralph Waldo Emerson

THERE IS NO God, Father says. Religion is just a crutch for weaklings.

But I want to believe.

So late at night, I lay in bed listening to the quiet. When I am sure everyone else is asleep, I crawl out from under the covers and slide to my knees beside the canopy bed. I open the wooden jewelry box on the nightstand, the one I got at a neighbor's garage sale, and hollow notes tinkle out. The ballerina twirls and twirls and twirls. Pink taffeta tutu on a narrow waist. Tiny chiseled face. Delicate fingers. Long sculpted legs. Girly. Graceful. Thin. Not like me.

When the song ends, I close the box and steeple my fingers so my thumbs press against my breastbone. I bow my head until my fingertips touch the end of my nose. I bow some more until the edge of the mattress touches my forehead. The room is cool, quiet. The clock ticks on nightstand, its florescent face glowing.

I want to believe. I want to believe. I want to believe.

My prayers go something like this: our Father who art in Heaven, please make me skinny I don't want to be fat anymore and forgive me for I have sinned please stop the kids at school from making fun of me please make *me invisible please make them find someone else to pick on I don't want to look like this I don't want to be seen please make my family love me bless me and the cat and the horses across the street and the toads in the pond and please make everyone stop calling me names and I'm sorry for whatever I did just please God make me skinny I don't want to be fat and bless my teachers especially Mrs. Andrews and you are good and kind and the lunch lady says you are all-powerful and can do miracles so you could make me skinny you could it's the only thing I'll ever ask for that one thing it's not too much to ask amen.*

I squeeze my eyes shut, clasp my hands tighter, press my forehead into the mattress.

"Please."

The word is a tiny puff of air against my fingers.

"Please."

Then I stop praying and I wait. There's a knot in my stomach. My heartbeat pulses in my fingertips. I wait and wait. A breeze hits the window and rattles the pane. Snowflakes gather in the corners then die on the warm glass. The furnace kicks on and sends heat spinning through the floor vent, swishing the hem of my nightgown.

"Please . . . please . . .please . . . please . . . please . . . please."

But no one answers.

After a while, when my bare feet get cold and my knees hurt from being smashed against the carpet, I crawl back into bed and pull the covers to my chin and stare up at the ruffled canopy in the dark.

"Where are you?" I ask.

But no one answers that either.

I am ten years old.

SOMETHING YOU NEED TO KNOW

Trusting yourself really is the very first secret to success, not just for weight loss but for life in general. Honestly, would you put your life in the hands of someone you didn't trust? Me neither. But the truth is this: your life is already in your hands. It's up to you how you want to live it.

When you don't have self-trust, you don't listen to yourself. You don't listen to the wisdom inside yourself. And that wisdom is there, I assure you that it is, in the form of your intuition. That wisdom knows what you most deeply want. It knows (oh yes, it does) how to take steps to get it. It knows the direction in which you most need to go.

But when you don't trust yourself, you look outside yourself for answers. You listen to the guidance of others, even if that guidance flies in the face of what your own intuition is telling you. And that's where the problem lies because other people will give you advice based on their own fears and limits. And in that way, suddenly, their fears and limits will become yours. You don't want that, I assure you that you don't. And finally, when you don't trust yourself, you sabotage your own efforts out of fear that you aren't capable of handling whatever comes. You choose to go around in cycles/circles in your life and get in your own way because that's easier, safer, and/or more comfortable (or so you tell yourself) than trusting yourself.

SOME THINGS YOU NEED TO DO TO BUILD YOUR SELF-TRUST

PRACTICE SELF-COMPASSION

One of the most important things you may ever do in your entire life is to have some self-compassion. Compassion is that feeling you get when you see someone else struggling or suffering or hurting and your heart breaks for them so you want to help. Self-compassion is turning that same feeling of tenderness/kindness and wanting to help ease the struggling/suffering/hurting inward toward yourself. Self-compassion really is what you most need to heal you. You will never come to trust yourself if you're being in any way harmful, derogatory, belittling, mean, and the like to your own self. You won't trust that you can take care of yourself. You won't trust that you can be kind and gentle with yourself. You won't trust that you have worth and value, and for those reasons alone, deserve to honor and respect yourself. You won't trust that you deserve to have beautiful things. You won't trust that you are strong, courageous, tenacious, determined, intelligent, and on the list goes. So you be nice to you even if (*especially if*) no one else is being nice to you.

Another part of self-compassion is having patience with yourself. Patience isn't always easy, I get that, especially when you think you should have/be/do/know better by now. But the truth is you are where you are right now, and that's okay. You're human, like everyone else; you make mistakes, like everyone else. You are still learning and growing. It's going to take some time before you get to where you most want to be. If you lose patience with yourself during the process, you're bound to start beating yourself up, which will: 1. cause you to abuse food to numb yourself and 2. shred your self-trust. Honestly, would you trust someone who was always berating you? No, you would not. So don't do it to yourself. Nothing can bloom when it's being mowed down.

One of the best ways I've found to practice self-compassion is to write your own life story.

So do this:

1. Jot down experiences: a memory here, a memory there. You don't have to write a whole memoir.
2. Separate your story from yourself so you can look at your life objectively.
3. Read it back so you can see the places where you were committed and tenacious, where you had perseverance and determination, where you had resilience and overcame your critics, where you were so much stronger than whatever it was that tried to defeat you. This will give you a bird's-eye-view of what you lived through, how challenging it may have been, and yet you still made it, you're still here.
4. Now write down what each of those experiences taught you.
5. Then realize that each of those experiences served a purpose in your life as lessons either about yourself or about others.
6. Know this: once you see all that, you'll naturally start being more compassionate with yourself.

LISTEN TO YOUR OWN INTUITION

Again, your intuition is full of wisdom. It'll *never* tear you down or berate you or harm you. It will *always* encourage you, strengthen you, and help you grow, even if what it's saying you need to do to move forward in your life scares you. It's also likely that your body knows the choice(s) you need to make long before your mind does. Your body reacts immediately and makes an instant judgment. Your mind filters information through a lifetime of knowledge, feelings, thoughts, and experiences then does pros and cons. So keep this in mind: your intuition includes both your body (how your body feels/reacts) and your mind (thoughts and feelings, usually the quieter ones).

It seems everyone has an opinion or some advice to offer and many of them will give it to you whether you ask for it or not. But what matters most when you make a choice, *any* choice, is that you listen for what your intuition (also known as that voice of wisdom inside you) is telling you and you choose that. And if you're confused about what is your intuition and what is not, then ask yourself this: *What feels (deep down, where it's quiet and still) like the right thing to do?*

There is power in your intuition. Your intuition will guide you to what's good for you and what you need to do to fulfill yourself. It will guide you about what's right for you and what's wrong for you, what you want to be doing with your life, which people you want to be spending time with and who you want to be gone from your life. It will tell you when you screw up and need to apologize but also when you're right and you need to stand your ground, when to say *yes* and when to say *no*, when it's time to dig your heels in and charge ahead or when it's time to stop clinging and leave. Your intuition will even tell you which foods you really want to eat and which foods you'd rather not.

Yes, it's trial and error at the beginning, but eventually you'll come to recognize your own intuition. You'll know when you're listening to it and also when you're flying in the face of it. Your voice of wisdom, if you let it, will prove to you that you can take care of yourself and that you can handle life as it comes. It will prove to you that you don't need anyone or anything else to make you whole. It will prove to you that you matter, your voice matters, what you do matters, and your life matters. You'll come to learn that you really do know what you most want, what will make you happy, and what's best for you. *You empower yourself by listening to your intuition and doing what it says.* And eventually, when you listen to your intuition every single time and do what it guides you to do, you'll come to trust yourself implicitly.

Now whether you listen to and act upon that wisdom inside yourself or not is another story. Be aware that every time you fly in the face of your own intuition and choose something else, you're betraying yourself, and it's the self-betrayal that has chipped away, if not shattered, your self-trust. You're not hurting anybody but yourself when you refuse to listen to your intuition, when you refuse to do what it tells you to do. And also be aware that listening to someone else's advice at the expense of your own intuition is dangerous because when things go south (as they're likely to do), the person who gave you the advice is not going to be the one dealing with the consequences, it's going to be you.

And finally, your intuition may say some scary things that throw you outside of your comfort zone (like: quit your job or end this relationship or move to a different city/state/country). I know it can be terrifying. It can make you want to stopper your ears with your fingers and pretend you can't hear. It can make you want to sprint in the opposite direction. But still, if you are ever going to learn to trust yourself implicitly, you will need listen to your intuition and do what it says every single time. It's just fine if you take action in tiny steps, because tiny steps will still get you where you want to be, just slower and with far less fear; what matters most is that you're moving in the direction your intuition tells you to go. Let your intuition be your roadmap, let it guide you, and two things will happen: 1. you'll learn to trust yourself implicitly and 2. success won't be far behind.

UNDERSTAND THE EXCESS WEIGHT AND/OR FOOD ABUSE IS JUST A BAROMETER, MEASURING YOUR SELF-TRUST

You can measure your self-trust by how many pounds overweight you are or how much you abuse food. The less you implicitly trust yourself, the more pounds you carry or the more often you abuse food, at least that's been my experience. The extra weight and/or food abuse is a way to hide yourself or keep yourself safe or avoid something you don't want to deal with or [insert your self-trust issue here].

What it all comes down to, though, is that there is something in your life (something that happened before, something that's happening now, something that might happen in the future) that you don't trust yourself to handle either emotionally or physically. And so you abuse food to make the memories go away or to give yourself a sense of courage or to numb the fear you have, and on the list goes. But what it all boils down to, all of it, is that you don't much trust yourself in some area of your life. I know this is true because I didn't used to trust myself much either. I didn't trust myself enough to (a partial list):

- Get out of bad relationships (including soured friendships, toxic romantic partners, unsupportive family members, overbearing supervisors, and the like).
- Go after what I wanted and not settle (so I accepted something I didn't really want, something less than, taking the scraps of what was left over instead of requiring nothing less than the best, and then tried to convince myself it was really okay. And I'm not only talking about food here but also about relationships and work and things that fulfilled me).
- Listen to my own intuition (so I listened to everyone around me—including strangers, self-help gurus, and people who didn't have my best interests at heart—and did what they said instead).
- Take care of myself (financially, emotionally, physically, and spiritually, so I let other people have the power in my life to control those things).
- Deal with my body reacting/remembering in certain situations (panicking in small spaces where I felt trapped, flinching if anyone made sudden moves around me, and the like), handle bad memories that kept playing on a loop in my head (which I felt powerless to stop), and protect/defend myself by saying *no* (because I had no hard, clear boundaries nor did I believe I had a right to have and defend hard, clear boundaries).Being overweight was the excuse that allowed me to stay deep in my comfort zone.

So be open, just be open, to the idea that all the excess weight and/or food abuse is simply showing you that you need to strengthen and fortify your self-trust.

CHANGE WHAT YOU BELIEVE

Self-trust starts with you. Specifically, with what you believe about yourself. Do you believe good things about yourself? Or bad things? The answer matters. Here's something I assure you is true: *you will live out whatever it is you believe about yourself.* Believe you can't and you won't. Believe you can, even if you have to repeat it in your head over and over, and eventually you will. Believe you don't have what it takes and you'll quit. Believe you're able and, even if it's hard, you'll keep going. Believe you're an addict, and you will forever remain an addict who never rises above. Believe you have the "disease" of being overweight and/or obese, and you will remain someone sick whose situation is beyond their control. Or instead, choose to believe that you are so much stronger than this food craziness that's trying to defeat you and watch yourself rise to the challenge and do whatever it takes to be victorious.

Again, beliefs are simply the same thoughts you've had over and over and over again; thoughts that have worn a neural pathway in your brain. You no longer question those thoughts (*Are they true or false? Do they strengthen you or weaken you? Do you even want them in your head?*), you just believe them. Because you live out what you believe, you need to form beliefs that work for you, not against you. That means you need to be thoughtful and deliberate about the things you choose to believe. You can accept or reject any belief that you want; that choice is always up to you. So do yourself a kindness and choose to hold on to beliefs that help you and not harm you. Choose to believe that both you and what you're doing matters. Choose to believe you can achieve anything you set your mind to. Choose to believe that you are capable and strong and intelligent and committed and determined. Choose to believe that you are worthwhile and deserve to have the life you most want. Choose to believe all those things because they are true. Until you change what you believe about yourself and your chances and what you deserve, you won't ever change your life.

Since you're reading this book, I know that you want to be thinner and/or to stop abusing food. I'm sure you want to feel comfortable in your own body. You likely want your self-confidence back. I'd bet too that you want to stop the insane diet-go-around and/or obsession with food and weight. You can have all that, I assure you that you can. It starts, first and foremost, with knowing what beliefs you hold that build you up and which ones tear you down.

So do this:
1. Let thoughts and beliefs just come into your mind.
2. Then pay attention to how your body feels when you think about those thoughts and beliefs.
3. Know this: anything that drains your energy, makes you feel less than or smaller, fuels a desire to abuse any substance/behavior, and/or limits/confines you, that is a thought/belief that's not serving you.
4. So simply change your mind.
5. Reject the thoughts that weaken you and/or don't help you move forward to where you most want to be.
6. Repeat (*repeat, repeat*) the thoughts that strengthen you until they become the beliefs that guide you.
7. Know this too: it's simply a matter of choice and repetition, that's all.
8. And remember: you're beating pathways in your brain all the time. So why not beat ones that make you into the person you want to be?

ALWAYS KEEP YOUR WORD TO YOURSELF

The quickest and best way to earn your own trust is to keep your word to yourself. *Every. Single. Time.* Say you're going to do something then do it. Say you believe something then stand your ground and defend it. Say you want something then go after it and fulfill yourself. Say you will handle whatever gets thrown at you (because you absolutely can) then rise to the challenge when it comes. Say you will listen to your own intuition instead of relying on others to guide you then do what your intuition says, even if that thing scares you.

Keep your word to yourself *every single time*, and the self-trust will come.

You made a commitment to yourself way back in Chapter One that you have started down this path to free yourself from the diet-go-round and from the food craziness. You made a commitment that you're going to keep going and stay at it until you find what works for you. You made a commitment that you're on this journey until you see it all the way through to the end. You gave yourself your word. Do yourself a kindness and build your self-trust by keeping your word.

MANAGE YOUR DISAPPOINTMENT (AND OTHER FEELINGS) WITHOUT FOOD

You're going to be disappointed in this life. Sometimes, you're going to be disappointed daily. Someone is going to let you down. Sometimes you will let yourself down. You'll have expectations that don't get met. Or goals that you'll think you should've reached by now. Or aspirations that haven't yet come to pass. You may have dreams that seemed close when you first started going after them but now they seem so far away. Or maybe the work you produced doesn't turn out as good as it was when it was just an idea in your mind. You'll get knocked down and not want to get back up again. You're going to make mistakes. At some point, you're going to fail.

Food will never fix your disappointment. It just won't. Ever.

So do this:
1. Go somewhere where you can be alone if possible.
2. Feel the disappointment. Sit with it and just let yourself fully feel it for at least 90 seconds.
3. Don't abuse food (or some other substance/behavior) to interrupt the feeling.
4. Don't drag up your history into the present moment.

5. Just feel. Curl into a ball and sob, scream as loud as you can, pound your fist into a pillow, whatever you need to do to express that feeling.
6. Then let go of both the feeling and the thoughts about what caused the disappointment.
7. Now move on and take a step forward (tiny, if need be) in the direction you want to go.

Every time you choose to feel your feelings instead of numbing them by abusing food, you'll build your self-trust that you can handle any emotion that comes up. Every time you choose to not drag up your history so you don't get stuck in the story of your personal narrative, you'll strengthen your self-trust that you don't have to be trapped in the past. Every time you choose to let go of your thoughts about whatever caused the feelings, you'll increase your self-trust that you can move on. Every time you take a step forward and keep going in the direction you want for your life, you'll fortify your self-trust that you can reach the goals that deeply matter to you. Do all that long enough, and you'll trust yourself implicitly. And when that happens, you won't let any situation derail you because you'll know you have everything you need inside you to overcome whatever gets thrown at you.

CHOOSE YOU

This one is really crucial to self-trust, especially if you have a history of being one of the last people picked or the one left behind or the one singled out or, in general, have a sense that you just don't belong.

You need to choose yourself.

Choose to make yourself happy and fulfilled regardless of what anyone else does or doesn't do for you. Choose to believe in your own self-worth regardless of how others treat you. Choose what you want out of your own life. Choose your own standards to live up to. Choose your own definition of success. Choose the beliefs and values that matter to you and serve you most. Choose to support yourself and your decisions. Choose to give yourself your own stamp of approval. Choose (because, yes, it's a choice) to trust yourself.

Every time you choose yourself, you will trust yourself a little bit more. You will trust yourself to meet your own needs, to fulfill your own wants, to build yourself up, to seek out what gives you joy, and to find what makes you come alive and go do it. You won't have to spend any time worrying that you'll throw yourself under the bus or sacrifice yourself for the wants of others or measure your own self-worth on a sliding scale based on numbers (your weight, your body measurements, your pant size, and the list goes on). If you regularly choose yourself, you'll come to trust that you matter to you, and once that happens, you'll finally come to realize that's reason enough to put yourself first.

CHANGE HOW YOU VALUE YOURSELF

Again, my guess is that you don't put much value on yourself; I know this because I used to not value myself much either. Maybe you feel worthless. Maybe you believe you have nothing to offer or what you do have to offer isn't worth much. It's quite possible that you're either trying to value yourself with food (*I'm worth having this [insert any type of food here]*) or you're covering up the fact that you feel worthless by numbing yourself by abusing food (*I just want it to all go away with [insert any type food here]*). It's also entirely possible with any kind of food abuse that you (consciously or subconsciously) are reinforcing your own belief in how little value you have (*I don't matter so what difference does it make anyway*). But none one of those scenarios is helping you.

Food is fuel for your body, that's it. It has no emotional attachments at all except for what you give it. Food is not the currency of self-worth. It cannot give you as a person any value at all. It will never—hear me: *never*—mirror back to you a person who has something worthwhile and valuable to offer. All those things— emotional support, validation, feelings of importance, proof that you matter, and the list goes on—that you're looking for from food are choices that fall, I say this kindly, squarely on you.

Along those same lines, the number on the scale does not equal your self worth. Neither does the amount of hours you spend at the gym. Or how many steps you take today. Or how much water you drink. Or how closely you weighed and measured your food. Or how little you ate (or how much either). Or how much money you make. Or how many titles you have after your name. Or how many friends you have. Or how much you have accomplished. Or your rankings. Or anything that many diets and/or society may say is important.

Again, your worth and value are innate. Period. You were born with them and *no one* can take them away from you. However, you can choose not to value yourself. You can choose not to believe in your own worth. It's a choice, *your choice*, to value yourself as-is, right now, just as you are, warts and all, regardless of your size or how you view food. It's your choice to believe that your gifts, talents, and passions are worthwhile. It's your choice to value what you do.

You'll never trust yourself implicitly if you don't start valuing yourself and what you have to offer *regardless of what others may say/think/do*. Why? Because: 1. you'll be seeking validation elsewhere (and what if they don't give it to you?), 2. you'll be putting the power over your well-being into someone else's hands (and what if they fumble?), and 3. there'll be a rift inside of you (caused by the fact that the power over your life belongs to you but you're giving it away). Know this: self-trust withers and dies (slowly, yes, but that's what is happening) every time you abuse food or some other substance/behavior, whether that's in an attempt to give yourself value and make yourself feel worthy or for any other reason.

So how do you value yourself, your gifts, talents, passions, and the work that you do? You start by changing your thinking because your brain is your most powerful ally and tool.

So do this:
1. Say these words aloud to yourself (even better do it while meeting your eyes in a mirror): *My worth and value are innate. I have worth and value because I am alive. What I say and do matters because I matter.*
2. Repeat (*repeat, repeat*) those words often in your mind.
3. Stop looking outside yourself for anyone or anything to give you value or worth.
4. Validate your own life by prioritizing and cultivating your own gifts, talents, passions, interests, whatever they may be.

LIKE YOURSELF

Would you like or trust somebody who had mostly negative things to say to you? Would you like or trust somebody who did anything that diminished you as a person? Would you want them to be with you every minute of every day? Would you want to hang around that person at all? Well, that's what you're doing if you're the person being mean to you. You won't ever grow your self-trust by being mean to yourself. Just how are you being mean to yourself? Well, here are some examples (again, just a partial list of my own):

- Talking down to yourself and calling yourself names.
- Always thinking there's something wrong with you and you're in need of fixing.
- Refusing to forgive yourself for something you did or failed to do.
- Comparing yourself to other people in any way.
- Not liking your entire self and/or parts of yourself.

Do yourself a kindness and stop fighting yourself and start liking yourself instead. You need to decide to like yourself *even if no one else seems to*. Just like you should never allow disparaging, demeaning, and/or disrespectful behavior from other people toward you, you must never allow that same negative behavior toward yourself either. It's a choice. So choose, over and over, to like yourself.

Remember: you get to accept or reject any thought that comes into your head. It may take a little time and effort to change your thinking (brain neuroplasticity, if you recall), but if you keep at it, negative self-thoughts will come less often and when they do, you'll reject them immediately instead of letting them linger. And once you come to like yourself and then to trust yourself, a whole world of new possibilities (many of them things, people, and/or opportunities that were there all along but that you just couldn't see) will open up to you.

BE YOUR OWN BEST FRIEND

Trust isn't just given, it's earned. Self-trust is the same way. You are with you 24/7. You are the only person guaranteed to always be in your life. You are already the closest and best friend you'll ever have. So grow your trust in yourself by being the kind of friend you most need: the one who always listens with a compassionate ear, who (lovingly) gives you a kick in the pants when you need it, who helps you out of a jam, who is there at three o'clock in the morning to save your behind, who just loves you through all of it, who you can count on to be there whenever you're in need, and the like.

You need to be that kind of friend to yourself.

So do this:
1. Resolve to have your own back *always*, no matter what.
2. Stand up to yourself when you're doing something wrong and tell yourself the truth even if it hurts.
3. Motivate yourself with love and compassion, not by talking down to or shaming yourself.
4. Love yourself no matter your mistakes and failings.
5. Help yourself and support yourself and encourage yourself as best you can.
6. Like yourself as-is without expecting you to change or to prove anything or to be somebody you're not.
7. Want to see yourself succeed and be genuinely happy for yourself when good things come your way.
8. Don't compare yourself to anyone else.
9. Listen to yourself and don't judge.
10. Don't let yourself give up.

If you want the self-trust to come, you need to be for yourself the kind of best friend you've always wanted to have. There's no way around this one, you won't succeed at weight loss or the cessation of abusing food (or much else in your life, I would argue) without befriending yourself first, so do yourself a kindness and choose to be the best friend to yourself that you could ever have.

EMPOWER YOURSELF BY BEING THE AUTHORITY IN YOUR OWN LIFE

You already are the authority in your own life whether you acknowledge that fact or not. You may choose to give that authority (and hence your power) to someone else, but that's *your choice.* When you're sneaking food or not waiting until you're hungry to eat or not stopping when you're full, you're not sticking it to anybody else. When you justify why you're abusing food and refuse to find an exercise you enjoy and make excuses as to why you don't want to live in a healthy body and procrastinate about changing your life, you're only sticking it to yourself.

Whenever you're disempowered in any area of your life, you simply don't trust yourself enough to handle that particular area of your life. It's the lack of self-trust that makes you feel powerless. Every time you don't trust yourself (to make decisions, to know what's best for you, to protect yourself, to put yourself first, and on the list goes), you put a crack in the foundation of your own life. Put enough cracks in it and your foundation will crumble beneath you, leaving a power void. I've come to learn that whenever there's a power void, someone or something will come to fill it: either by you willingly giving them permission to take the reins of your life or by them simply stepping in and taking control while you do nothing about it. Then at some point (days, weeks, years, decades) later, you wonder (and are sometimes even quite perplexed) how you ended up where you are. It's because somewhere along the line you gave up power over your own life.

You have given your power to food. Oh yes, you have. You feel powerless in some area, you don't trust yourself to handle it, and then you abuse food (overeat, binge, starve, and/or purge) to give yourself some sense of control over what's happening to you. Except that food will never—I repeat, *never*—give you control. The only thing that will give you any control over your life is you taking action to fix what's wrong. Maybe you're having a hard time enforcing your boundaries. Maybe you hate confrontation and the only way out of the situation you're in is to confront someone. Maybe you're miserable in your career but afraid to change to a different one. Maybe you feel like you need to move on and you're terrified to step out and do it. Maybe you're socially awkward and afraid of people but horribly lonely and the only way to solve that is to be vulnerable and put yourself out in the world. Whatever it is (and as you can tell a lot of it is fear-based), you have the power to take some action and fix it.

Sometimes, the choices are hard. Sometimes, they throw you so far out of your comfort zone that you can't even see its boundaries anymore. Sometimes, they make you tremble or scream or cry or brace yourself for the onslaught you believe is coming. Sometimes, it may take everything inside you just to simply hold your ground and not back away from the choice(s) you know you need to make. In the end, it all comes down to this fact: *all the choices are still yours and no one else's.* Know this: even if you choose to give your power away, that's still a choice, *your* choice. The only way you're ever going to trust yourself implicitly is to stop looking outside yourself for someone to be the authority (for weight loss or for anything else).

Again, no one is coming to fix it. You know what you want. You know what you need to do to get it. Never let anybody, including yourself, tell you that you can't have it. Self-trust thrives when you take responsibility for your choices so you can get to where you most want to be, when you make choices that build you up and strengthen you and help you grow. So you take your power back, *right now*, and make the choices you know are best for you.

REALIZE THAT YOU CAN NEVER GET ENOUGH OF WHAT YOU DON'T NEED

You simply cannot build self-trust if you won't give yourself what you *actually* need. You need enough food to keep your body functioning at an optimal level. After that, food is just extraneous. You simply don't need any more. But when you're abusing food, there's just never enough it seems (bingeing, never enough food; purging, never enough vomiting; starving, never enough days in a row). *That's because abusing food is not actually what you need.* Keep that in mind. Here are some things I *really* need instead of abusing food (a partial list):

- To define success for myself instead of letting the world define it for me.
- To get out of comparison with others and get into creation of the life I want.
- To choose abundance over scarcity. There is enough. *Always.*
- To believe in the importance and value of myself, of my work, and of the causes that deeply matter to me.
- To encourage myself to keep going even in the face of both fear and what seems like overwhelming obstacles.
- To see a glimmer of hope even when there seems to be no hope at all.
- To confront someone or something I've been avoiding.
- To talk to a friend.
- To relax into uncertainty, let go of the outcome, and believe that everything, in the end, works in my favor.
- To take a break from the things that are causing me stress and anxiety and to do something that makes me happy instead.

I mention this process again because it's so important. When you want to abuse food (including eating when you're not hungry and/or not stopping when you're comfortably full), simply do this*:
1. Take a breath and a pause.

2. Don't put anything in your mouth. Don't go running off to some other substance/behavior. Move away from the refrigerator, cupboard, drive-thru window, and/or wherever you have your stash of comfort foods. If you are in the midst of abusing food, take a breath and a pause (yes, you can, I say kindly; it's a choice) and step away.
3. Say **out loud in a calm, kind voice**: *"What's the matter, [insert your name]? What do you need?"*
4. Go somewhere that you feel comfortable and safe, preferably by yourself, and let yourself feel whatever it is that's coming up.
5. Then when the feeling passes, take a deep breath in through your nose, hold it for three seconds, then let it out slowly through your mouth with an audible sound. Pull your shoulders down away from your ears. Feel your body relax.
6. Then take some time to address exactly what you need (that is not food-related) to make yourself feel safe, comforted, and supported in that moment. Trust yourself to know.
7. Now take action to do whatever it takes to meet that need(s) for yourself.
8. Then watch your self-trust grow.

*For the full explanation of this process and why it's so important to your healing, see *Eat Calmly* in Chapter Two.

QUIT PROCRASTINATING

Would you like it if you asked your friend to do something for you and he/she kept giving you excuses? Or putting you off? Or never getting back to you? You'd start to wonder if that person actually liked you, if he/she were really your friend. If they did it to you enough times, I guarantee that you wouldn't trust them anymore. You'd roll your eyes when they told you that you could count on them. You'd snort and say, *yeah, right.* Eventually, you'd stop asking them to do you any favors at all. Maybe you'd even cut them out of your life entirely. Thing is, you're doing that same thing to yourself when you're procrastinating about doing the things you need to do for your own well-being. Every time you put off dealing with your health and your weight and the abusing food, you're ditching yourself.

Hear me on this: *You will never build trust with yourself if you keep failing to follow through.*

So don't wait to do the next right thing. Do the next right thing *now.* Remember you're training your brain all the time. If you put off doing what you know you need to do, you're telling your brain it's okay to procrastinate the next time. This is especially important when you make a mistake (be it with food or something else). You're setting yourself up for failure by not *immediately* either fixing what you can or learning from what you can't. Why? Because the next time you make a mistake (and there will be a next time, no reason to believe there won't be), your brain's response will be whatever you did previously, be it taking decisive action or putting off dealing with the problem. This is especially important if you blow it with food then instead of simply waiting until you're hungry again, you choose to start over tomorrow morning, on the next Monday, and/or on New Year's Day of the following year. You are training your brain *all the time*, so make it easier on yourself and get back on track *right now*.

So do this:
1. Know this: procrastination is always rooted in fear.
2. So write an answer to this: *What am I afraid of?*
3. Make a list. Fill it with everything you can think of that scares you about moving forward.
4. Circle the biggest ones.
5. Find the thread that connects them. That thread is likely the fear that's driving your procrastination and why you keep putting off doing what you know you need to do.
6. Okay, with that as your starting point, what's the tiniest step you can take to get you moving through that fear? (Maybe look in a mirror and smile and tell yourself words you really need to hear. Or go do something that nourishes you. Or sit with whatever you're feeling until it passes. You get the idea.)
7. What's the next tiniest step after that? (Maybe ask for help. Or write a letter, telling someone how you really feel. Or perhaps, sit down to work a little more on that project you've been putting off. And the list goes on.)
8. The only thing you have to do when fear happens is to take a deep breath then take the next (tiny, if need be) step in the direction you want to go. That's it. One deep breath and one tiny step, one after another after another.
9. You'll overcome the fear, crush the procrastination, and *fortify your self-trust* if you'll just carry on.

DETERMINE WHOSE VOICE IS IN YOUR HEAD

My guess is that at some point you've been shamed and/or humiliated by someone. Someone in your life, maybe even somebody you really cared about, has probably used some disparaging, derogatory, or belittling term about you. Maybe they thought they were being funny at your expense. Maybe they did it to be cruel and build up their own low self-esteem. Maybe they did it in hopes that it would spur you on to change your life. Whatever the reason, all those demeaning words they used to describe you just put their voices inside your head. Problem is, those voices shout so loudly, they drown out your own voice. And the only way you're ever going to build your self-trust is by listening to and speaking with your own voice.

If you've replayed their voices over and over, you've internalized their words to the point that you believe them. You may have heard the echo so much that you think it's your own voice saying those things. But it isn't. Hear me: you are not what they said (or say) about you. *You are only what you say and think and believe about yourself.* So do yourself a kindness and stop repeating their words. To stop abusing food, get the weight off and keep it off, and be healthy and whole, you must challenge those voices in your mind, let them go, and then let only your own voice be the one that guides you.

I keep a journal. A lot of times, other people's voices that echo in my head take shape on the page. Here are some of the things they've said (a partial list):

- You are no good at this.
- No one likes you.
- You don't have what it takes. You're never going to make it.
- You are alone. No one will help you.
- You've wasted your life.

It made me sad to see, there in my blue-ink scrawl, all the hurtful things other people have said to me that I had now starting repeating to myself. I repeated their words both out loud and in my mind because I didn't trust my own voice. So one day, out of sheer desperation, I decided to befriend myself and picked a different color ink and wrote responses in the margin. My own voice said (a partial list):

- Do it because it matters to you. Do it because it makes you happy and it makes you feel alive. You do beautiful work when you do it just for you.
- I know this hurts. You need to do this for your own healing. You just have to heal yourself. And you can, darlin'. You surely can.
- You will get to where you want to go. You just need to listen to yourself, doll, that's all. The wisdom, it's all inside of you.
- No matter what you achieve or look like or screw up or choose, I love you. I am your friend even if you eat every piece of sugar in this house. I am your friend. I will never judge you or leave you or be mean to you or berate you or compare you. I love you as-is. I am your friend.
- You are lovely and beautiful and talented and generous and kind. You have so much to offer.

It is your head after all. *You're the one that gets to edit what it's thinking.* You won't learn to trust your own voice if you can't discern whether the one in your head belongs to you or to someone else. You can't listen to what your own voice has to say if you don't even recognize it. You won't ever learn to trust yourself if you allow the negative voices of others to drown out your own.

So do this:

1. Write an answer to these: *What negative words/phrases are echoing around in my head? Whose voice(s) do those words actually belong to?*
2. Circle any words/phrases coming from a voice that isn't wholly yours (meaning it belongs to a parent, sibling, teacher, authority figure, and the like).
3. Now write an answer to these: *How is it serving me to allow these other people's voices in my head? What do I hope to gain?*
4. Choose to reject any voice that isn't wholly yours and/or isn't serving to strengthen you, encourage you, and help you grow.
5. Now start listening for your own voice: the quieter one that is kinder to you, the soft-spoken one that believes in you, the one that does not (and never will) berate you or tear you down.
6. And start repeating (*repeating, repeating, repeating*) what it has to say instead.
7. You can write down what your own voice says, like I did. Or mull it over in your head. Or speak it out loud. Whatever you choose, make sure you do something to recognize and repeat what your own voice has to say.
8. Know this: if you do that long enough, your own voice will be the one to drown out everything else, which is how it should be.

SPEAK STRENGTH TO YOURSELF

Words have power, both to build and to destroy. In the end, it's not what others say about you but what you say about yourself that will determine whether you're victorious or defeated. Read the two lists of words below (some of which you may have, at some point, either heard said about you or even used on yourself) and pay close attention to how your body *feels* as you read them:

FIRST:

Worthless, useless, lost, conformed, small, trapped, alone, unable, incapable, stuck

SECOND:

Strong, powerful, courageous, tenacious, determined, awesome, talented, growing, amazing, intelligent

That first list is full of words that diminish your self-trust. I bet that as you read that list, your energy level dropped and maybe you cringed and/or contracted into yourself, making yourself physically smaller. The second list is full of words that increase your self-trust. That second list likely did the exact opposite of the first, raising your energy level and making your chest expand and making you want to reach and grow.

The point is this: you will live out whatever it is you're repeating to yourself (because what you repeat to yourself is what you come to believe). That's true regardless of what others are saying to you and/or about you. So you need to choose words that describe you (or that you want to describe you, even if you don't quite believe them yet) that enlarge your self-trust and expand your life and give you strength. Then you need to speak those words to yourself.

So do this:
1. Pick three words that feel expansive when you use them to describe yourself.
2. Those three words are your foundational words. Your phrase will be: *I am [foundational word, foundational word, and foundational word]*.
3. Then look yourself in the eyes in a mirror *every morning for at least 66 days* and say those to yourself like a kind friend would say them to you.
4. Say those words to yourself as often as you need to throughout the day.
5. Repeat (*repeat, repeat*) those words, making a new neural pathway in your brain, changing your beliefs, and providing the nourishing environment you need for your self-trust to grow.

RELAX INTO IT

You really can make it through anything (oh yes, you can!) if you'll just keep breathing deeply, stop focusing on the fear, stress, and/or discomfort of it, and instead just let yourself relax into it (whatever it is).

You need to understand how you got to where you are (the choices you made or didn't make, the advice you took or didn't take, the power that belonged to you that you gave away), so that as you move forward, you won't make those same mistakes again. Your self-trust will grow rapidly when you give yourself some room to breathe and screw up and learn and try again, all the while having some self-compassion and not beating yourself up along the way.

SETTLE IN TO THE IN-BETWEEN

The in-between is that place of the unknown where you let go of the familiar (and so you think safe) and you venture out into something brand new (where safety is not assured). It's where you embrace change so that you can have/be/do/say what you most want during your lifetime.

Your self-trust will expand exponentially (oh yes, it will!) when you let the space between where you are now and where you most want to be motivate you instead of scare you.

REFUSE TO GIVE UP ON YOURSELF

You can conquer anything (oh yes, you can!) if you'll just keep showing up and trying and learning and growing, if you'll just refuse to abandon yourself, if you'll just refuse to quit. Your self-trust will become a rock-solid foundation, one you can confidently build your life upon, when you steadfastly refuse to give up on yourself.

A SPECIAL NOTE FOR SURVIVORS OF ABUSE (ESPECIALLY PHYSICAL AND/OR SEXUAL ABUSE)

FAT TISSUE IS A POOR SUBSTITUTE FOR SELF-PROTECTION AND ABUSING FOOD IS A POOR SUBSTITUTE FOR POWER/CONTROL

If you have been physically or sexually abused, it's entirely possible that you believe the excess fat tissue on your body will keep you physically safe. All you want to do is make yourself a flesh cocoon, fat tissue that will hide you and protect you so you will never be attacked again, fat tissue that will make you feel secure. Nobody hitting you or shoving you or knocking you down. Nobody catcalling or ogling or copping a feel. Nobody fondling or molesting or raping you.

You may think that, because you are overweight, people will take less notice of you, not think much of you, and therefore pass you by and leave you alone. Go after somebody else. Let you fade into the background. I used to believe those things, too. But here's the truth: fat tissue is a poor substitute for self-protection. It traps *you*. It becomes *your* prison. It keeps *your* life small. It keeps *you* contained and confined. If the fat tissue is like the flesh of a peach, you're the seed stuck there in the middle. And in the end, all of that fat tissue offers no guarantee that you won't get hurt in the future. None whatsoever. Not even a little bit.

Likewise, abusing food will not give you the control over your life, your body, and/or the actions of others that you seek. Abusing food will not give you any power. It will give you the *feeling* of control and power, but that's just an illusion, a short-lived (twenty minutes, remember) figment of your imagination. It's not real because food is simply fuel for your body: your body converts food into energy so you can go do things. Food has no power on its own. None. It's just an object (not unlike a brick) that sits there until you tell it where to go. It has no feelings, no emotional attachments, no thought processes.

You give food the power it has by what you believe about it. And when you're abusing it, you're no longer looking at food as fuel so you can take action but instead as a crutch that you need to get yourself through. At that point, you believe food has the power to fix something in your life by changing how you feel. And because you believe it has a power of its own (which you do, I say kindly, because you don't choose to soothe yourself and instead expect food to soothe you), you keep abusing it. At that point, you have given food psychological control over you. If you abuse it long enough, you'll end up believing that you can never break free, and that's how you end up with food in control as the master with you as its slave.

I have no doubt that at the moment(s) when you were abused, you felt that the person abusing you took your power away from you. I know that because that's what happened for me. You surely felt powerless in that moment and likely powerless in the hours/days/weeks/months/years after. Maybe the feelings of being powerless never left you and you feel powerless still. Maybe you doubted that you'd ever feel powerful again. Or that you were capable of being powerful. Or that you had the right to be powerful. And because of that, I say kindly, you didn't/don't seek out ways to truly empower yourself because you've come to expect food to fill that void where you feel powerless. And that is a terrible position for you to put yourself in. Do yourself a kindness and don't do that to yourself. You have given food your power, and like I said before and will say again, always and forever: *you never want to give your power away to anyone or anything—your power, along with your body, are the only two things that you ever truly have.*

And because that's true, this is true too: *you have every single right to defend yourself and your body against anyone or anything that would harm you.* Say that out loud. Take it into your heart and believe it.

Here's something else that's true: *you will never come to trust yourself implicitly if you don't empower yourself.*

So to build your self-trust, you need to learn how to *truly* physically defend and protect yourself against threats. How? Take martial arts and/or self-defense classes. Keep taking them. Practice until the movements become second nature. Get strong. That's real authentic control and power, and trust me on this, that's what you want. You will learn what to do if you get unwanted attention or tangled up with people who don't/won't respect your boundaries. You will learn how to *truly* keep yourself safe. You will also learn that you are worth having boundaries, worth feeling safe in your own body, and worth protecting, which are all priceless lessons to get.

You are absolutely worth the time and effort it takes to learn. Your self-trust will flourish and you won't have to live in fear when you learn to authentically protect yourself. You won't feel the need to keep hiding behind a flesh wall, hoping the fat tissue will be enough to keep others away and to keep you safe, and/ or abusing food to pretend that you're powerful and in control. Instead your muscles combined with your knowledge will become the real strength and power you need to keep yourself safe.

WE NEED TO TALK ABOUT SOME THINGS YOU'RE LIKELY TRYING TO NUMB BY ABUSING FOOD

SHAME

The dictionary defines shame as a painful emotion caused by shortcomings or a condition of humiliating disgrace.[1] Shame is like an attacker who snatches you and drags you into the dark, isolating you. It chokes you and keeps you from calling out for help. The whole time it's throttling your neck, it whispers in your ear that there's something wrong with you or that you're somehow less than. It says things like: *if there wasn't something so bad about you, this would've never happened to you* or *you are alone, no one else has ever felt this way* or *you are worthless* or *you are bad* or *you are different than everybody else* or *you are nothing* or *you don't matter*. It says it so many times that you believe it. You start repeating it to yourself.

Shame drains you until you feel small and unimportant, until you are convinced you brought whatever bad thing happened upon yourself and so deserve what is happening to you, until your own voice is silenced. Shame makes you believe there's something about you that is just plain bad or wrong. Shame is often filled with things—memories, events, behaviors, actions you did or were done to you, and the like—that you don't want anyone else to know, ever. Shame destroys your self-trust because you believe, deep down in your core where it matters most, that you as a person are just *Not Right*.

Shame is what you feel when the thing you did or was done to you becomes not about the event that happened but instead becomes about who you are as a person. People often confuse guilt and shame. Guilt makes you feel bad about something you did and can actually spur you to change. Shame, however, makes you feel bad about yourself and causes you to curl into yourself and hide; it makes you never want to face anyone or anything again. Guilt says: *That was bad, I shouldn't have done that.* Shame says: *I am bad, I shouldn't be who I am.* Shame is a dead-end road that leads to self-hatred (and it's your choice, I say kindly, if you want to walk down it).

If you feel guilt when you overeat, well, okay you know you messed up so you'll do better next time. If you feel shame when you overeat, you pinch your thighs/butt/belly/arms and call yourself derogatory names, and the end result is that you head for the refrigerator again to numb yourself. Shame, in my opinion, is the number one reason people stay stuck in behaviors that don't serve them, including addictions. According to a psychotherapist friend of mine, shame is the most painful emotion there is; a person's first instinct is to avoid it at all costs, and if they can't avoid it, then to numb it immediately by whatever means necessary.[2] Because you're reading this book, you're most likely numbing yourself by abusing food. Guilt can motivate you. *Shame never will.*

Shame, gone unchecked, will color every action you take or refuse to take; it will color everything you believe about yourself and your chances and your place in the world. It will make you stop speaking the truth about who you are, what you want, and what you need. Shame is what makes you refuse to look in the mirror or have your picture taken or step on the scale. It's the reason you sell your own self a lie and won't face the truth about your weight or how much you eat or why you feel the way you feel. It's why you seek out excuses instead of facing yourself and your choices. It's why you won't admit to and/or talk about overeating, bingeing, bulimia, anorexia, and/or abusing food to others and get yourself the help you need. Shame is why you look down and/or away when people try to look you in the eyes; it's also why you believe you deserve it when they look at you and their face pinches up like they sucked on something sour and/or they frown. It's why you hide in baggy clothes or in the back of rooms or behind others or in your home or in the dark so no one can see you. It's why your face goes red and you try not to cry or you fake laugh when nasty comments are shouted/whispered/hissed your way; it's also why you won't stand up and roar and defend yourself.

Shame is the reason you feel less than and unworthy and embarrassed by your own self whenever you're not numbing yourself by abusing food and/or some other substance/behavior. You are in shame's vice grip when you shy away from anyone and remain in stunned silence, when your voice is a hoarse whisper that even you can barely hear, when you don't believe you're worth the effort to ask anyone for help, and/or when you feel like you ought to apologize for even being alive.

You will know you are trapped in shame by how your mind reacts. Do you believe that something about you is just not right? Do you feel bad about who you are? Are you afraid to face yourself? Are you afraid to face others? Is there a sudden and insatiable need—you'll do anything, anything at all—to numb yourself with substances/behaviors just to make the pain of the shame stop?

You will also know you are caught in the grip of shame by how your body feels and reacts. Do you feel yourself shrinking back in any way? Do you hang your head? Do your shoulders slump forward? Do you physically curl into a kind of fetal position with your chin to your chest or your arms wrapped around your middle or your legs drawn up? Do you try to make yourself small and/or hide yourself? Do you back away or fade into the shadows? Do you refuse to meet anyone's eyes? Does your throat or chest or belly constrict? Do you feel like a heavy weight has settled onto your chest and/or shoulders, pressing down? Does your breath catch in your throat? Do you feel trapped? Do you feel uncomfortable in your own body?

Shame thrives in secrecy. You think you're the only one who feels this way, the only one that something bad has happened to, that you're alone and no one else would understand, all of which serves to reinforce your belief that there's something bad/wrong with you. The best way I've found to let go of shame is to speak the truth about it aloud.

So do this:

1. Find someone you *trust* (extremely important that they are *trustworthy*), who will listen and not judge or condemn you, and tell them what's going on with you and how you feel. Yes, you'll have to tell your secrets, the parts of you that are causing you to feel shame, both what's happened to you and what you've done. But once you heal the burden of shame, you'll find that trusting yourself and believing in your own self-worth will come a lot easier.

2. Say words *aloud* to yourself like: *That's something that happened to me; it's not who I choose to be. I lived through it because I am strong. They tried to break me, but I'm not broken.* And always, always, always: *Food will not fix it.*

3. Remember from Chapter Two: speaking out loud activates a different part of your brain and gets you out of emotional reacting and into the logical, decision-making part of your brain. So, even if it feels odd to you, still speak out loud to yourself.

4. Choose self-compassion and befriend yourself and be that kind, encouraging person you need. Speak strength to yourself *out loud* because words of encouragement spoken to yourself in your own voice will also increase your self-trust and decrease the shame. You'd trust someone who was being authentically kind to you, right? Who was genuinely trying to help you without trying to get something in return? Who honestly wanted to see you succeed? Be that person for yourself.

5. Be proud and protective of yourself. Say this aloud: *I am proud of myself, I took care of myself, I made it through, I have nothing to be ashamed of.* Or if you're still in the midst of going through something: *I am strong, I will take care of myself, I will make it through, I have nothing to be ashamed of.*

6. Know this: you were and still are stronger than whatever it was that tried to defeat you. Yes, you are, because you're still here. Choose (because it is your choice) to believe that you are *always* worthy, valuable, capable, amazing, forgiven, and lovable no matter what—regardless of the choices you make or fail to make, regardless of what happens or doesn't happen to you, regardless of what you do or don't do, regardless of what is done or not done to you.

7. Realize that shame, while it feels real in the moment, in the end is just an illusion in your head. You're the only one who gives shame its power. So you can take that power away. Once you start telling the truth *out*

loud of who you are and what you've done or what's been done to you, you'll come to see that shame really is just a prison of your own making and you can set yourself free. Then choose to fill the space that shame took up in your life with ideas, dreams, passions, and goals that move you toward the life you most want.

VULNERABILITY (OTHERWISE KNOWN AS BEING YOUR REAL SELF)

Letting people see the real you can be downright terrifying, believe me I know, especially if you've spent any amount of time being trapped in shame and/or rejected for who you are. Safer to put on a show, be who you think they (whoever they are) want you to be. Safer to make a wall between you and them and graffiti it up with what you think they want. But here's the thing: when you sacrifice who you are at the altar of other people's approval or praise or admiration, you only end up enslaved to the opinions of others.

The truest thing I know is this: when you fake being who you are so others will accept you, like you, be kind to you, not single you out, and on the list goes, you risk two things: 1. being trapped in a mirage because the person you're presenting to the world is partly/mostly/completely not real, and 2. being confined to moving through your life as a shimmering figment of your own imagination, which, I assure you, will take an enormous emotional toll on you, starting with decimating your self-esteem. At some point in the future, if you keep along that path, you will: 1. wonder who you even are, what happened to you, how you got so lost from yourself that you ended up where you are in your life, and 2. realize that you wasted a lot of time not being the person you most wanted to be; time that you can't ever get back. I assure you that one of your biggest regrets, looking back, will be all the years you spent not being true to yourself and therefore unfulfilled when you just never had to be.

You may tell yourself it's safer to abuse food and/or create a flesh wall: one that will be both an emotional barrier to keep you numb and a physical barrier behind which you can hide. You may think those walls are keeping you safe. Here's the thing though: having walls may give you the illusion of safety (and it really is just an illusion, life is still going to come at you regardless of your size), but what those walls do mostly is keep you stuck and trapped in a prison of your own making.

So do this:
1. Write an answer to this: *What am I afraid is going to happen if I show my real self to the world?*
2. Then answer this: *Am I willing to free myself from that fear so I can be myself?*
3. Know this: you free yourself by showing up in the world as your real self.
4. Know this too: the biggest part of self-trust is being true to yourself; it's being your authentic self all the time regardless of where you are and choosing to live in a body that feels like the real you.

REJECTION

Science has shown that the pain of rejection and social exclusion stimulates the same regions of the brain (the right ventral prefrontal cortex and the anterior cingulate cortex) that a physical injury does.[3] That means, emotional pain hurts just as much as a hook shot to the body. So it's completely natural that you would want to avoid that pain at all costs.

However, you will be faced with rejection at some point because not everyone you meet is going to like you no matter what you do. So do yourself a kindness and don't make them your focus. The easiest way to do that is to stop wasting your time chasing after those people who don't want you or don't like you, trying to win them over. Do this instead: figure out who you are at the core: what you believe, what matters to you, what you stand for. Then don't back down or waver or hide those things from the world. People who value the same things as you will gravitate toward you, and those are the kind of people, trust me on this, that you want in your life.

Rejection from people you love is tough. It might be one of the toughest things you ever have to face and go through. It often leads to shame, like we just talked about, because they (especially if they are family) are supposed to love you back and accept you as you are. Sadly, sometimes that doesn't happen and the people you hold most dear are the ones who hurt you the deepest when they reject you. There are a myriad of reasons they may reject you, many of which have their origins in something that person is feeling about themselves and what they lack. They see something in you that reminds them of something they dislike about themselves, and instead of acknowledging that and healing that in themselves, they get scared/angry, lash out, and reject you. So you see, in many cases, their rejection of you is about them; it's truly not about you. I know it may not feel that way, but I assure you that's true. So whoever it is (family or otherwise), don't take their rejection into your heart and hold it close. Learn what you can from it. Use that knowledge to grow yourself. Don't chase after them (which may be hard for you, I know, because it was hard for me, but you'll be doing yourself a huge, enormous kindness if you do). Just wish them well and let them go (which may also be hard for you, and we'll be talking more about how to do that in Chapter Four).

You may also reject yourself. You may reject your whole self or just parts of yourself, but either way, know this: you are causing yourself pain, destroying your self-esteem, and shattering your self-trust in the process. That's why it's so vital to like and accept yourself as you are, right now, no matter where you are in your life.

You're also going to face other kinds of rejection, which will cause pain and also which you're likely to take personally. Rejection like: the dream(s) you hold close and work toward doesn't materialize, you can't get a foothold in the career you've always wanted, someone you care about leaves you, no one is interested in the thing you created/produced, someone you thought was a good friend betrays you, and on the list goes.

The important part is this: how do you handle that rejection? Do you pick yourself up, dust yourself off, learn what you can, help yourself grow, and keep going in the face of it? Or do you tell yourself that whoever rejected you was right in their assessment of you and then give up on yourself? The answer matters: the first builds self-trust, the second destroys it.

If you like yourself and believe in your own capabilities in the face of people rejecting you, you'll strengthen your self-trust. If you steadfastly refuse to reject yourself, you'll solidify your self-trust. If you continuously believe that your own good opinion of yourself matters more than what anyone else thinks of you, you'll increase your self-trust even more. You get decide what to think and believe about yourself (so you think and believe: *I am worthwhile, I am lovable, I will have my own back always, I can do this, I am capable and strong and intelligent and committed and determined, I will not give up on myself*) and in that way, regardless of what anyone else is doing or saying with regards to you or where you might currently be in your life, you'll be fortifying your unshakeable foundation of self-trust.

And that, the unshakeable foundation of trust in yourself, is what will help you keep going in the face of rejection. You'll come to understand that rejection isn't always personal. You'll see that the rejection, while painful, is just an event, something that happened to you, and is over now. And many times, after the sting and the crying jag and a little time and distance, you'll come to find out (just like I did) that many of the rejections you'll face, even from loved ones, are just a way for you to stop heading down a path you aren't supposed to be on, and that the rejection will actually point you in a direction that is better suited for you.

So do this:
1. Go somewhere by yourself if possible.
2. Sit with yourself for at least 90 seconds and let yourself fully feel the rejection, how much it hurts.
3. Don't abuse food or any other substance/behavior. Give yourself permission to let yourself feel whatever comes up for you without judging and without numbing. You may feel anger, bitterness, resentment, jealousy, sadness, and/or a deep sense of loss. You may take it personally and feel ashamed, humiliated, and/or not good enough.
4. Know this: whatever you feel is okay.
5. And remember: be kind to yourself and don't bring up your history of all the times you've been rejected before into the present moment.
6. Then take a deep breath and choose to accept, like, and love yourself regardless of the rejection.
7. Let the feeling pass.
8. Let go of the thoughts about the stimulus (what caused you to feel rejected) so the loop of rejection feelings and physiological reaction doesn't begin again.
9. Now move on and take action in the direction of where you most want to be.

LACK OF CONTROL

There's uncertainty everywhere. I get how nerve-racking that is. I, myself, don't do well with vagueness. Personally, I like all my ducks clearly defined and in a row. Thing is, though: life's not like that. Again, life often happens without asking your permission first. While it's true that you can take steps to prevent negative events or unwanted outcomes or avoid danger, there are still no ironclad guarantees of either security or comfort in nature. In many, many things, you often have little-to-no control over what happens.

Food, as we already talked about, will never give you control. It may give you the illusion of control for a brief time, but that is not real. (See the full explanation in the section *A Special Note For Survivors Of Abuse* a few pages back).

To grow your self-trust, you need to learn to let go of those things you cannot control. You need to: 1. be okay with not knowing everything ahead of time, and 2. embrace change, which gets easier every time you do it (brain neuroplasticity, remember), and 3. believe, *really believe*, deep down that you're strong enough to deal with whatever comes your way (because you're capable of asking for help or finding other resources or making different choices or learning new things, and the list goes on). And once you believe that deep down in your core, you will trust yourself to handle whatever shows up (unannounced or otherwise) in your life.

It also helps if you choose to believe that everything that's happening in your life is somehow working out for your good. I don't know how exactly, but I know it is. I'm also well aware that it often doesn't feel that way, especially in the moment when you're going through it. But if you choose to see it that way, it will make whatever you're going through easier for you to handle emotionally. I've come to find that everything, no matter how painful it was at the time I went through it, became either: 1. a lesson to me about something in my life and/or 2. something I could use as inspiration/material later in my life.

Rather than seeking control and trying to wrestle what's happening to you into submission, you'll be better served to fix what you can and then start looking for the lesson in what you can't. I assure you that if you'll choose to do that, you will move through that period in your life easier and let go of it quicker. The lesson may be the size of a pinprick and heavily camouflaged and not at all easy to find. But look and look again until you find it. If you make the choice to look for what life is trying to teach you (and not give up until you do) instead of trying to exert control, you'll come to find that the lesson really is a gift to you (if you'll just choose to look at it that way). Learn from that gift and let it make you stronger and grow your self-trust in the process.

FEAR

The major reason that people fail to achieve their goals/hopes/dreams and/or their calling is fear. It'll either slow you down, maybe to the point that you grind to a halt, or maybe it'll paralyze you before you even have a chance to start. Fear of the unknown or failure or rejection or success or financial ruin or humiliation or responsibility and on the list goes. You're going to get hit with fear at some point. You will be afraid to take a risk, afraid to move forward, afraid to listen to your own intuition, afraid to do what you know needs to be done, afraid of your own power, and the list goes on.

Fear comes in two types. One should stop you every single time & sometimes it doesn't. The other should never stop you & often it does. That's why you need to know & recognize the difference. The first is *real fear*. That's the kind that you feel when you're in danger of bodily harm or death. When you feel it, you need to heed it (oh, the suffering you will save yourself if you'll just heed it) and start running in the opposite direction or start fighting to save your life. The second kind is *head fear*. That's any fear that doesn't leave you emotionally/physically maimed or lead to your death. When you feel it, you need to walk right through it (oh, the suffering you will save yourself if you'll just walk right through it the first time) or you'll spend your life waiting, putting off, backing down, and then wondering why you are where you are and why you can't get where you most want to be.

Head fear can, if you let it, stop you in your tracks when opportunity comes. It can keep you from moving forward and pursuing things you want to do, need to do, and/or feel like you're supposed to do. You sit trapped on the sidelines and don't participate in your own life. And in that way, head fear causes you pain that, in turn, you numb by abusing food or some other substance/behavior. When you're scared, even with head fear, often your first instinct, understandably, is to bolt. Run and keep on running. But in which direction is safety? Like we already talked about, there is no sure thing because there are no guarantees in nature. Not a one. Even in your comfort zone, things you're afraid will happen can still befall you.

So do yourself a kindness and don't fall into the trap that you'll start living—going after whatever it is you want, having the experiences you want to have, being the person you most want to be—once the fear subsides. Here's something that is absolutely true: you won't be any less scared a week, a month, or even a year from now. You just won't. The only thing waiting does is make you lose time that you can't get back.

So do this:
1. Go somewhere that you can be alone.
2. Think about something you really (maybe even desperately) want to have/be/do/say but the thought of having/being/doing/saying it also scares you tremendously.

3. Now sit with all those feelings of fear and really feel the fear for 90 seconds.
4. Don't do anything to numb or block or avoid the fear.
5. Pay attention to how your body feels/reacts to fear; especially any differences between real fears (bodily harm/death) and head fears (no risk to your health).
6. Take note: you're still alive; nothing bad happened to you by feeling the fear.
7. Know this: this exercise helps train your brain (and you) to distinguish between real fear and head fear. That will make it easier for you to push through head fears and move forward.

Now do this:
1. Know this: beyond head fear is where you'll find freedom.
2. Start with whatever it was you were just thinking about that you really want to have/be/do/say.
3. Now listen for your intuition and write an answer to this: *What steps do I need to take to move right through that fear?*
4. Then take a deep breath in through your nose, hold it three seconds, then let it out slowly through your mouth. Repeat often.
5. Now take the first step (tiny, if need be) through that fear.
6. Repeat daily, one deep breath and one (tiny) step, over and over again.
7. Know this too: the *only* thing you have to do when head fear happens is to take a deep breath then take the next (tiny, if need be) step in the direction you want to go. That's it. One deep breath and one tiny step, one after another after another. You'll overcome the fear if you'll just carry on.

The absolute worst thing you can do for yourself when facing your head fears is to back down. (Score: Fear-1, You-0). Why? Because remember: you're training your brain all the time. When you back down, you're creating a neural pathway that makes it easier for you to back down the next time. When you push through, you're creating a neural pathway that makes it easier for you to push through the next time. If you'll just push through and keep pushing through, you'll overcome your head fears and build your self-trust.

Know this: abusing food will not take away your fear. It may numb you, but the fear will still be there when the numbness wears off, stopping you from all that you could have/be/do/say. You don't need to be numb to be brave. You're already brave. I know that's true because you're still reading this, you're still trying, you haven't quit. Real courage is when you begin and you keep going no matter what gets thrown at you and you see whatever you started all the way to the end. There's always going to be something that scares you. *Always.* If you keep abusing food in an attempt to conquer your fear, you'll spend your life numb, unfulfilled, and in a body that doesn't feel like you.

So right now, begin:
1. Take a deep breath.
2. Then take a single (tiny, if need be) step in the direction you want to go without abusing food as a crutch.
3. Then keep going, one (tiny) step *every day* all the way until you finish, all the way to the end.

OH, SOME SCIENCE (PART ONE)

Remember how we talked back in Chapter One about the fact that your brain does some 400 billion actions per second. Well, here's something else you need to know: you are only conscious of roughly 2,000 of those actions.[4] What does that mean for you? It means that the vast majority of the time, your subconscious is running the show.

So if you've ever wondered why you find yourself stuck in bad habits or doing things you don't want to do or making choices that don't serve you at all, here's your answer: you don't have to look any further than your own mind. You hold subconscious beliefs that steer you toward the decisions and choices you make. Maybe those beliefs stem from things you were once taught in school. Or you got them growing up, being raised the way you were. Or you heard them told to you over and over and over again by someone in authority and decided to internalize them yourself. Or they were shouted at you by others and you chose to repeat them and believe them. Or you told them to yourself in a moment of weakness and decided they were true. Whatever the reason, now those beliefs are lodged in your head.

Your body, to put it incredibly simply, is just a series of electrochemical feedback loops. Basically, your brain takes in all the information it's constantly getting from your body (both the external senses and the internal cells), integrates it, makes some calculations, and decides what to do. All of that happens in a split second. Then your brain sends either electrical impulses or biochemicals to communicate with cells. Your cells take the feedback from the brain and react by either sending their own electrical impulses and/or by secreting biochemicals to make adjustments as needed, both doing their own job as well as communicating with other cells based on what your brain has told them. Those other cells then take that feedback and react/communicate, and on it goes from one cell to the next in a loop that leads all the way back to the brain. Then the cycle starts again. There is a specific movement to feedback loops and they run nonstop.[5]

All that takes place at the cellular level. Tiny. So small you can't see it with the naked eye. Electrochemical reactions triggered by thoughts (conscious and mainly subconscious) are what drive your behavior. It's your behavior that has an impact on your well-being. And the only control you have over those electrical impulses and biochemical reactions that are happening because of your subconscious mind is to change the thoughts and beliefs that are lodged there.

Again, beliefs are just thoughts that you've repeated over and over again in your head. The problem arises when the things you believe limit you and keep you contained and don't allow you to grow into the person you most want to be. You need to change your beliefs, *most importantly the subconscious ones.*

So do this:
1. Go somewhere that you can be alone. Then get still and quiet.
2. Write an answer to this: *What beliefs do I have that are holding me back?* (about yourself, about life in general, about your place in the world, about others, about your own gifts and talents, about your chances, and/or about anything else you'd like to address)
3. Let your intuition be your guide and write quickly (so no overthinking and/or editing) anything that comes up. If you don't overthink or edit, you'll find it's the full truth, and not a watered-down version of it, that lands on the page.
4. Now write an answer to this: *What would I rather believe instead that'll help me?*
5. Write quickly (again no overthinking and/or editing) anything that comes up.
6. Then choose to think those new thoughts that will spur you forward.
7. Repeat (*repeat, repeat*) those new thoughts over and over again until they become the beliefs that guide you.

The old thoughts will pop up, of course, because they're a habit. Remember: you get to challenge every thought that pops into your head, you get to accept or reject every one; that's *always* your choice. If you keep at it, repeating those new thoughts that serve you best, eventually the new ones will be the ones lodged in your subconscious, those will be the ones that drive your behavior.

You really will not succeed at becoming the person you most want to be, at getting the weight off and keeping it off, at not abusing food as a balm for your emotional state, until you examine your thought life, uncover the subconscious beliefs that drive you, then change those beliefs. You're going to believe something no matter what you do, so why not cultivate beliefs that are going to help you?

OH, SOME SCIENCE (PART TWO)

Dr. Caroline Leaf, a cognitive neuroscientist, states that you will believe what you *feel* to be true. What that means is this: you can be given evidence and proof, logic and reason, statistics and graphs, and even an ironclad scientific study about the truth of something, and yet, you will not believe that information to be true unless the limbic system in your brain lets you *feel* that the information is true.[6] The converse also applies: you can be given all kinds of evidence and proof, etc., to show that information is false, and yet, if your limbic system lets you *feel* that the information is true, well, it will be true for you.

Why does that matter to you?

Emotions are simply chemical and electrical reactions in the brain. The limbic system is the seat of where these reactions for emotions take place. It's the limbic system and *not your logical, thinking brain*, that's determining what information you deem to be true for you. It's your limbic system that decides which information is real and which is not, which information is important and which is not. Your limbic system is unique to you, which means it processes memory and thoughts and information in an individual way (based on a variety of factors like your personality, your learning style, your reasoning skills, and the like).[7] What that means is this: you can be provided with the exact same information as someone else and come up with a wildly different conclusion as to the veracity of that information *based on how you feel about it* (you believe some but not all, you believe all, you believe none, etc.).

That's why the beliefs you hold about yourself and the story you tell yourself about your history and your present circumstances, who you are and what you're capable of, where you belong in your community as well as in the larger world, and on the list goes, is so vital. You repeat your beliefs and that story to yourself and to others. You *feel* that your beliefs and that story are true. And so, whether your beliefs and/or that story are *actually* true to reality or not, they are true for you. And so, because they are true for you, you will abide by your beliefs and that story, and you will live them out every day of your life. You will absolutely live out what you believe to be true, which is all the more reason to *question not only the actual truth of but also your feelings about* the thoughts, beliefs, and story/stories circling in your mind.

THIS IS A PRACTICE AND A PROCESS

Yes, I keep saying this, and I will remind you every single chapter because it's that important: *Figure out what works for you and do that*. Also, you will not do any of this perfectly, so don't expect to. Cut yourself some slack. You'll forget stuff. You won't do things that you know you should. You're going to make mistakes. Just make a point to learn what you can from them, so you can come at it again from a wiser perspective, then move on. The goal is to be kind, gentle, and patient with yourself along the way because you deserve to take it easier on yourself. Nobody can grow by cutting themselves down, remember that. And remember too: every mistake is simply a brand new chance to do it better the next time.

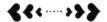

CHAPTER FOUR

SURRENDER

OR

Relinquish
control and
free yourself.

Chapter Four

"Let go or be dragged."
—Proverb

THE CONCEALER IS *not a dark enough shade. I dab it on with my finger, wait for it to dry, then dab on another coat. But still the long string of purplish bruises across my cheekbone shows through. I walk the school hallway with my head hung low and tilted to the right, my hair falling down and partially covering my left cheek. I hold my books tightly against my chest like some sort of shield. My gaze jumps from the dented metal lockers to the yellowed linoleum squares on the floor to the sunlight falling in a long rectangle through an opened classroom door. That gaze never settles on any one thing, especially not on someone else's eyes.*

I stand at my locker and spin the dial, clicking toward twenty-four.

"Shelli is fat!"

I stiffen. Without thinking, just pure reaction, my chin lifts, my eyes cut toward the voice then just as quickly cut away. A popular jock. Dark-haired, stocky, Italian, moving through the school with a posse of friends. My face goes hot. The locker dial goes still. Sweat runs along my spine, soaks into the waistband of my jeans, leaves an oval stain under both armpits of my T-shirt. I blink a half-dozen times but still my vision goes blurry. I spin the dial again, clicking toward the number six.

"Shelli is faaaaaaaaaaaaaaaat!"

I tighten my grip and the books press hard, flattening my chest. My hand shakes. I fumble with the dial and it spins too fast. I think: please don't let me screw up the combination, please don't make me start over, please let me get my stuff, please let me get out of here.

No one tells the jock to shut up. The hallway goes mostly quiet and still. I stop spinning the dial and instead tighten my grip on it to keep my hand from shaking. I close my eyes briefly, hoping someone will defend me, hoping someone will make him stop. A few kids laugh.

"Shelli is fat! F-A-T! Fat!"

I pretend I don't hear. It's someone else they're talking about. It's not me. No one is staring at me. No one is pointing at the rolls of flesh under my not-baggy-enough shirt. No one is laughing at my thick thighs. No one is spreading their arms wide behind themselves and mimicking my huge rear end. It's not me they are laughing at. I spin the dial slowly. Click. Click. Click. I count the numbers in my head. Thirty-seven, thirty-eight, the dial stops at thirty-nine. I yank the handle and the locker pops open.

"Fat chick with dirt on her face!"

I toss my books inside then grab the books I need. I slam the door with a loud clang, but too hard because the latch doesn't catch and the door swings back open. My eyes sting, and I blink back tears. I say, "It's not dirt." The words are too soft for anyone to hear.

The bell rings. The jock wanders into an open doorway, his posse following a step behind. I let out the breath I've been holding. I brush my sleeve across my eyes, crush the books against my chest again, then hurry off to class.

At home after school, I eat without tasting. Fast, faster, fastest. Stale animal crackers in a big plastic jar. Candy corn from last Halloween. Hard sugar cookies in the shape of Christmas trees, decorated with green frosting. Beef jerky, which I don't really like, but that's not the point. A half-dozen big marshmallows. A couple handfuls of cereal from three different boxes. I move through the kitchen like that, hands whirling like blades, not discriminating too much, grabbing this, that, the other thing as long as it's already opened. Mother or Father is less likely to notice what's been eaten or how much is gone if some of the package was already missing when I started eating from it. I snatch a handful here, a handful there. Never a lot from any one bag or box, just a little bit from everything.

Hiding in plain sight, I think.

Then I hear the jock's voice: Shelli is fat.

It's loud as a marching band inside my head: Shelli is faaaaaaaaaaaaaaaat!

I choke back a sob. Then I chew, swallow, barely chew, swallow hard, a lump in my throat, wash it down with a couple swigs of cola right from the bottle. Spoon in hand, I sit cross-legged in front of the refrigerator door, the linoleum cool on my backside. Cold air spills out onto my sweaty face. So does a circle of light from the bulb above the top shelf. Leftovers in plastic containers form a semicircle around me. I open the lids and scoop a little from each one. Tiny bites. Lots of tiny bites. I push the remaining food around with the back of the spoon, flattening it down, filling in the holes, leveling out the surface. Try to make the scoops unnoticeable. No questions asked. No more fingers pointing at me. Why are you so fat? What are you eating? No child of mine is going to be fat. No daughter of mine is going to have a double chin.

Then I hear it again, echoing, a refrain inside my head: Shelli is fat. Faaaaaaaaaaaaaaaaaat! Fat chick with dirt on her face!

I close my eyes against the memory.

Another one lands in my head: just the day before when Father rushed into my bedroom after I hollered a slur at Mother. His face was red, hard and angry. His hands were balled into fists. He towered over me where I sat on the floor, grabbed me by the upper arms, lifted me, then threw me onto the bed. He yelled about my loudness, that I wouldn't treat Mother and him that way, as he climbed onto the mattress, his head hitting the lace canopy and making it sway. His knees pressed on either side of my chest, his backside against my groin, my legs dangling over the edge. I struggled to sit up, trying to leverage my elbows beneath myself. I kicked my feet, trying to find traction. But Father was a big man, six foot two, easily two-hundred-thirty pounds. He gathered both my wrists in his big left hand. He yanked them above my head and pinned them against the mattress. I was not going anywhere. He raised his right arm above his head then the flat of his hand came down.

I shove mashed potatoes from two days ago into my mouth. Chicken noodle soup with a thin skim of congealed fat on the top; who knows how old it is, doesn't matter. I slurp a third of it then seal the plastic lid again. Sausage links. What if someone counted? I don't think anyone would have. Just to be safe, I only eat two. Leftover peas and fruit cocktail and sliced cheese and whipped cream straight from the can. Fried chicken that I suck the last of the meat off of, lick my fingers, then later bury the bones in the bottom of the trash can where no one will look to find them.

Father's voice had gone low and dangerous. He hissed at me with each hit. The words mostly jumbled inside my head. His palm slammed into my cheek. Pain exploded across my face. My head rocked to the side. Again and again and again. All the while, three words echoed inside my skull. Fat. Ugly. Stupid. Fat. Ugly. Stupid. Fat. Ugly. Stupid.

I stand and open the freezer. TV dinners that would take too much time to microwave. Other things in plastic bags, frozen leftovers, which would take too much time to defrost. Popsicles. I count how many—eight—are left in the box. Three, I think. I could get away with three. They won't miss three. I tuck the damp sticks into the back pocket of my jeans when I'm done. Later, I'll hide those in the garbage can in the garage, shoving them underneath the other trash, where no one will notice.

And then Mother's voice joins the fray in my mind: Not so hard, dear.

And then, I hear my own scream.

I remember how it chafed the back of my throat, how it was sharp and loud at first then, less than a minute later, petered out into nothing.

And Father, who looked up at Mother standing at the edge of the room beside the door, said: "She's crazy. No wonder she has no friends. No one else likes her either."

Then to me as my mind slowly moved away from my body, he said: "You'll never amount to anything. You are evil. Rotten to the core."

Father crawled off of me then stormed out of the room, leaving as quickly as he came in. Mother stood there for a time, quiet, wringing her hands and shifting her weight and not speaking. I rolled onto my side, away from Mother, facing the wall. My stuffed animal collection was piled in the corner, all those teddy-bear eyes staring. My face was hot, my left cheek swollen and throbbing. My head ached. My neck hurt from the tendons straining. There was pain in my chest and hips and the low part of my belly where his weight had pressed down. There was the start of a round bruise on my right heel from kicking the metal frame of the bed.

The door shut, the catch making a soft click as it fit itself into the groove. Mother left almost soundlessly, and I was alone.

F-A-T! Fat chick with dirt . . . .

But the jock's voice is faded now. So is Father's. Mother's is too. The words just don't have the sting like they did, like a blade going in every time I remember them. My stomach hurts, but I don't want to remember any of it at all. If I eat more this time, will I forget? If I eat more, can I pretend to be someone else? Not this person who's fat and ugly? Not someone crazy? Not this stupid person who no one likes?

I find a gallon of Rocky Road ice cream in the back underneath a couple of leftover pork chops and a bag of frozen green beans. The container's only half-full. At some point, it must've melted and refrozen, the surface covered in ice crystals, the consistency harder than it should be, the taste odd. But I don't care. I'm sure no one will miss it. And I need the voices to fade altogether, to wink out like a candle extinguished and be gone. So I gobble down the entire thing: scraping the sides with a spoon then licking the lid. I pad down to the garage, lift the trash can lid carefully so it doesn't clang, then scoot sawdust and newspaper and a couple of greasy rags out of the way. I bury the wooden Popsicle sticks and the ice cream container then arrange the trash so you can't see them.

I stand in the quiet, no sound except for the buzzing of the florescent light above my head. Their voices are soft, indistinct, like the static coming through the car speakers when the dial's between radio stations.

The problem is this: I'll never get thinner if I keep all that food down.

So I lock the bathroom door then stand in front of the toilet, shifting my weight from one socked foot to the other. I have done this before. There's a fuzzy beige cover on the lid, like shag carpeting, that matches the bath rug and the shower curtain and the soap dish and the tiny flowers on the wallpaper. Coordinated, Mother said, just perfect. I lift the lid. The tank seal is loose and water trickles down the sides of the bowl. Tiny bubbles swirl and float across the surface.

Brother is in his room. Music vibrates through his closed door, down the hallway, AC/DC cranked up because no one else but he and I are home. The song: Hells Bells. I don't think he'll be able to hear, but I'm not one for taking chances. I spin the sink faucet and cold water splashes against the drain. Background noise. Hopefully loud enough to drown out what I'm about to do. I slide to my knees on the fuzzy mat. I lift the toilet seat.

With one hand, I hold my hair out of the way. With the other, I jab my index and middle fingers down my throat. I do that again and again, my stomach cramping and my throat burning, until all I'm throwing up are long strings of saliva. There's a lightness afterward. It's more than the food being out of me. There's a calm. A sense of relief. And something powerful, too; I'm the one in control. I flush the toilet. I wipe the rim with a wad of toilet paper then flush that, too. I wash my hands and face then rinse my mouth out. I scan the bathroom one last time to make sure I've left it just as I found it. Then I tilt my head and listen.

Their voices are finally gone.

I am fourteen years old.

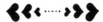

CHANGE IS YOUR FRIEND

So we've come to the part that very few people like; the part where you need to start letting go of all the things in your life that are no longer serving you. That requires change. Most people (yes, my hand is raised, too) don't like change. But like I said before, you can't have your life be different (read: better) if you keep doing the same stuff over and over.

You can't expect other people, places, and/or things to change either because that: 1. takes the power over your life away from you and plunks it right down onto those other people, places, and/or things, and 2. turns your life into a waiting game that sticks you fast and keeps you stuck until those other people, places, and/or things do something. So you're going to have to be the one to change, which means you're going to have to start trusting yourself like we talked about last chapter.

Again, change is so much easier when you believe: 1. whatever happened in the past, is currently happening now, and will happen in the future is somehow working out for your good, 2. you will grow and be stronger because of it, and 3. deep down in your core that you can take care of yourself no matter what happens. Change also means that you're going to have to take a deep breath and release your vice grip on all those things that no longer serve you. Because if you choose not to, well, like the proverb that started this chapter says, you'll just end up being dragged. And I suspect, having been there myself, that you've been dragged along far enough.

You'll also come to find that when you start letting go of things that no longer serve you, the insatiable want to binge, purge, starve, and/or abuse food will ease if not leave you altogether. If you refuse to let go of things that no longer serve you, just know this: that will cause you some kind of pain (emotional, surely, but maybe also physical, depending on what it is you need to let go of), which will, in turn, make you want to abuse food and/or some other substance/behavior to numb yourself.

SOME THINGS YOU'RE GOING TO HAVE TO LET GO OF (A PARTIAL LIST)

- Using food as a crutch
- Having a scarcity mentality
- Your failures
- The past & what happened to you & who you used to be
- Regret and lost time
- Who you think you should be by now and/or what you think your life should look like by now
- Someone else's idea of success
- Comparison
- Pretending to yourself
- Lying to others
- Self-doubt
- Self-abuse
- Not forgiving yourself and not forgiving others
- Trying to impress others
- Trying to save others
- Expecting others to make you happy
- Choosing powerlessness over being powerful
- Panic, despair, and worry
- Things the don't belong to you and/or aren't about you
- Getting in your own way
- Trying to control

USING FOOD AS A CRUTCH

I know food has been your friend when no one else was around. Food gave you comfort when you needed it most. Food numbed you and made you feel not so afraid, hurt, sad, or whatever it was that you didn't want to feel. Food was the thing you could one hundred percent count on, and you could never say that about anyone/anything else. Food dulled the pain. It could also be that food made you feel alive or at least that life was worth living. Or it gave you courage and made you feel like you could rise to the challenge. Or maybe food gave you an excuse sometimes, too: an excuse to not risk, to not grow, to stay home curled up on the couch with a pint of ice cream instead of out there in the world, going after what you most wanted for your life.

As I keep saying, food has one intended purpose: it's simply fuel for your body. That's it. Any other meaning food has in your life is because that's the meaning you give it. And using food for anything other than its intended purpose makes food a crutch.

If you continue to use food as a crutch to make it through your days, you will never learn to stand on your own two feet. And if you can't stand without a crutch: 1. you've given your power away (you need the crutch, and so it's the crutch that has the power and not you), 2. you'll never be able to realize your full potential with an obstacle you can't overcome (the crutch will constantly be in your way), and 3. you won't be free to create a life you love (because the crutch will always be there, zapping your time and focus and energy).

So how do you let go of using food as a crutch?* I mention this process again because it's vital for your success. Do this:
1. Pause.
2. Take a deep breath in through your nose, hold it three seconds, then let it out slowly through your mouth with an audible sound.
3. Speak strength to yourself *out loud*. You are brave and tenacious and strong and intelligent and *you have everything it takes to achieve everything you want* (oh yes, you do). All those things are true. I know them about you. Now you need to believe them and say them about yourself.
4. Remind yourself over and over: *Food will not fix it.*
5. Ask yourself **out loud in a calm, kind voice:** *"What's the matter, [insert your name]? What do you need?"*
6. Now let yourself feel whatever it is that's coming up in you.
7. Then, once you're a bit calmer, take some time to address the origin of the feeling that caused you to want to abuse food. (The answer to the first question: *What's the matter?*)

8. Then take some time to address exactly what (that is not food-related) will make you feel safe and comforted and supported in that moment. (The answer to the second question: *What do you need?*) Then do whatever it is you need for yourself.
9. Then ask yourself: *How is using food as a crutch serving me? Is it helping me or harming me?*
10. Then answer this: *What do I need instead of food to fix the situation I'm in?*
11. Now do for yourself what you believe food is doing for you. (The power food has to be a crutch is just an illusion; you and you alone give food the power and meaning it has in your life. So you be your own rock, because *you are strong*, and you lean on yourself. You meet your own wants/needs and fix your own life.)
12. Separate your emotions from food. Food, again, is not a balm for your emotional state.
13. Choose to stop looking at and using food as anything but fuel. Yes, food can (and absolutely should) be delicious and enjoyable as long as you are physiologically hungry. Just listen to your body and stop eating when you are comfortably full.
14. And finally, take action (even tiny steps) to move yourself in the direction you most want your life to go.

*For the full explanation of this process and why it's so important to your healing, see *Eat Calmly* in Chapter Two.

HAVING A SCARCITY MENTALITY

A scarcity mentality is believing that there's just not enough for you. What it really is though is plain old fear dressed up as something else. Fear that there's not enough to go around for everyone. And so, it leads to unhealthy competition, grasping for what's yours, feelings of unfairness, desperation, struggle, frustration, comparison, and on the list goes.

A scarcity mentality also leads to rushing. If there's not enough to go around, then you've got to rush to get yours. So you rush to get the weight off, without stopping to think or listen to what your intuition/body is telling you. You rush to get things and create relationships and go places, not pausing to decide whether those things/relationships/places are really ones that *you* actually want. You rush into decisions and make hasty/bad choices that, in the end, take you further and further away from your goals.

So how do you let go of having a scarcity mentality? Do this:
1. Pause.

2. Take a deep breath in through your nose, hold it three seconds, then let it out slowly through your mouth with an audible sound. Repeat until you calm down.
3. Then ask yourself: *How is having a scarcity mentality serving me? Is it helping me or harming me?*
4. Then choose to believe in abundance. Consciously tell yourself all your needs will be met and life is generous toward you. Say that over and over—*life is on my side, there's more than enough for me, I get everything I need*—until it's the story you believe and so live out in your life.
5. Then start a daily gratitude journal (written or verbal) and take note of at least one *different* thing *every day* that you're thankful for, one thing that makes your life more rich and full.
6. Remember: your brain is your most powerful ally. If you change the thoughts running around in your subconscious, you'll come to find abundance coming into your life, sometimes with little or no effort on your part at all. (I have watched this happen over and over again in my own life.) And even if you don't believe me, try it anyway (just make sure it's an *honest* effort: try it with an open mind and with the belief that it will work for you). You don't have *anything* to lose by giving it a shot.

YOUR FAILURES

This one is hard, I know. It's often easier, although not more productive, to beat yourself up over what could've/should've/would've been than it is to forgive yourself for your mistakes. But hear me on this one: all those things you thought you failed at were just learning experiences. Maybe they were colossal, knock-you-on-your-behind, make-you-cry teaching moments, but still that's what they were. In the end, you're still breathing and so you're stronger than whatever it was you thought crushed you. You simply—no matter how painful and shocking and devastating it was to go through—got a lesson in what didn't work. In the end, you got an opportunity to learn something. And since you're still alive, there's still time to come at it again, whatever it happens to be, from a position of increased knowledge and strength.

You're human, so cut yourself some slack. You're going to screw up. You're going to get challenges thrown at you. At some point, you're going to fail. Remember: the first secret of success is to trust yourself. The second secret of success is this: stand back up, dust yourself off, learn what you can, and try again. Know this: the *only* difference between those who succeed and those who fail is that the former group doesn't let their failures or their fears derail them.

So how do you let go of failure? Do this:
1. Pause.

2. Take a deep breath in through your nose, hold it three seconds, then let it out slowly through your mouth with an audible sound. Repeat until you calm down.
3. Then ask yourself: *How is holding on to my failures serving me? Is it helping me or harming me?*
4. Then just stop believing in failure. (Easy as you want to make it, remember.) It's your mind; you get to change it whenever you want.
5. Reframe events so that you've got two choices from now on: 1. you're either going to succeed or 2. you're going to learn. Yes, it may take you a lot of tries to get it right. That's okay. You get *unlimited* tries so just keep on going.
6. Make this your new mantra: *I believe there's only success or learning.* Repeat, repeat, repeat so you can train your brain.
7. Then turn each and every one of your failures into gifts. You do that by looking at each one for the lesson it has to offer that will help you grow.
8. And one last point: take heart because sometimes success is just a matter of timing, which means you need to cultivate patience. So be extra kind to yourself while you're learning what works and what doesn't, applying it for the next try, and moving forward.

THE PAST AND WHAT HAPPENED TO YOU AND WHO YOU USED TO BE

You already know this but it bears repeating (because, sigh, sometimes we forget): you can't ever go back and change any of the things you did or didn't do; you can't change the things that happened or didn't happen to you. You can't go back and say *yes* when that opportunity came. You can't go back to stand up tall and full of courage instead of what you did, which was to back down in fear. You can't go back and make a different choice. You can't go back and undo what you did. Or maybe your past was so much better than your life now (or so you've convinced yourself), and all you want to do is go back to the way life used to be. Sadly, you can't do that either. I know that, intellectually, you understand all this. Emotionally, though, maybe you're holding out hope that somehow, if only you could go back, you could make it all different.

The most disempowering thing you can do to yourself is to try to live in the past. First, it zaps your time, energy, and focus on a fruitless quest (it's impossible to live in the past because the past is over). Second, right now, this moment, is the only place where you have the power to change anything. And change is the only way you're going to get out of the funk that you're in. If you've been hanging on to the ugly details of your life, if you've been beating yourself up over them, if you've been reliving them in your mind and trying to give them some kind of shine to make them prettier, you've got two choices: 1. hang on and stay stuck, 2. release your grip and let go.

So how do you let go of your past and what happened to you and who you used to be? Do this:

1. Pause.
2. Take a deep breath in through your nose, hold it three seconds, then let it out slowly through your mouth with an audible sound. Repeat until you calm down.
3. Then ask yourself: *How is holding on to my past and what happened to me and who I used to be serving me? Is it helping me or harming me?*
4. Know this: you hold on to your history at the expense of your present and your future.
5. Then change the story you tell yourself about your history. For instance: that moment that you tell yourself was a life-crushing mistake, what if it was just an error in judgment? Or a decision made out of anger or arrogance or fear? What about that horrible thing that happened to you that you say marked you and made you who you are today? What if it was there to show you how determined you are, how much perseverance you have, how you are so much more courageous than you give yourself credit for? What if it happened to teach you compassion or forgiveness or generosity or leniency (toward others, yes, but also toward yourself)?
6. It's your own voice in your head, so all you need to do is simply edit what it's saying. Do yourself a kindness and write a new story about your history.
7. Remember: you live out the story that you believe about yourself.
8. Now change the story you tell yourself so that you can live out a different one.
9. Know this too: when you choose to describe events/mistakes in a different light, you'll begin to accept the ugly details of your history. When you do that, you'll come to see that you really can move forward to be the person you want to be and to make the whole of your life into something beautiful.

REGRET AND LOST TIME

Know this: All the regret in the world won't change a thing. Lamenting the lost time won't change a single thing either. Both regret and lamenting lost time will, however, zap your energy in the present moment. They will keep you stuck and forever looking behind you, focused on the past. They will keep you busy running in emotional circles instead of moving forward in the direction you want to go. But neither will change a single thing. *Not a single thing.*

Your history doesn't define you unless you let it. (Yes, I say this kindly, that's a choice that is squarely up to you.) What happened to you doesn't define you. What you allowed or didn't allow doesn't define you. What you did or failed to do doesn't define you. Your mistakes and failures don't define you. What you choose to do about all of those things afterward is the only thing that defines you. Do you learn and grow or get stuck and stagnate? Do you accept responsibility or assign blame? Do you use events/mistakes as fuel to propel you forward to a better and more meaningful life? Do you use happenings, failures, and/or choices as an excuse to accept defeat and quit? Do you choose self-punishment or self-compassion? The answers matter. The answers are your character and who you are right now. And if you find that you don't like your answers, you can always change them by changing yourself so you can become who you most want to be.

So how do you let go of regret and lost time? Do this:

1. Pause.
2. Take a deep breath in through your nose, hold it three seconds, then let it out slowly through your mouth with an audible sound. Repeat until you calm down.
3. Then ask yourself: *How is holding on to regret and lost time serving me? Is it helping me or harming me?*
4. Then choose to let the happenings and the failures in your life be the lessons that make you into the empowered person you want to be.
5. So learn from them.
6. Then choose to change the story you tell yourself. Choose to look at it this way: you wouldn't be the strong, determined, tenacious person you are today if it had not been for your history.
7. And choose to believe that there is no lost time. Because, have no doubt, that's a choice. There is learning. There is coming at it again from a more informed perspective. There is progress and growth and perseverance. There is believing that everything, in the end, works out for your good. But there is no lost time, not as long as you choose to find the lesson in it.

WHO YOU THINK YOU SHOULD BE BY NOW AND/OR WHAT YOU THINK YOUR LIFE SHOULD LOOK LIKE BY NOW

I know we all want what we want *right now*. Waiting is hard, I get it. I know most of us (yes, my hand is raised, too) believe there's a timetable as to when we should've achieved this or that, usually gauged by reaching a certain age. That line of thinking only adds stress to an already-stressful situation.

Sometimes, the thinking turns defeatist and the question becomes: *I'm X years old; if I start now, do you realize how old I'll be by the time I achieve that?* The answer: *the same age you'll be if you don't start*. In the end, all that defeatist thinking does is increase the odds that you will abandon yourself and quit. Remember: you're in your body for the entirety of your life. As long as you're still alive, that's how much time you've got left to create a life that: 1. matters to you, and 2. fulfills you. So regardless of your age, it's not too late. Just start where you are, today.

The fact of the matter is this: you are not where you want to be at this moment, your life does not look the way you imagined it would look at this point in time, you are not the person you most want to be at this exact second. That doesn't mean those things can't change. All it means is that you had high expectations and you didn't reach them . . . *yet*. You will. No need to worry. So cut yourself some slack. Your choices got you to this point in your life. Your choices can also get you to a different place in your life. If you listen to your intuition and trust yourself, you'll know who you want to be and where you want to be. You'll know what you need to do to get there. That's the majority of the battle right there (and if you honestly don't know, well, no worries because we'll be talking about that in Chapter Six). Now, all you have to do is keep moving in the direction that will get you there. Again, it doesn't matter (truly, it doesn't) how slowly you go, just as long as you don't stop.

So how do you let go of who you think you should be by now and/or what you think your life should look like by now? Do this:

1. Pause.
2. Take a deep breath in through your nose, hold it three seconds, then let it out slowly through your mouth with an audible sound. Repeat until you calm down.
3. Then ask yourself: *How is holding on to who I think I should be by now and/or what I think my life should look like by now serving me? Is it helping me or harming me?*
4. Then you choose acceptance. Plain and simple. Who you are right now is who you are. Where you are right now is where you are. And that's okay. You start where you are.
5. Say this out loud: *I accept who I am right now. I accept where I am right now.*
6. You'll come to find that once you stop fighting the way things are and the way you are and instead accept them and yourself as-is, the insatiable want to binge, purge, starve, and/or abuse food will ease.
7. You'll also come to find that the pressure will lessen and moving forward toward who/where you actually want to be will become so much smoother and easier.

SOMEONE ELSE'S IDEA OF SUCCESS

You don't have to venture too far before you get bombarded with what society thinks you ought to have and ought to be doing. But here's the thing: living up to someone else's ideal of success will never make you happy, will never fulfill you, will never give you the meaning, acceptance, love, or whatever it is that you're searching for. Ever.

The moment you start allowing people to tell you what they want for your life is the moment you start living for someone else. And if you do that, you'll end up enslaved to the ideals of others. You'll forever be chasing those ideals (ideals that don't belong to you, mind you). Even if you do manage to achieve those ideals (you're a millionaire, you're the most popular person in the group, you have a mansion/yacht, etc.), will you honestly be fulfilled by achieving an ideal that isn't yours? The other thing that comes into play is that at some point, your fortunes may change, and everything that you used to define success for yourself could be taken away from you in the blink of an eye. The only thing that doesn't change is: 1. who you are at your core, 2. what deeply matters to you and what you're going to do about it, and 3. what gifts and talents you have to offer to the world. And keep this in mind, too: even if you look successful to the outside world, if you don't feel successful inside yourself where it matters most, well, I'd argue that's not success at all.

So how do you let go of someone else's idea of success? Do this:
1. Pause.
2. Take a deep breath in through your nose, hold it three seconds, then let it out slowly through your mouth with an audible sound. Repeat until you calm down.
3. Then ask yourself: *How is holding on to someone else's idea of success serving me? Is it helping me or harming me?*
4. Then you simply write a definition of success for yourself, what a having a successful life looks like to you, and you decide that *it's okay to want whatever it is that you actually want.*
5. You determine what you want for your life, make goals based on those wants then reach them solely for you, and be positive that whatever you choose to pursue *deeply matters* to you.
6. Your intuition will tell you what you most want to have/be/do/say. Follow it. That's the only way you'll ever be happy and fulfilled.
7. So with that in mind, write a list of what's most important to you without judging yourself or letting others judge you. Is it money? Prestige? A title? Power? Your picture in a magazine? Or is it time to pursue your passions? The freedom to do what you want with your life? Being able to look yourself in the eyes after the decisions you've made? Feeling comfortable in your own skin?
8. Know this: *whatever it is, you must define what's important to you and choose it for yourself.* You need to know exactly what you're striving for, based solely on what you want for your life and not because someone, somewhere, told you what your ideals should be.
9. Let your own definition of success be your focus because what you focus on grows.
10. And then, here's the most important part: you get busy working toward your own ideal of success.

COMPARISON

People who lack their own firm definition of success tend to fall into comparison with others. They look around, yardstick in hand, trying to gauge their own success based on the achievements/possessions of those around them as if they should want those same things, too.

Comparison is a horrible act of self-abuse that shines a spotlight on all the things that you feel are lacking in your own life because you've defined success by someone else's standards. That, in turn, makes you feel bad about yourself. On the heels of that feeling, you'll likely turn to abusing food and/or other substances/ behaviors to numb yourself. Like I said before: there will *always*, at some point, be someone more -er (skinnier, richer, smarter, prettier, [add your -er here]) than you. This one's a no-win game. So do yourself a kindness and don't play it.

Another byproduct of comparison is that it tends to lead to unhealthy competition, which keeps you working hard to one-up someone else. Instead of striving toward what matters to *you* and creating a life *you* love, your goal instead becomes knocking someone else down a notch. That kind of competition is usually in an effort to prove something. Maybe that you're better? Or more worthy? Or deserving? Or not the [fill in the blank] that someone once said you were? Or perhaps not as small and insignificant as you believe you are? Whatever the reason, that kind of competition leads to making your motivation to achieve about someone else and not about you. And like I said way back in Chapter One, you need to check your motivation first and foremost before you embark on changing your life.

So how do you let go of comparison? Do this:

1. Pause.
2. Take a deep breath in through your nose, hold it three seconds, then let it out slowly through your mouth with an audible sound. Repeat until you calm down.
3. Then ask yourself: *How is comparison serving me? Is it helping me or harming me?*
4. Then you be positive that your definition of success was and continues to be defined solely *for yourself.* You decide what you want your life to look like. You let others have their own lives. You wish them well because there's more than enough for all of us.
5. Again, you choose to believe in abundance. You change your mindset and tell yourself, over and over until you believe it and it becomes the story you live out in your life, that there is more than enough for you.
6. You choose to believe in *more life for everybody,* which means you support everyone achieving their own ideal of success.

7. You choose to believe that you're capable of achieving what you most want from your life and that you're capable of becoming the person you most want to be.
8. You get into creation. You let others have their achievements and then, here's the most important part, you get busy working toward your own.

PRETENDING TO YOURSELF

Pretending is lying to yourself. There is no strength in pretending that your life is different than it is. There is no power in pretending that you are anything other than who you are right now: just as you look, how much you weigh, where you live, what relationships you have or don't have, what shape your finances are in, what dreams for your life haven't come to pass, and on the list goes. Pretending, like abusing food, is about avoidance.

I get that pretending is easier. Don't make waves. Don't confront anything. Don't risk. Just live in a fantasy of your own making. But pretending never really works in the long run. You can pull it off short-term, sure. But it takes time and energy and focus to pretend. Eventually all the lying to yourself grinds you down to the nub. You lose your sense of self. You end up, even if you don't realize it, enforcing the belief that you're not enough as-is. You lose respect for yourself. And once you lose respect for yourself, you allow any behavior from both yourself and others, no matter how bad it is for your well-being. On top of all that, reality will always (always, always) catch up with you at some point.

I also understand that sometimes we all need an escape. That's why you need to take extra good care of yourself during this process and do things you enjoy every day. It's really okay to take breaks and take your mind off your struggles. You sometimes need to sprawl out in your comfort zone for a bit to relax, rejuvenate, and refresh. It really is necessary for your mental health to play and have fun and do things that fulfill you. Pretending, though, is not a short break; it's you regularly sticking your head in the sand and using substances/behaviors to avoid reality and lie to yourself that your life is different than it is. Know this without a doubt: *you will never be empowered by avoiding and lying.*

I happen to believe that visualizing is a great way to imagine the reality that you want, seeing a future that matters to you in your mind's eye. Visualizing can help you shape that future by spurring you to take action to achieve that vision. Just to be clear: pretending is not visualizing. Pretending is imagining that what is really happening, right now, in your life is not actually happening. It's a facade you're using to cover up and hide reality from yourself so you don't have to make (some potentially hard) decisions. Pretending will not help you solve the real problems in your life. It won't help you move forward either. You will remain trapped in a mirage, not able to allow yourself to just start where you are, not able to change, not able to take action, if you refuse to admit the truth to yourself.

So how do you let go of pretending to yourself? Do this:

1. Pause.
2. Take a deep breath in through your nose, hold it three seconds, then let it out slowly through your mouth with an audible sound. Repeat until you calm down.
3. Then ask yourself: *How is pretending to myself serving me? Is it helping me or harming me?*
4. Then be honest with yourself. Stop avoiding, and instead, choose to stand firmly in reality. Who you are right now, in the body you're in, is who you are, period. What you're doing with your time and what you're facing in your life, right here and now, is part of the path you've chosen.
5. Now find a mirror, preferably full-length. Take a long look at your reflection. Look yourself in the eyes. Smile because yes, no matter where you are in your life, you deserve to be kind to you. Tell yourself that it's all going to be okay, because, in the end, both it and you will be.
6. Then go somewhere alone. Take stock of your life by writing down *the way it is right now*. Career. Finances. Relationships. Family. Education. Goals (reached and unreached). Dreams (fulfilled and unfulfilled). The status of your weight loss. Add anything else important to you.
7. Stay where you are. Don't run away (physically or mentally). Don't abuse food or anything else to numb yourself. You got this. This is who you are. This is where you are. Period. And that's okay.
8. Now you can truly just start where you are.
9. Take another deep breath.
10. Know this: the path you're currently on is the path you've chosen. If you don't like that path, you can choose differently (oh yes, you can). You can simply make different choices and start down a new path that will get you to where you most want to be.
11. So for each life area you've taken stock of, answer this: *What choices/changes do I need to make and what actions do I need to take to make my reality a place where I actually want to live?*
12. Then honor yourself and make/take them.

LYING TO OTHERS

You're going to have to tell the truth not only to yourself but also to others as well. The truth about what you're doing now in your life The truth about what you want to do with your life in the future. The truth about who you are. The truth about who you want to be. The truth about what you truly love and believe. The truth about how you really feel and think. Maybe you've been lying to protect yourself from pain/rejection. Or to protect others. Or to live up to someone else's standards. Maybe you're scared to reveal the truth of who you are because you're afraid of the unknown, and the most unknown thing is what'll happen if you tell the truth. Maybe you've built an entire life based on a lie (pretending) and telling the truth would shatter the whole thing.

Lying to others is also not being true to yourself. It is definitely not finding your voice and stepping into your own power. You know (deep down, you do) this is not what you want to do, not who you are, not who you want to be, and yet you keep trudging down the same path out of fear of how others will react. You don't cultivate your own gifts and talents. You don't honor and respect your own wishes and desires. You don't speak your own thoughts and beliefs and truth. Instead, you show up as someone not quite you and/ or someone entirely not you. Someone tailored to the opinions and/or wants of others in an attempt to get something (approval, money, attention, permission, and the list goes on) from other people. What all that amounts to is this: you are betraying yourself.

Not being true to yourself causes pain. It causes suffering. It reinforces the belief you likely hold that there's something wrong with or missing in you. And those beliefs cause pain, too. All that pain leaves you in a state of constant internal strife between knowing who you are but keeping up a facade to others that you are someone else. You will never be healthy and whole when you're fighting a battle with yourself. You know the truth plus you refuse to speak it equals a war inside you. In the end, lying to others does not keep you safe and protected, nor does it free you; what it does instead is keep you confined and stuck in a prison of your own making.

I'm fully aware that the truth can be hard and awkward and uncomfortable. That's especially true when others (or even you) don't want to hear it. Sadly, you'll come to find that many people prefer the lies you tell: they don't mind fake as long as everything stays the same, nothing at all changes, and they don't have to confront their own lives. It's even possible that you, yourself, may prefer the lies because they are something to hide behind. The lies provide a way to keep from being vulnerable and stepping out of your comfort zone and growing as a person. And so, in that way (you think), the lies keep you safe.

But when you lie to others, you risk three things: 1. you won't know what's real and what's not anymore, 2. you'll lose respect for yourself, and 3. you'll feel like you're living a life that doesn't matter to you at all. And here are the perils with that: 1. you'll fall out of touch with your own intuition, which you vitally need to guide you, 2. you'll allow all kinds of behaviors that don't serve your well-being at all, including abusing food, and 3. you'll never feel fulfilled (that hole inside will forever be there) if you choose to never pursue those things that matter to you because you need to keep up a facade for others.

So how do you let go of lying to others? Do this:

1. Pause.
2. Take a deep breath in through your nose, hold it three seconds, then let it out slowly through your mouth with an audible sound. Repeat until you calm down.
3. Then ask yourself: *How is lying to others serving me? Is it helping me or harming me?*
4. Then tell the honest-to-goodness truth about what you do, who you are, what you want, and what you really love. Lay it all out. Write it all in a journal to start if that makes it easier for you. Your preferences, whatever they may be, are okay.
5. Now speak it *out loud*, even if your voice quakes and your body trembles when you do it. Admit it to yourself. Admit it to others (start with people you *trust*). This is what you do, who you are, and what you want. Period. And that's okay. Because you are enough as you are, right now.
6. Then act on it by pursuing those thing that deeply matter to you.
7. And let the chips fall where they will. Know that you're strong enough (oh yes, you are!) to handle whatever fallout comes.
8. Always remember: this is your life you're working to save. It truly doesn't matter what anyone else thinks of you or believes about you; the *only* thing that matters (truly, the *only* thing) is what you think and believe about yourself.
9. Repeat (*repeat, repeat*) that to yourself—*I am saving my own life by telling the truth about who I am*—as you stand strong, hold your ground, and tell the truth.
10. Prepare yourself now because, I'm sorry to say, the fallout will come. Some people you love will leave you. Your boss, coworkers, and/or clients may no longer be happy with you. You will have to be stronger than you ever thought yourself capable of being. The entire trajectory of your life may change in ways you never imagined. But know this: eventually the people who like/love you for the real you are the ones who will stay and/or come back and those are the people you truly want in your life.
11. And even with all that, tell the truth because the tradeoff is that you, finally, get to be free of the food craziness, of the burden the lie creates, of living a life that doesn't feel like you, and on the list goes. In the end, I know this to be true without a doubt: living in your truth and shining your truth to others is the only way to a body and a life that matters to you.

SELF-DOUBT

Self-doubt, in my experience, tends to be a self-worth issue, you don't believe in your own innate worth and value, you don't believe that you have a purpose for being alive and a much-needed part to play in the larger world, you don't believe that you have gifts, talents, and passions that are unique to you, you don't believe in your own potential, and/or you are afraid you are not enough as you are.

Failure often leads to self-doubt. Failure is an action, it's something that happens (to all of us, mind you, so you are not alone; you are, in fact, in excellent company with the rest of us who have failed). Failure is a learning experience. Failure is an opportunity to do it better the next time. Failure is not a character trait. You failed, sure, but you, yourself, are not a failure, I assure you that's true. It doesn't matter how many times something you tried didn't work; you as a person did not lose a single ounce of value because of it. Remember this: failure is *only* what you believe it to be and how you choose to look at it.

Criticism, both from others and also from yourself, can also lead to self-doubt. When someone starts telling you their opinion about you or your work, you need to discern whether they're genuinely trying to help you or if they have more sinister motives. If they are trying to help you improve, you need to not only be open to their advice but also discerning (by listening to your own intuition) if that advice rings true to you. If they are trying to tear you down, you must choose (yes, it's *always* your choice) to outright reject what they're saying. In either case, if you take any criticism (both helpful and especially harmful) and attach it to your worth as a person, well, that's when self-doubt gets a foothold in your psyche. Everyone has an opinion, that's true. What's also true is that someone else's opinion is formed and also clouded by that person's own fears, limitations, self-beliefs, insecurities, and on the list goes. Always remember, even if you think the person giving the opinion has some kind of authority on the subject: *an opinion is not the same as the truth.*

Comparison can lead to self-doubt too, especially if you're comparing other people's outsides to your insides, comparing other people's highlight reels to your everyday life, and/or comparing yourself as a beginner to someone who already has years/decades of experience. Comparison hits your self-worth because you've stacked yourself up against someone else and found yourself lacking in some way. Again, comparison is an act of self-abuse and it's quite likely fueling your self-doubt, which is all the more reason to do yourself a kindness and free yourself from it.

And finally, playing to your weaknesses, in my experience, is one of the major reasons behind self-doubt. Believing in yourself is so much easier when you play to your strengths. Look, there are some things that you are naturally gifted and talented to do (I assure you that's true even if you may not know what those gifts and talents are just yet—and if don't know, hang on because we'll get to figuring that out in Chapter Six). Then there are other things that you just don't have the aptitude for doing (even if you really, really wish you did). Good news is this: someone else out there is great at doing your weaknesses. So let them. You don't have to be good at everything. You just have to be good at your strengths. So focus on and hone those. Why? Because what you focus on grows. If you continue to focus on what you're *not* good at, you risk the following: 1. constantly feeling incapable, inept, useless, stupid, and/or frustrated because you can't seem to get good at a particular skill, 2. delaying becoming the person you were meant to be by keeping yourself busy with activities that just aren't your forte, and 3. failing to find joy and/or meaning in what you're doing (mostly because you're trying hard to be somebody you're just not).

So how do you let go of self-doubt? Do this:

1. Pause.
2. Take a deep breath in through your nose, hold it three seconds, then let it out slowly through your mouth with an audible sound. Repeat until you calm down.
3. Then ask yourself: *How is self-doubt serving me? Is it helping me or harming me?*
4. Then know this: self-doubt simply started as a thought that you let ruminate in your mind, repeating it until it strengthened into a belief or maybe even a string of beliefs that became the story you tell yourself about your life. Again, you will *always* (always, always) live out what you believe.
5. So take everyone else's opinion out of the equation. Again, you are saving your own life here. This isn't about what anyone else wants, thinks, wishes, and/or hopes for your life. This is about what you need to do so you can be healthy and whole.
6. Then change your thoughts. It's your mind after all; you're the only one who can change what's circling around in there.
7. So *you* decide what to believe about yourself. Be thoughtful and deliberate about what you choose to believe about yourself, especially that you have worth and value, that you are capable and strong and intelligent and committed and determined, that you can do anything you put your mind to (oh yes, you can), that you can handle anything that comes your way (oh yes, you surely can), and that you are enough as you are.
8. Then *you* decide which things *matter deeply* to you and that you want to spend your time on.
9. Now identify what skills you do well so you can achieve those things that matter deeply to you.
10. Focus on improving, growing, and mastering those skills.
11. Hire or barter with others to fill in the gaps where your skills are weak.
12. Breathe deeply, speak strength to yourself, and keep going. Overcoming self-doubt is simply a matter of perseverance. You will crush self-doubt if you'll just keep your focus, carry on no matter what, and not stop until you finish.

SELF-ABUSE

Anything you do to yourself that tears you down or diminishes you instead of builds you up and strengthens you is self-abuse. Hurting yourself in any way (physically yes, but also emotionally and mentally) is self-abuse and also self-betrayal. Period. The end result of self-betrayal is self-loathing. And if you hate something (even yourself), you don't care what happens to it. Nothing will demotivate and demoralize you faster than turning on yourself.

I know how it can be easier to put the bullseye on your own chest and take out your frustration, anger, disillusionment, and other such feelings on yourself than to direct those emotions toward the person or people to whom they actually belong. It's easier, say, to be angry with yourself than it is to be angry with your spouse, parents, children, siblings, boss, and the list goes on. It's easier to turn on yourself and berate yourself than it is to face someone else and speak the truth of how you feel. It's easier to take shots at yourself because you know you'll just sit there and take it since, up until now, you haven't fought back.

Self-abuse is also a distraction and a method of self-sabotage. It's a way to avoid your feelings, minimize risk, keep yourself small, and remain tucked inside your comfort zone. You don't spend your time stepping out and moving forward; instead, you spend your time hurting yourself. Self-abuse is also a way for you to validate your own belief that you are worth very little. And in that way, self-abuse becomes a cycle: you decide you're not worth much or that you hate yourself; abuse yourself; then because of that abuse, you reinforce the belief that you have very little value or goodness inside you; then because of that belief, you decide you're unworthy of your goals, passions, and dreams while also deciding that you're not worth the time and effort to help yourself; and so you abuse yourself some more, and the cycle begins again. You're trapped, around and around in that cycle, until you choose to break free.

Believe me when I say this: self-abuse exacts an enormous toll on you because there's just no getting away from your attacker, ever, because all day, every day, you are with you. You end up trying to destroy the part of you that feels worthless and/or broken. Except that it's hard to tell where exactly that part starts and you end. And so when you abuse yourself, you end up destroying all of you in the process.

So how do you let go of self-abuse? Do this:
1. Pause.
2. Take a deep breath in through your nose, hold it three seconds, then let it out slowly through your mouth with an audible sound. Repeat until you calm down.
3. Then ask yourself: *How is self-abuse serving me? Is it helping me or harming me?*
4. Then choose self-compassion *every single time* because self-compassion is what you most need to heal yourself. You befriend yourself and start being kind, gentle, and patient with yourself, *especially in your weak moments.*
5. Choose to believe in your own worth and value, no matter what.
6. Choose to have your own back *always* and take full responsibility for how you treat yourself in the good times and the bad.

7. In any moment, when you want to abuse yourself, instead ask **out loud in a kind, calm voice***: *What do I most need to hear right now?*

8. Then channel the kindest, nicest person you know and tell yourself, *out loud*, what it is you most need to hear. Better yet, go find a mirror and look yourself in the eyes and say it.

9. Make your own mantras out of what you most need to hear. Make ones that fly in the face of whatever thoughts/feelings got you rolling toward self-abuse. Say them *aloud*. For example, a few of mine: *There's still time. Quitting will not get me where I want to be. I am healing and whole. I have every answer I need inside me.*

10. Contact someone you trust (key: *trust*) and tell them you are struggling. Ask for their support. Ask for what you need. You are worth asking for what you need.

11. Now go do something (not food-related) that gives you joy, that nourishes and fulfills you, instead of being self-abusive (more on why this is so imperative in Chapter Six).

12. Know this: you'll come to find out that once you start actively making yourself happier and more fulfilled, you'll be less inclined to abuse yourself.

*Remember: out loud matters because to activate the rational/thinking part of your brain. See *Eat Calmly* in Chapter Two for a refresher as to why.

NOT FORGIVING YOURSELF

Yes, you've screwed up, misjudged, acted out of emotion, and you should've known better so you would've done better. But you didn't. And whatever it was that never should have happened did. All you can do now, I say kindly, is fix what you can and learn from what you can't. You need to forgive yourself for all the things you did and failed to do. Even if someone else, whoever they are, won't forgive you, you still have to forgive yourself. You don't need anyone else's permission to forgive yourself; you only need to decide that you're done hauling around each and every mistake you've made, and beating yourself up for them, wherever you go.

Part of self-compassion includes forgiving yourself as many times as it takes. Just like you get *unlimited* tries, you can (and must) forgive yourself an *unlimited* number of times because that's the only way you're ever going to find peace. Even if it ends up being a million times, then that's how many times you will have to forgive yourself because you're going to continue to make mistakes for your entire life; you're human and there's no way around that fact. And so self-forgiveness is nonnegotiable (you must do it) and an ongoing practice (likely daily). It's also a practice, so you'll get better at it the more you do it.

So how do you let go of not forgiving yourself? Do this:

1. Pause.
2. Take a deep breath in through your nose, hold it three seconds, then let it out slowly through your mouth with an audible sound. Repeat until you calm down.
3. Then ask yourself: *How is not forgiving myself serving me? Is it helping me or harming me?*
4. Then start by checking your motivation. You need to forgive yourself because you want to, not because someone else says you should.
5. Then take an honest inventory of your unforgiveness. Write a list of events, mistakes, failures, happenings, and the like from your past that you refuse to forgive yourself for.
6. Read through the list you just wrote in Step 5 (all the things you refuse to forgive yourself for) and write the age you were when that particular item occurred. Subtract your current age. That's how much time you've been imprisoned in unforgiveness.
7. Then for each item on your list, ask yourself: *Is it possible I just made a mistake, that this was simply an error in judgment? Or I made a decision out of fear, anger, arrogance, loneliness, sadness, and the like? Or maybe I was young and naive? Or maybe, no matter my age, I simply didn't know better and so I didn't do better?*
8. Now for each item on your list, ask yourself: *What do I need to do to let this go?* Your answers might include: make amends, apologize, fix what is fixable and learn from what is not, change your choices/behaviors, deal with the consequences, have a small ceremony, and the like).
9. Then love yourself enough to do whatever it is you need to do to forgive yourself.
10. Part of loving yourself enough is to believe you are forgiven. So look yourself in the eyes in a mirror and say out loud: *I forgive you, I am forgiven.*
11. Repeat (*repeat, repeat*) *daily for at least 66 days* until the fact that you forgive yourself and you are forgiven becomes part of the story that you believe about yourself.
12. And lastly, love yourself enough to forgive yourself over and over and over again, as many times as it takes. A hundred. A thousand. A million. It doesn't matter. Love yourself enough to give yourself unlimited chances, as many times as it takes. Love yourself enough because, again, that's how you'll find peace.

NOT FORGIVING OTHERS

Yes, you're going to have to forgive others for the things they've done or said to you. Forgive them for making your life so difficult. Forgive them for treating you as if you were small and unimportant like a smudge beside the main point. Forgive them for humiliating you or berating you or abusing you or choosing someone else over you or not loving you back. Forgive them for the myriad of other ways they may have hurt you.

But, you say, you just don't understand how awful it was, what that person (or people) put me through. I don't doubt it was awful. Maybe even soul-crushing. That's not the point. The point is you need to forgive them *for you* so that you can let them go. Refusing to forgive them is like chasing after a bad debt: you can spend your time and energy and resources trying to get what you think you're owed (which you're unlikely to get) or you can say enough is enough, you don't owe me anything, I release you so I can move on without you. When you chase a bad debt, you think about that person all the time, you stew in your feelings of anger, betrayal, disillusionment, and on the list goes, you contemplate how you can get what's rightfully yours or get even, and your focus becomes not your own goals, dreams, talents, gifts, wants, and wishes but becomes instead whomever it was that hurt you. When you refuse to forgive somebody, you end up giving them power over your life until they acknowledge what they've done to you. While it's possible they may come around and make amends, you're still stuck waiting until they do.

Sure, you can choose not to forgive. Lots of people do. They are the ones who are trapped carrying around all that hurt. And because they don't want to feel how much it hurts or how powerless they believe they are or how much they've lost, many of them abuse their substance/behavior of choice (in your case, abusing food) to numb and avoid. Then it becomes a cycle: you are wronged by someone; so you feel anger, betrayal, disillusionment, and the like; you demand they admit what they did and make it right; when they refuse, you abuse food to numb the pain; then the numbness wears off so the feelings of anger, betrayal, etc. return; you start right back up, demanding of them until you abuse food to numb yourself. Again and again. Make no mistake: it's cyclical. It never ends until you end it. So choose to forgive them and end it.

And keep this in mind, too: it's your choice entirely whether you want that person in your life anymore after you forgive/release them. Even if they are family, you still have a choice to keep them out of your life. I know there's loyalty and bonding and blood ties involved. But sometimes some of the most damaging people to you are the ones whom you love the most or who are supposed to love you the most. You always have permission (given to you by yourself) to choose who is in your life and who isn't. *Always.* And if you don't believe me about the importance of that, we'll be talking about it in Chapter Five.

So how do you let go of not forgiving others? Do this:
1. Pause.
2. Take a deep breath in through your nose, hold it three seconds, then let it out slowly through your mouth with an audible sound. Repeat until you calm down.
3. Then ask yourself: *How is not forgiving others serving me? Is it helping me or harming me?*

4. Then realize and take to heart that people are fallible. You. Me. Everyone. We all make mistakes. We all have weaknesses and failings. We all do badly sometimes. We all don't do better when we don't know better. Sometimes, we do know better and still don't do better. We all make lousy choices on occasion. We all have hurt somebody at some point. We all have lied, cheated, stolen, and/or [insert your transgression here] sometime during our lives. We are all here without much of an instruction guide, trying to figure out life.

5. Then answer these: *Do I really want to exchange my life for chasing after others and traveling in a circle? Or would I rather move on without them in a straight line toward where and who I most want to be?*

6. Then do yourself a kindness, don't wait. You be the one to break the cycle, *right now*. You get yourself out of that circle. Like I said before, the only way to get your power back is to take it. So take it back. Release them from their bad debt to you. Move out of that circle and onto your future.

TRYING TO IMPRESS OTHERS

True freedom only happens when you strive to be true to yourself and you stop needing to impress anyone. The moment you start trying to impress is the moment you believe you're not enough on your own, as you are. Trying to impress leaves you enslaved to the wants, opinions, judgments, and/or criticisms of others. Likewise, seeking approval for your knowledge, cleverness, creativity, and the like only serves to: 1. diminish the strength of your own belief in your gifts and talents, 2. put the power over your gifts and talents in someone else's hands (at least in your mind, anyway), and 3. change your motivation from yourself to someone else. If your motivation is not to fulfill yourself with your gifts and talents but rather to impress other people, you will constantly be attached to the outcome. (*Will they be happy with you? Like you and what you've done? Think more of you? Accept you and ask you to hang around?* And on it goes). That outcome will likely include some kind of judgment and/or critique, which you will get whether you're ready for it or not and which (especially if it's harsh) just may derail you.

So don't ever get suckered into believing that you need to do the dog-and-pony-show for anyone. Know this: when you're trying to impress others, your gifts and talents cease to be about your uniqueness and expressing your authentic self and bringing you joy and instead start being about trying to get something from others (usually starting with their approval) along with an endless cycle of the question: *Am I enough?*

Another thing that happens when you're trying to impress is that you don't ask the questions that truly matter like: *Is this what I actually want to be doing? Am I happy? What do I love and want more of in my life? What deeply matters to me? What brings me joy? What does a successful life look like to me?* Trying to impress is a distraction that can also keep you going in circles, chasing after the favorable opinions of others. Your focus ends up being honed in on someone else and what they will think of you and/or your work (and so their opinion of you becomes more important than your opinion of you), instead of on figuring out who you really are, what you really want, and taking the actions you need to take to get yourself to where you most want to be.

So how do you let go of trying to impress? Do this:
1. Pause.
2. Take a deep breath in through your nose, hold it three seconds, then let it out slowly through your mouth with an audible sound. Repeat until you calm down.
3. Then ask yourself: *How is trying to impress others serving me? Is it helping me or harming me?*
4. Now check your motivation (see Chapter One if you need a reminder) and make sure the reason you're doing/being whatever it is you're doing/being is *solely for you*. You make your *only* motivation a desire to become the person you most want to be, to achieve all those things that matter deeply to you, and to improve your own well-being.
5. Always remember: your worth and value are innate. You were born with them and no one can ever—hear me: *ever*—take them away from you. No matter what happens to you, your worth and value will *always* be intact. You are enough as-is. You *never* need to impress anyone to have worth and value.
6. Change your focus from outward (them) to inward (you).
7. Monitor your focus. You'll consciously have to make a few tweaks or rein yourself back in if your motivation changes from you to them. All you have to do is refocus and change it back. Repeat as many times as it takes.
8. Instead of striving to impress, you strive to be true to yourself and for your own standards of excellence and to make yourself fulfilled. Then what other people think, believe, and/or say about you doesn't matter nearly as much as what you think, believe, and/or say about yourself.

TRYING TO SAVE OTHERS

Again, there is only one person's life in this world that you can truly save, that's your own. You are one hundred percent responsible for your own choices and actions. You are one hundred percent responsible for how your own life turns out.

You are not, however, responsible for any other adult who is capable of taking care of themselves. I know how easy it is to get roped into trying to fix someone else's life. Maybe you genuinely want to help them. Maybe you want them to like you. Maybe you want to make yourself look good. Maybe you think it's the right thing to do. Or maybe you just want a distraction so you don't have to look at what needs fixing in your own life.

But here's the thing: trying to save others rarely works. Why? Because if you're doing all the work to save them, they take no ownership of their problems and so they don't involve themselves in finding solutions. If they don't do the work for themselves, they will never be invested in how it all turns out. Eventually, you'll get tired of trying to rescue them (yes, you will) and so you'll stop trying to save them. And when that happens, they will likely turn on you, getting angry, bitter, resentful, and the like at you. You'll also come to find that the odds are extremely high—because there was no commitment on their part to see the thing through to the end—that they'll go right back to the mess they were in when you found them. You'll come to find out the hard way that all the time, energy, money, focus, and on the list goes that you spent to help them will be for naught. That's when you're likely to feel like you've been suckered. And it's the feelings of being taken advantage of and/or duped that will likely have you running to numb yourself by abusing food.

So how do you let go of saving others? Do this:
1. Pause.
2. Take a deep breath in through your nose, hold it three seconds, then let it out slowly through your mouth with an audible sound. Repeat until you calm down.
3. Then ask yourself: *How is trying to save others serving me? Is it helping me or harming me?*
4. Then believe, deep down, the fact that all the time, energy, money, and focus you're using turning other people's problems into your own is all the time, energy, money, and focus taken away from you meeting your own goals and dreams.
5. Then make a list of everyone whose life you are trying to save.
6. For each one, answer this: *Are they capable of saving themselves?*
7. If the answer is *no*, then answer this: *How can I help them so they can be capable of saving themselves?* (in a temporary way and in a supportive role, mind you, so they don't become your main focus)
8. If the answer is *yes*, then you gently but firmly tell them that they need to take the lead on fixing their own problems.
9. Then you step back and let them. You *empower* them by doing this. You empower them by making them do the work to get out of the hole they dug for themselves. You empower them by letting them make their own choices and learn from their own mistakes. Be supportive of them, yes. Be responsible for them, no. And you also empower yourself by getting rid of the distractions (yes, everyone you are trying to save is a distraction) that are keeping you from forging ahead toward creating the life you want.

EXPECTING OTHERS TO MAKE YOU HAPPY

Your life is passing you by as you hem and haw, expecting someone else to deliver happiness to your doorstep. Happiness is a choice, your choice. You, and you alone, are responsible for your own happiness. When you expect others to make you happy, you wait (and sometimes wait and wait and wait and wait) for them to get around to it. On top of that, you're often disappointed because they: take too long, don't do exactly what you want so you're not as happy as you could be, leave your life so leave you waiting on happiness, and/or the list continues on.

You have zero percent control over the actions of other people. You have one hundred percent control over the actions of your own self. So play the better odds and take the power back in your own life. You are going to get busy doing something, so you might as well get busy making yourself happy. And keep this in mind: overeating, starving, purging, and/or abusing food is a choice. You have a choice before you start doing it. You still have a choice while you're doing it. You may feel crazed and out of control, but still, you are making a choice. Does overeating, starving, purging, and/or abusing food make you genuinely happy? If not, you can and need to choose differently.

So how do you let go of expecting others to make you happy? Do this:
1. Pause.
2. Take a deep breath in through your nose, hold it three seconds, then let it out slowly through your mouth with an audible sound. Repeat until you calm down.
3. Then ask yourself: *How is expecting others to make me happy serving me? Is it helping me or harming me?*
4. Then define for yourself *exactly* what makes you happy. Saying you just want to be happy is too nebulous, there's nothing concrete to move toward. So do yourself a kindness and write down what *specifically* makes you happy. Not what *should* make you happy but what actually *does*. Not what makes someone else happy but what makes *you* happy.
5. So answer these: *What is/was happening in my life when I'm at my happiest? What activities make/used to make me feel alive? What do I enjoy doing and/or lights a spark in me? Who do I enjoy being around? Where do I feel most at home? What do I most want to be doing with my time?* Those answers will tell you what makes you happy.
6. Then get busy creating a life around your own answers. So take action. Don't like your job? It's time *now* to find a new one. Miserable in your relationship? It's time *now* to either take steps to improve it or to break it off. Unhappy where you live? It's time *now* to find a place where you feel like you're home.

7. Don't put it off. Don't wait until you've gotten rid of the weight and/or stopped abusing food to start moving in the direction of your own happiness. I assure you that the weight will come off and/or the food abuse will ease with less struggle from you when you are already pursuing your own happiness.
8. Don't make the mistake of telling yourself you'll be happy when you are thin, rich, married, divorced, and/or [fill in the blank].
9. Know this: telling yourself that you'll be happy at some point in the future just means that you're missing your life *now*.
10. Know this too: time doesn't stop and wait for you. Don't come to find out (as I did) that your biggest regret will be all the time you spent being unhappy when you could've made changes and had a life that you loved. You absolutely can have a life you adore, a life that makes you excited to wake up in the morning, a life that makes you happy. There's not a doubt in my mind. You can. Don't leave your happiness up to chance or up to someone else, make it up to your choice.

CHOOSING POWERLESSNESS OVER BEING POWERFUL

At any given moment, you can choose to either be powerless or be powerful. The thing is: you can't be both at the same time. You get to choose: be the victim or be the hero/heroine of your own story.

If you choose victim, you choose to give your power to someone else and hope they do something to help you. If they don't, well, you don't have any control over that. Choosing to be a victim anchors you where you are and keeps you moored for as long as you spend waiting for someone else to come fix it. If you choose to be a hero/heroine, you choose to keep your power and make choices that move you forward right now. You have control over yourself, what you'll allow and what you won't. You take charge and fix what needs fixing. Plus, there's no waiting. You move at your own speed in the direction that you want to go.

Here's something else to keep in mind: nothing boxes you in and leaves you powerless like telling yourself that you have no choices. You do. You *always* have choices. Sometimes, there aren't any great choices. Sometimes, the choices are really hard. Sometimes, the choices fill you with fear. But still, there are always choices.

So how do you let go of choosing powerlessness over being powerful? Do this:
1. Pause.
2. Take a deep breath in through your nose, hold it three seconds, then let it out slowly through your mouth with an audible sound. Repeat until you calm down.

3. Then ask yourself: *How is choosing powerlessness over being powerful serving me? Is it helping me or harming me?*

4. Then stay in the present moment and look at the situation you currently find yourself in (so not the past where you can't change anything or the future that hasn't happened yet). Write a list of everything that's not the way you want it to be.

5. Then next to each item on that list, write what you need to do to change it for the better. Answer these: *What choices do I need to make that will improve my situation? What choices are best for me? What choices will move me in the direction that I want to go?*

6. Speak some strength to yourself (*I can do this. I've got this. I have what it takes. I will save my own life.*)

7. Then get busy working your way down that list.

8. Action will empower and embolden you. It's true that a body in motion tends to stay in motion. The more action you take, the more action you will want to take. And if you make some mistakes along the way (which you will), learn from them and choose more wisely the next time.

9. And remember: your life belongs only to you. When all is said and done, you're fully responsible for where you end up. With that in mind, refuse to be the victim. Instead, be the hero/heroine of your own story and keep making the choices that are best for you.

PANIC, DESPAIR, AND WORRY

There are two kinds of fear, like we already talked about. One: *real fear*, which includes anything that could cause you bodily harm. Real fear protects you by keeping you out of dangerous situations. And two: *head fear*, which includes everything that scares you but that won't actually physically harm you. Head fear keeps you from achieving what you want for your life.

Panic is head fear.

Panic is the crazed, I-don't-know-what-to-do-what-do-I-do feeling that happens when you aren't prepared and/or you don't believe that you can handle anything and everything that comes your way. Panic makes you stop thinking and start reacting. People (myself included) tend to make terrible and sometimes life-altering mistakes when they panic.

176 | Start Where You Are Weight Loss

So how do you let go of panic? Do this:

1. Pause.
2. Take a deep breath in through your nose, hold it three seconds, then let it out slowly through your mouth with an audible sound. Repeat until you calm down.
3. Then ask yourself: *How is panicking serving me? Is it helping me or harming me?*
4. Then speak strength to yourself *out loud*, telling yourself words you really need to hear.
5. Take a step back from the situation if at all possible and wait to make a decision.
6. Then, once you're out of panic and thinking rationally again, look at all your options and come up with a plan.
7. If it's a true emergency, still speak out loud to yourself and take deep breaths to keep yourself out of panic so you can make better decisions.

Despair is head fear, too.

Despair is believing there is no hope. Despair is the quickest way to quitting. If you can't ever see your life changing for the better then what's the point of trying? Why bother if things will never improve? Despair leads to (often overwhelming) pain because you believe that you're never going to get where you want to be or get what you want to have. Here's something else that's true: despair (like shame) is a dead-end road that leads only to numbing behaviors like abusing food. It's your choice, I say kindly, if you want to walk down that road or not.

So how do you let go of despair? Do this:

1. Pause.
2. Take a deep breath in through your nose, hold it three seconds, then let it out slowly through your mouth with an audible sound. Repeat until you calm down.
3. Then ask yourself: *How is despair serving me? Is it helping me or harming me?*
4. Then choose hope.
5. Choose to believe there's hope for you, for your situation, for whatever it is you're going through. Look for that hope. Keep searching for it even while you fumble around and go in the direction that you think is forward and do the best that you can with the information you have. Hope says it will get better. Hope says that it's only a matter of time before you find those people, places, and things that fulfill you and give your life meaning.
6. Cultivate patience. This too shall pass (yes, it will).

7. You choose to believe that everything is working out for your good, and you hang on to hope (because that, I say kindly, is a choice).

Worrying is yet another head fear.

Worrying does two things, neither of them good: 1. it keeps you out of the present moment because you're concerned about what might or might not happen in the future, and 2. it focuses your time and energy on a fruitless pursuit. Know this: all the worry in the world will not change the outcome of anything one bit. Not even a little. Nope, not at all.

So how do you let go of worry? Do this:
1. Pause.
2. Take a deep breath in through your nose, hold it three seconds, then let it out slowly through your mouth with an audible sound. Repeat until you calm down.
3. Then ask yourself: *How is worry serving me? Is it helping me or harming me?*
4. Then take action.
5. Now make choices that will fix whatever situation it is that you're worrying about. Make decisions that will move you forward. Do what is in your power to do. Ask for help for those things that aren't in your power to do.
6. Choose to believe that you're strong enough to handle anything that life hands you (because you most assuredly are).
7. And choose (yes, it's a choice) to take life as it comes.

THINGS THAT DON'T BELONG TO YOU AND/OR AREN'T ABOUT YOU

Sometimes you pick up things that don't belong to you. I'm not talking about stealing here, although if you're stealing, you need to stop that and give the stuff back because that's an act that is: 1. not being true to yourself and 2. coming from a place of scarcity. What I'm talking about here is emotional baggage. You may also pick up things that aren't about you, meaning that someone felt some way about themselves and projected/dumped that feeling, for whatever reason, onto you.

All that emotional baggage belongs to other people, which you pick up and take into your own heart, hold it close, carry it with you, and let it change who you are and/or who you could become. You really need to be discerning as to what is actually yours and what isn't.

I'm talking about (a partial list):

- other people's insecurities/fears/limitations/beliefs/etc.
- other people's opinion(s) of you and/or reaction(s) to you
- other peoples wishes/hopes/dreams/wants/etc. for your life
- other people's choices/feelings
- other people's blame and/or responsibility for other people's actions

We've talked about most of these already, but I'm adding them all together here because it's important that you realize you need to let go of anything that isn't wholly yours. I would also argue, having done this and continuing to do it, *letting go of things that don't belong to you and/or aren't about you may be one of the most important things you ever do for your weight-loss journey and for your healing.* You need to really see and take to heart that: 1. these things don't belong to you and/or aren't about you, 2. it's a choice to carry them around, and 3. they weigh you down (both in your heart and in your weight loss; they are significant part of the reason you abuse food), which makes it harder for you to soar high.

So how do you let go of things that don't belong to you and/or aren't about you? Do this:
1. Pause.
2. Take a deep breath in through your nose, hold it three seconds, then let it out slowly through your mouth with an audible sound. Repeat until you calm down.
3. Then ask yourself: *How is holding on to things that don't belong to me and/or aren't about me serving me? Is it helping me or harming me?*
4. Take an inventory of things inside yourself that you may be struggling with and/or that don't feel true to you.
5. Separate what belongs to you and what belongs to others. For each item on your list, ask yourself: *Is this true for me? Do I actually believe this? Do I want to believe this? Who does this actually belong to?* Or for blame/responsibility: *Is this actually my doing?*
6. Then reject (oh yes, you can) all those that don't belong to you. Lay them down or give them back mentally. Say it aloud: *This doesn't belong to me; I'm not carrying it with me anymore.* Write it down and burn the

paper if that'll help you. Let your intuition guide you and do whatever you need to do that will allow you to release them.

7. Don't wait. Do it now. Free yourself of the burden of the weight they put on you.
8. Let them fall wherever they land, just as long as they are out of your own heart and mind.
9. Step around them and keep on going.
10. Actively repeat these steps because you'll find that as long as you are alive and interacting with others, you will likely find yourself picking up things that don't belong to you and/or aren't about you. (No worries, though, because it's a practice: it'll get easier and you'll get better at it the more you do it.)

GETTING IN YOUR OWN WAY

We talked about this in Chapter Two (in the section, *Sabotaging Yourself*). I mention it again here because if you didn't address it then, you really will need to address it now. Sabotaging yourself is a significant part of why you continue to abuse food. You need to face it and heal it in yourself, I say kindly, or you will find yourself getting in your own way and sabotaging your own efforts (and not just with food either) for your entire life.

Getting in your own way, like self-abuse, is about minimizing risk. You sabotage yourself so you don't have to step out of your comfort zone. Or if you're already out of your comfort zone, you sabotage yourself so that you can jump right back into that zone. Sometimes, you get in your own way to keep yourself non-threatening and/or less intimidating to others. You self-sabotage so they'll be comfortable around you, so you'll belong and be liked and blend in. Or you self-sabotage so they'll stick around and you won't be alone. Or maybe you do it because others prefer you small and so you stay small.

Many times too, getting in your own way is about reinforcing (often subconscious) beliefs you already hold about yourself. Maybe you believe you don't deserve good things. Or you believe that you're not likable. Or you believe that you aren't worthy of success, money, relationships, fulfillment, and the like. So you sabotage your own efforts, either not achieving what you most want (by giving up before you reach it or not even trying to reach it at all) or achieving what you most want then making choices that take that achievement away from you. Self-sabotage also includes knowing what triggers abusing food and/or numbing behavior for you and choosing to do it anyway.

You sabotage your own efforts because that is safer (you think) than trusting yourself and facing whatever it is you fear. And make no mistake, getting in your own way is all about not trusting yourself, ignoring your intuition, and cowering to fear.

So how do you let go of getting in your own way? Do this:

1. Pause.
2. Take a deep breath in through your nose, hold it three seconds, then let it out slowly through your mouth with an audible sound. Repeat until you calm down.
3. Then ask yourself: *How is getting in my own way serving me? Is it helping me or harming me?*
4. Make a list of all the benefits you gain by being overweight and/or abusing food. *Be honest.*
5. Go back and reread your answers from Chapter Three (in the section, *Oh, Some Science (Part One)* that address beliefs that are holding you back.
6. Now write a list of moments (both big crossroad-type moments and itty-bitty moments) in your life where you regret the choice you made, especially if that choice took you further away from what you wanted.
7. Then for each one, listen for your intuition and write the first answer that pops into your head (so no editing and/or overthinking) to this: *Why did I sabotage myself in that moment?* (Hint: the answer likely has something to do with fear.)
8. Read through the answers you just wrote and find the common thread between them. Write it down. That thread is likely your biggest fear and the major reason that you keep getting in your own way.
9. Now listen for your intuition—which, remember, includes *both your body (reactions) and mind (thoughts/ feelings)*—and let it guide you.
10. Take a deep breath in through your nose, hold it three seconds, then let it out slowly through your mouth with an audible sound. Remind yourself to relax into the journey and not take it all so seriously. (Remember: look at your life as an experiment or a game.)
11. Then choose to trust both yourself and your intuition.
12. Now take action (even tiny steps taken slowly) and do whatever your intuition tells you to do even if that scares you.

TRYING TO CONTROL

We talked about this in Chapter Three (in the section, *Lack Of Control*). I mention it again here because if you didn't address it then, you really will need to address it now for two reasons: 1. there are no ironclad guarantees of either security or comfort in nature, and 2. food will never give you control.

Control is just an illusion. You have complete control over your own choices and actions, but that's about it. You have no absolute control over anything else. Honestly, other people are going to do what they are going to do. Events (accidents, illnesses, job losses, and the like) are just going to occur. Again, life does not ask your permission first, and the outcome will ultimately be whatever it's going to be. Trying to control will leave you: 1. banging your against the wall in frustration and 2. abusing food when things don't go the way you want them to.

So how do you let go of control? Do this:

1. Pause.
2. Take a deep breath in through your nose, hold it three seconds, then let it out slowly through your mouth with an audible sound. Repeat until you calm down.
3. Then ask yourself: *How is trying to control serving me? Is it helping me or harming me?*
4. Then honor yourself by following your own passions and cultivating your own gifts and talents, whatever they may be.
5. Respect yourself by making clear boundaries as to what behavior you'll allow and what you won't from others. Defend those boundaries by speaking up for yourself and/or taking action to protect yourself.
6. Determine what you want for your life, make goals based on those wants then reach them solely for you, and be positive that whatever you choose to pursue deeply matters to you. Then pursue what you want for your life to the very best of your ability. That way, regardless of what other people do or say, regardless of what happens or doesn't happen at the end, you will still have a deep personal fulfillment and satisfaction from having done the work for yourself.
7. Keep moving forward *without delay*.
8. Believe without a doubt that life is rigged in your favor. Again, what that means is no matter what life brings, you are strong enough to handle it, you will learn from it, and somehow it is happening for your good.
9. Believe without a doubt that there is a lesson in everything that happens to you, and that lesson is a gift to you (truly it is, if you'll just look at it that way).
10. Know this: believing those two things—life is rigged in your favor and there's a lesson in everything—deep down in your core, where it matters most, will get you through everything without abusing food for relief.

OH, SOME SCIENCE (PART ONE)

Peptides, if you recall, are molecules that carry information to and from the different systems of the body; they are what allow your cells to communicate with each other. Your body processes every thought, emotion, impulse, action, etc. as either an electrical impulse or a biochemical reaction; all those processes run in constant feedbacks loops, like we talked about before. Peptides are an integral part of those feedback loops; they need to be able to flow freely in order for those feedback loops to work the way they are designed to.[1]

According to my layman's understanding of how the brain/body connection works, if you continuously refuse to let go of things that don't serve you, you disrupt the flow of those feedback loops and destabilize the entire communication system between your body and brain. Steadfastly hanging on to those things that no longer serve you causes stress, which floods the body with high levels of various biochemicals, including cortisol and adrenalin. Your body is designed to handle temporary stress (a fight-or-flight reaction). Your body is *not* designed to have continuous high levels of those biochemicals present at all times. Chronic high levels of those biochemicals interfere with and interrupt the proper flow of those feedback loops.[2]

As you may remember, those feedback loops run in a fraction of a second, one after another, never stopping. Once you interrupt the flow of those loops, they can very quickly and easily spiral out of control. That means your body and brain are no longer communicating effectively or efficiently. That's not good for you, especially when those feedback loops are what drive the mental processes that actually create motivation and behavior, and so control your attitude and your actions.

When you let go of things that don't serve you, you decrease your stress, which in turn decreases the high levels of biochemicals in your body. When that happens, the delicate workings of those feedback loops are able to be restored. Remember, those feedback loops are also serving your subconscious, which controls the vast majority of your brain's activities. Your subconscious is a powerful ally that you need on your side. Once you let go and those peptides are able to flow freely again, your brain will have an easier time guiding your actions (both consciously and subconsciously) in a way that changes the scope/shape of your life for the better. All that to say when you let go of that which no longer serves you, you are physiologically changing the odds greatly in your favor that you'll open yourself up to creating the body and the life you most want, a body and a life that you love.

OH, SOME SCIENCE (PART TWO)

I'm of the belief that you can make your way through pretty much anything by just breathing deeply. I've also learned from experience that deep breathing is one of the best ways to support yourself through letting go.

Your body is always looking to remain in homeostasis, which is basically an optimal balance. Science has shown that controlled slow deep breathing (4-10 breaths per minute) will help you achieve that. Your diaphragm, the muscle under your lungs that you actively use when you breathe in, is normally passive when you exhale. To do controlled breathing, you need to activate your diaphragm for the exhalation also. You do that by breathing out slowly to a count of 4-6.[3]

Deep breathing regulates your heart rate through the vagus nerve, which is part of your body's parasympathetic nervous system (that's the system that works to slow down your body's processes). Your heart rate naturally increases slightly when you breathe in then decreases when you breathe out. Slow, controlled exhalations will slow your overall heart rate, helping your body return to homeostasis during a heightened response. Science has also shown that deep breathing, practiced over time, will improve your body's fight-or-flight response to external stimuli (from my layman's understanding: it will better regulate the bursts of biochemicals flooding your system during a heightened response so you'll react more calmly the more you practice deep breathing techniques). In short, controlled deep breathing has been shown to help your body react better to stressors (both physical and mental) so it can remain in a more internally stable state. And finally, if all of that didn't give you enough reason to start breathing deeply, then know this: deep breathing has also been shown to help people in general live longer.[4]

THIS IS A PRACTICE AND A PROCESS

Don't fall into the trap of believing that you'll let go once and move on. For some things, you very well may be able to let go easily. Other things, you'll let go and snatch them back up again (because they feel safe and familiar, even if they're bad for you) and you'll have to let go all over again. So you be kind and gentle and patient with yourself. Don't get frustrated if it takes you a few or even a lot of tries to let someone/something go. I, myself, sometimes still struggle to let go. I still pick things back up and carry them for a while before I let go of them again. Like I keep saying, there's no doing this perfectly. You do the best you can, you keep trying, and whatever you do, you don't give up on yourself. And always remember: every mistake is simply a brand new chance to do it better the next time.

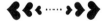

CHAPTER FIVE

BANISH THE VAMPIRES

OR

Get rid of that
which sucks the life
out of you.

Chapter Five

**"Let me fall if I must fall. The one I will become will catch me."
—Isreal ben Eliezer**

I BEND AT the waist, hands on my knees, searching the refrigerator. Cool air spills out onto my socked feet. A plastic-wrapped bowl tips, red liquid sloshing, staining the thin clear covering like blood. A half-empty can of chicken noodle soup on the top shelf. A moldy orange that's caved in on one side. I push it away and keep looking.

I feel Father before I see him. The air shifts and flattens. The hairs on my nape rise. My scalp prickles. I know he's in the kitchen, watching me, even though he doesn't make a sound. I straighten up and shut the refrigerator. The bottles in the door clink softly. I turn to face him. Water drips from the sink faucet. The clock behind me ticks loudly. The refrigerator kicks on, humming. Everything so normal except for Father who is standing near the sliding glass doors, backlit in the bright sunlight, his body stiff.

Behind me, there are two slices of bread on a plate, peanut butter slathered on one. It was the grape jelly I'd been looking for. My thigh muscles tighten. My mouth goes dry. My whole self tenses. Fight or flight. I am ready to spring. I don't like being alone with Father. I don't trust him. I don't feel safe. Fear simmers, a roiling boil in my belly. I take a few small steps back until I bump into the countertop. The knife clatters to the floor, peanut butter splattering across the linoleum. I look beyond him, the glass doors to the deck closed and locked. He's broad-shouldered, filling most of the kitchen doorway, and his arm span gives him a long reach. I could try to bolt, but I know I won't make it.

He crosses the kitchen in two long strides and grabs me by the arm, hard enough that in a little while there'll be bruises in the size and shape of his fingers. He yanks me closer, his face above mine, looking down, so close I can see a fleck of something green (Lettuce? Oregano? The skin of a Granny Smith?) on his top front tooth. His breath, hot and tinged with onions, washes over me.

"What're you doing here?"

What should I say? What does he want to hear? His nostrils flare as he breathes. His fingers squeeze harder. Anger comes off him in waves. I can feel it. It raises the hairs on my neck, on my arms. It tightens my stomach. It makes my heart throb in my chest. My scalp prickles again in warning: danger, danger, danger. But it's too late. He has a hold of me. There's no getting out of that grip. What can I do now?

"Well?" Father says. Smells come off him in waves too, sharp and glittering like shards of broken glass: grease from his overalls, wood shavings caught in his hair, a metallic scent that reminds me of winter air.

I swallow hard. I can still taste the peanut butter I'd eaten: three heaping spoonfuls before I went searching for the jelly. There's a hot, thick mass in my throat. All the words I want to say are tangled inside it.

"I'm talking to you. What's this mess?"

I make a soft gravelly sound, a tiny throat clearing. "A snack?" It comes out like a question. Is that the answer Father wants to hear?

"You're big enough," he says. "Last thing you need is another snack."

His grip tightens again. Tears spring into my eyes. Without thinking, just pure reflex, I yelp.

"No daughter of mine is going to have a double chin. You got that?"

Don't cry, I tell myself. Don't you dare cry.

"Huh? Do you?"

I give a single nod. I'm sweating, although I didn't realize it before. Tendrils of damp hair slap my face, stick to my cheeks, one of them catches fast in my mouth.

"You better be careful or I'll knock you into next week."

He raises the hand not holding me, fingers clenched in a fist. I flinch. He yanks me away from the countertop and shoves me hard. I spin and stumble backward, socked feet not finding purchase on the linoleum floor, arms windmilling. The oven door handle hits me midback, the metal hard against my spine. The momentum bounces me forward, arms outstretched, and I land oddly, bending my index and middle fingers back, hyperextending my wrist so that I hear a quiet pop and then heat and pain blaze through my hand and down my forearm. I slide to the floor, on my side, facing him.

Father cocks his leg at the knee.

I roll away from him, curl into a fetal position, hold my head in my hands. I learned that at school. Tornado drills. Turn yourself into a ball, protect your vital organs, protect your head. But my back is still exposed.

The kick strikes low, just above my kidneys.

I'm sniffling. The scream is there in my throat, trapped in the hot, wet, pulsing mass where all my words are caught too. I clench my jaw, grind my teeth, try to keep the sound contained. Showing weakness, I know, will add fuel to the fire. At some point, I must've bitten my lip. The blood tastes like I've been sucking on a rusty nail. I hold onto my skull with both hands. My back throbs. Heat radiates out from my spine. I wait for the next strike. Protect yourself. Tighten up. Hold your breath.

But no more strikes come.

He says, "You turn eighteen and you're out of this house. I can't wait for that day to come."

Then he steps over me, boots squeaking across the linoleum, laces dangling down and frayed at the ends, little clods of dirt from the soles leaving a trail behind him. He doesn't turn back. He doesn't say anything else. He just walks around the corner into the dining room and disappears behind the wall.

He's never stopped at just one. Never. He's coming back.

I push myself until I'm sitting. I suck in a sharp breath, wince at the throbbing in my back and my wrist and my fingers. I cradle my injured right hand, bend the joints this way and that. Painful but nothing broken. The knife is still on the floor, glinting dully in the low-angled late-afternoon light. My sweatshirt is dotted with tiny smears of peanut butter, so are my jeans. I scoot myself across the floor toward the countertop, grab a hold of the edge, use it to leverage myself up.

I stand there for a time, leaning, holding on to the lip of the counter, light-headed, the room faded black at the edges. In just a few seconds my blood pressure will equalize and I'll be able to move. Just a few seconds. Father won't come back in a few seconds, will he? I've got time? I can get away? Is he coming back?

I cock my head and close my eyes and listen hard.

The clock above the sink still ticks. The faucet drips in a slow rhythm. The television in the den is on now, low decibel voices talking about the weather, the unseasonable heat for spring. There's a clicking, like gears with their metal cogs catching, and I know that Father has just kicked back in the recliner, feet up, iced drink on a coaster on the side table. He's not coming back.

Hand skimming the countertop for balance, I shuffle slowly over to the peanut butter jar. I screw the lid shut, set the jar back in the cupboard. I set the plate in the sink then take the two slices of bread and limp over to the garbage can, step on the rubber pedal so the lid shoots up, and dump them inside. I bend at the knees, trying to keep my torso straight because that eases the pain, and pick up the fallen knife then set it quietly next to the plate in the sink. I wipe the countertop down, scoot the breadcrumbs into my cupped palm, blow them into the sink too. I scan: it's just like I was never here.

The television drones on, something about the raw power of electricity, lightning and discharges, completing a circuit. I turn so I can catch the reflection of my back in the sliding glass doors. I lift my sweatshirt. There's a violent scarlet mark already. Not long before it turns navy then a deep shade of purple. I find a bag of peas in the freezer, wrap it in a plaid dish towel, press it to my low back. I think: at least no one will see the bruise where it is, oversized pants and baggy shirts will cover it. I hide my body every day. I'm good at hiding things.

I am sixteen years old.

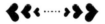

THE MOST IMPORTANT THING YOU MAY EVER LEARN ABOUT WEIGHT LOSS (& POSSIBLY LIFE IN GENERAL)

This may very well be the most important chapter in this entire book. So why is it closer to the end? Because you need to stop abusing food first so you can think clearly. Then you can learn to befriend yourself, so that you can trust yourself enough to listen to your own intuition and know without a doubt that you can take care of yourself no matter what. Then you will be to the point where you can let go and move on. And then (and only then) will you be able to do some of the most important work you may ever do by banishing your vampires. The vampires in your life are all those things that no longer serve you and are, in fact, sucking the life out of you. They can be places, sometimes things, more often people.

Know this: vampires cling. Clinging, by its very nature, leads to withering and dying. Think of a vine growing wild over everything in its path. That vine clings. It smothers. It suffocates. It chokes the life out of whatever it's clinging to. That's what's happening in your life, too. You're the unsuspecting plant. Your vampires are the vine. I'll tell you right now that it'll be easier on you if you *voluntarily* let go. If you hold on to your vampires (which many of us—sigh, yes my hand is raised—are inclined to do), well you're clinging right back. Except in that scenario, you are choking the life out of yourself. When you cling to those people, places, and/or things that no longer serve you, you risk several things:

- Destroying your own self-esteem (because you believe you need someplace, something, and/or someone to be whole).
- Giving your power away (because whatever has a hold on you has most if not all the power over your life).

- Remaining in a holding pattern, waiting on your vampire to change or give you permission or love you back or [insert what you're waiting for here] (while both time and your life continue on without much input from you).
- Draining the joy, excitement, sense of wonder, and the like out of your life (which leaves you as a husk of who you once were).
- Being emotionally decimated when the vampire and you are parted not by your choice (either by the vampire's choice or by circumstances forcing you apart).

In any of the above scenarios, you're likely to be sent spiraling out of control emotionally, leading you to abuse food and/or some other substance/behavior in an attempt to numb/avoid. My point is this: there's no scenario of clinging to your vampires or letting them continue to cling to you that ends with you healthy and whole.

I am telling you, right now and without a single doubt, that *excising your vampires is the single most important thing you can do not only for your weight loss but also for your happiness in general.* Maybe you don't understand why you keep overeating, why you're so overweight. Or why you keep purging, starving, and abusing food. From my own personal experience, I can tell you it's because of the vampires in your life, the ones that, subconsciously or not, you're trying to keep at bay.

YOUR BODY WILL TELL YOU EVERYTHING YOU NEED TO KNOW

I'm sure you know (because deep down I always did) who and what your vampires are, how to get rid of them, and most importantly when it's time to move on without them. Your intuition tells you all of that if you'll just listen.

But sometimes, you still steadfastly refuse to get rid of them. Whatever reason you may give yourself for clinging to your vampires, it all boils down to the same single thing: fear. Those vampires, even though they're sucking the life out of you, are still familiar. And people often, mistakenly, equate familiarity with safety because unfamiliarity, we tell ourselves and so believe, is uncertain and unpredictable and therefore scary.

The question you need to keep in mind and answer for each of your vampires as you work through this chapter is this: *What am I afraid is going to happen to me when I let go of this vampire?* Your answers may include things like: a loss of their love or approval or acceptance, losing a sense of belonging or being financially secure if they are the ones footing the bills, being alone, and/or that you believe you can't take care of your own self without someone else's help. Or maybe you've always lived in a certain place and done things a certain way and you just fear change. Or perhaps, it can be too that you're simply drained/exhausted/tired of trying, and so you've given up fighting for yourself. Whatever the reason, you've come this far, so I'm going to ask you to go a little bit further because if you don't save yourself from your vampires, no one else will. (Because remember: *no one is coming to fix it*.)

Again, one last but very important thing to remember: your intuition *includes both your mind and your body*. You will know the vampires in your life without a doubt by *how your body feels and reacts* when you're around them or even just thinking of them. You'll either have a psychological reaction (like nervousness, anxiety, depression, a sense of unease, helplessness, hopelessness, a feeling like you're shrinking back or trying to hide or being drained, and the like) or a physiological reaction (trembling, muscle tension, sweating, dry mouth, exhaustion, trying to make yourself smaller by physically pulling away or curling into yourself, and the like) or you may have both. Most people don't listen to what their bodies are trying, often desperately, to tell them. That, right there, is the crux of the problem. Not listening to your body is what's gotten you into trouble and into the place you find yourself now.

When you're in contact with a vampire or even just thinking about one, your body will give you cues. Here's a partial list of signs you should pay attention to:

- Do your shoulders slump forward?
- Does your chin dip toward your chest?
- Are you in a posture of defeat?
- Is there a knot or a sinking feeling in your stomach?
- Does your chest feel caved in?
- Do you feel antsy?
- Do you keep fidgeting?
- Do you continually sigh?
- Does that voice of wisdom inside your head keep saying things like: *I don't want to be here* or *I don't want to be doing this*, over and over again?
- Do you feel trapped, like you have no power and/or no choices? Or do you feel like you just can't win no matter what you do so you might as well give up?
- Is there a constant nudge inside you pushing you toward doing something else?
- Does your face get hot?
- Do you start sweating profusely?
- Is your blood pressure sky high?
- Do you have ringing in your ears?
- Do you have heart palpitations?
- Do you have knotted muscles, especially in your back?

- Do you suffer migraines or frequent upset stomach?
- Do you have a tightness in your throat like you can't breathe?
- Do you suffer from autoimmune disorders? (Now mind you, I'm not saying the vampires in your life are the sole cause of autoimmune disorders but I would certainly argue, from my layman's perspective and also personal experience, that they are a contributing factor).
- And the biggest tell of them all that a vampire has gotten a hold of you: Do you have an insatiable hunger that you can't fill no matter how much you eat and/or a cavernous hole inside you that you can't fill no matter how much you abuse food?

Of course, some of these signs can commonly be caused by medical conditions, which is why you always need to be under a physician's care for your overall health and well-being. Just know that some of these signs can also be caused by vampires sucking the life out of you. So you will have to use your intellect along with your intuition and be discerning. You will recognize the difference. *Just listen to your body and how it feels and reacts.* I assure you that your body will tell you everything you need to know if you'll just listen to it. Trust yourself. Let your instincts, your intuition, your intellect, and your body be your guides. Your body has all the wisdom you need to make the choices that are best for you. So do yourself a kindness: *trust your body and listen to it.*

VAMPIRES YOU'RE GOING TO HAVE TO BANISH FROM YOUR LIFE (A PARTIAL LIST):

- People
- Places
- Thoughts and beliefs
- Addictions
- Armor

PEOPLE

You know who these people are, I assure you that you do. When you're around them, you feel like your energy just got zapped. Your mood turns dark. You wonder why you bother trying at all. When you're with them or even just thinking about them, you'll often feel: defeated, drained, diminished, less than, not good enough, there-must-be-something-wrong-with-me, why-can't-I-do-anything-right, and on the negative emotion/reaction list goes.

People who are vampires aren't interested in what they can offer you and/or bring to a relationship. They are interested in what they can get because they desire something you have. Be assured they are in your life because they want something for themselves and they think they can gain it from you. And take and take and take is what they will do. They will take your time and energy and focus and resources and sense of well-being and on the list goes. Make no mistake, vampire people, gone unchecked, will suck you dry until you are a mere sketch of who you used to be.

Part of the reason your intuition is so vital in spotting vampires in your life is because it won't be fooled by appearances. Some vampires seem sweet and kind and nice, but their behavior toward you exposes them as a vampire. They may say nice things and still be incredibly manipulative or horribly controlling. They may do or say kind things and yet lie to you. They may offer sweet things with the full expectation of something in return. It's a vampire's behavior that you need to pay attention to and *not make excuses for*. And that's incredibly important, whether they are kind/nice/sweet vampires or mean/vindictive/competitive vampires: you'll save yourself a lot of heartache & time if you stop making excuses for other people's bad behavior and instead see them for who they really are, *the first time*.

Vampires by their very nature are oppressive, even if their actions don't seem, at first, to come off that way. They are parasites. They feed off you. Off your kindness. Off your good will. Off your sense of loyalty. Off your fears, too. You can spot a vampire if being around them makes you feel powerless in any way, if you feel that your needs and wants and issues don't matter nearly as much as theirs, if you feel like you're in some kind of jealously-fueled, unhealthy, one-upmanship competition with them, and/or if you spend your time with them counting the minutes and hoping it'll be over soon and just trying to make it through.

And finally, three easy ways to spot a vampire in your life:

1. If they lie to you (little white lies included), they are a vampire. Period.
2. If they are in any way abusive (physically, verbally, sexually, mentally/emotionally) to you, they are *always, always, always* a vampire for you.
3. The biggest tell there is: if you react to anyone by abusing food and/or some other substance(s)/behavior(s) before, during, and/or after you're with them just to tolerate the encounter, that person is *without a doubt* a vampire for you.

This category includes people who are (a partial list):

FAMILY

A vampire family member includes: meddling parents, manipulative in-laws, overbearing siblings, and any other relation who thinks they can attach themselves to you and try to control your actions or dictate terms or treat you badly or make demands or monopolize your life for their own gain. Yes, just because these people are related to you does not make them immune from being vampires in your life. In fact, more often than not, it's your family members that turn out to be the biggest vampires in your life. Why? Because familiarity breeds a feeling of safety. Your family members think that since they know you, they are safe to act like vampires around you. That your love, loyalty, sense of duty, and/or [insert some familial bond here] will keep you from standing up to them and calling them out on their life-sucking behavior. It could be they (or even you) believe that because of those familial bonds, you are somehow required to put up with their behavior and keep them in your life. There's also the tendency for family members (and maybe even you) to believe that, since you're related, you have to accept them as they are and they don't ever have to change and they get a free pass to treat you however they like.

BOSS, CO-WORKERS, AND/OR CLIENTS/CUSTOMERS

A vampire boss is one who bullies, harasses, demeans, ignores concerns, uses you as a scapegoat, asks/expects you to lie, and/or other similar disrespectful and/or illegal behavior. Vampire co-workers are the ones who gossip, take credit for work you did, don't do their own work while expecting you to take up the slack, harass, intimidate, and/or other diminishing behavior. Vampire clients/customers are the ones who scream as they demand you meet their needs, are in a state of emergency most of the time, show little respect for you or your time, become irate easily, don't pay you on time, expect you to work for a deep discount/free, and/or other similar behaviors.

FRIENDS

Vampire friends (and I use the term "friends" quite loosely here) take more than they give, are self-absorbed, expect you to do all the work to maintain the relationship, are jealous of you, are not genuinely happy for you when good things come your way, dump their problems on you and expect you to listen/help but don't reciprocate, will not step up when you need them, have a lot of excuses without much action, add you to their list of friends then care more about the number of friends they can boast about rather than actually building a relationship with you, let you be the one to buy all the time, and other similar behaviors. Vampire friends are not really your friends regardless of what they may say to the contrary; they are in it for them, not for you.

BOYFRIEND, GIRLFRIEND, AND/OR SPOUSE

Vampire significant others take you for granted, blame you for their bad behaviors, don't put you at or even near the top of their priority list, cheat on you, lie to you, and the like. These are some of the most dangerous vampires there are because they will suck the life out of you with your permission; that's because you love them (or so you tell yourself) and so you stay. You even tilt your head and expose your neck. You don't run away screaming when their fangs hit your jugular. You don't even fight back. Instead, maybe you just close your eyes and think this is how love should be or this is the best that you deserve or it's not as bad as being alone or he/she needs you or [insert the reason you stay here], and so you just passively wait for their feeding on you to be over. This is especially true if you've been in the relationship for any length of time and you've been repeatedly drained by them.

ACQUAINTANCES AND STRANGERS

Vampire acquaintances and strangers attack you (verbally, physically, or otherwise), try to take you down a peg to build themselves up, believe they are better than you, scheme and/or con you, manipulate and/or control you, and other similar egregious behaviors. A special note on this one: your intuition will primarily be your guide with acquaintances and strangers. You may have a physiological reaction; however, you're more likely to get a gut feeling that something about them is not quite right. Your inner voice of wisdom will tell you to steer clear of them. Often, you can feel something (anger, neediness, power-hungry, a desire to dominate/manipulate, and the like) coming off them. You may just feel a general unease around them, something you can't quite put your finger on but that you don't trust about them. I can't say it strongly enough: *listen to yourself the first time, trust your instincts the first time!* Have no doubt that these people are vampires. Trust yourself then run fast and far away from them.

Some helpful tips:

- Do not, under any circumstances, doubt yourself when your intuition tells you that someone is a vampire for you.
- Do not, under any circumstances, make excuses for the behavior of vampires. When vampires show their true nature, *believe them the first time*, and do not give them a pass or another chance or invite them to stick around in your life. If you choose to make excuses for them, they will latch on and start sucking the life out of you. Once that happens, you'll have a much harder time freeing yourself from their grasp. I assure you that you'll save yourself a lot of days/weeks/years, energy, and feelings of helplessness/hopelessness if you recognize your vampires for what they truly are when they show you.
- Often, we stay in relationship with vampires out of fear. No matter the excuse you use to justify why you remain in the relationship with a vampire, the underlying motive is fear. And that fear will keep your vampire latched onto you and/or you onto the vampire until you do something to break the cycle. In the end, your vampires will drain you because that's their nature. Make no mistake, it's what vampires do. There's no point in fighting it. No point in trying to stick around and change them. No point in believing time will change them either or your love will heal them or if you just wish hard enough that they will be different. They won't be different unless they choose to change (and that's a BIG *unless*). You, however, will be changed—and not in a good way—by staying. That's why you have to let them go *now*.
- When you do let them go, you will probably feel like you've just dropped an overstuffed suitcase that you've been hauling around. You will likely feel: relief, freedom, and/or that you can finally take a rest and breathe. You will also probably finally feel like you can be yourself, be the person you want and were meant to be.
- And, as always, remember to check your motivation. You are living your life *for you*. You are saving your own life *for you*. So it doesn't matter what your vampires (or anyone else, for that matter) thinks of you, wants from you, wishes you would do, hopes for you, and on the list goes. Their opinions are none of your business. What is your business is this: figuring out what *you* want from your life and *healing yourself* so you can be whole.

What to do if you want to salvage the relationship and make it a healthy one:

1. Your best course of action is to have a conversation (polite but firm) with them in person, on the phone, or in a letter about how you feel.
2. Tell them what you're willing to accept or no longer accept from them.

3. Let them know how you need their behavior toward you to change.
4. Just know this going in:
   - You cannot demand, expect, hope, and/or wish that they will change; all you can do is ask.
   - You will not be able to change them; they must change themselves.
   - You need to have zero expectation that they will agree.
   - You are drawing a line around yourself to protect yourself, that is your boundary; you will only save your own life by enforcing your own boundary.
   - If they don't respect your boundaries and change their behavior, you need to be prepared to not back down; if they will not change, you will let them go and you will move on without them.

What to do if you can't muster the courage to communicate with them:

1. Don't feel guilty about it because that happens to all of us—including me.
2. Know this: you still need to let them go.
3. Remember: you will never be able to do the same thing over and over and get different results, so you need to be the one to break the pattern and leave the relationship and move on without them.
4. Cut off communication and get them out of your life entirely.
5. Be strong and do not go running back. There may be familiarity in what you know but there is not wholeness, I assure you of that. You may choose to revisit the relationship later, not running back out of desperation or need but returning to the relationship when you are in a better mental/emotional place. Or you may choose never to return to it. That's a choice that's entirely up to you.
6. Always remember: you are leaving the relationship(s) to save your own life. If they don't respect your boundaries and change their behavior, you need to be prepared to not back down; if they will not change, you will let them go and you will move on without them.

In either scenario (communicate with them or don't), you need to decide what you're willing to live with and what you're not, then make choices based on that decision. Always keep in mind that if being around or even thinking about your vampire(s) leads you to abuse food and/or other substances/behaviors to numb yourself, that's not living, that's surviving. And you deserve more out of your life (the only one you'll ever get, by the way) than to just survive it day-by-day.

What to do when you just cannot get your vampire(s) out of your life entirely:

You may run into these vampire people at work or where you live or at family functions or elsewhere. Remember: you still (and *always*) have choices.

1. Limit, to the best of your ability, the amount of time you spend with them.
2. Do something that gives you joy, that nourishes and fulfills you (not numbs you), *before* you have contact with them.
3. Do something that gives you joy, that nourishes and fulfills you (not numbs you), *after* you have contact with them, too.
4. Make your boundaries clear by stating them aloud (and remember *no* is a complete sentence: *No.*) then stand firm and defend those boundaries.
5. Always remember: you are worth taking excellent care of yourself, which includes both your physical health and your mental health, too.

What to do if you are somebody's vampire:

Sorry to say that it likely happens to all of us at some point in our lives: we chase after someone, desperately trying to get something from them, including: approval, security, praise, admiration, love, favors, and on the list goes. You, yourself, are exhibiting vampire behavior if you hang around someone with the motivation that you want them to be proud of you or say they love you or show you that you're worthwhile or in some way gain something you want from them. If you are latching onto someone, trying to get your needs met, you are a vampire and, in that state, you will never be healthy and whole.

So do this:
1. Own up to the fact that you're being a vampire.
2. Stop the behavior that's sucking the life both out of them and out of you, too (even if you don't realize it).
3. Apologize and change your ways if you want to salvage the relationship.
4. Wish them well and let them go if you can't/won't change the relationship dynamics because a life-sucking relationship is never good for anyone involved.
5. Resolve to stand on your own two feet and stop searching for anyone else to be your life source because, remember, *no one is coming to fix it.*

6. Then be compassionate (kind, gentle, and patient) with yourself and do not beat yourself up for the vampire behavior (which you will change, see Step 5 above) that cost you the relationship.

PLACES

Certain places can be vampires for you, too. You will know them by listening to your body. If you show up somewhere and start to feel sad, lonely, panicked, confined, suffocated, fearful, and the like, then you know that place is a vampire for you. When you find yourself in a vampire place, your body may react in a way that leaves you feeling like a weight is sitting on your chest or you may start trembling or your mouth may go dry. Just being in certain places can make your energy level drop and your anxiety level rise. That's especially true of certain places that were the location of bad memories for you. Places, maybe, where you felt small and powerless. Or where you were abused or attacked or hurt in some way. Or where you felt boxed-in by the environment around you. When you're in vampire places, you don't feel refreshed and rejuvenated. Instead, you feel defeated and diminished. You ask yourself questions like: *Why am I back here?* and/or *Why can't I ever break free?* And again, as always, the biggest tell of them all: being in vampire places will make you want to abuse food and/or other substances/behaviors to numb yourself from the discomfort you feel just being there.

You may stay in those places out of loyalty, familiarity, habit, family ties, because you just don't like change, and/or you listened to bad advice, just to name a few reasons. But, in the end, all of it boils down to fear. Fear of venturing out into the unknown. Fear of trusting yourself and your own instincts. Fear that you aren't strong enough to handle whatever comes your way. Fear of claiming your own power and putting yourself first. Fear of this. Fear of that. Fear of the other thing. The list of fears can be seemingly endless.

But forcing yourself to stay in a place that is a vampire for you will hurt you, *not* heal you. You may have heard the advice that you should remain where you are because a geographical cure won't work. Those misguided people argue that wherever you go, you and all your problems are still there. Know this: that is some of the worst advice I've ever been given. Fortunately, I didn't listen to it. You shouldn't either. Here's why: while it's true that you will always be there no matter where you go, not all of your problems will be. In fact, if you're suffering by being in a vampire place, I'd argue that one of your biggest problems—namely that vampire place—will be gone. If you're spending the majority of your time in a place that makes you feel unhappy, trapped, unimportant, dead inside, and the list goes on, then know this: you will more than likely have a negative outlook every single day. If you remain in a location where you are miserable, you will never wake up excited about your life, ever. Instead, you will drudge through your days wondering why you are stuck there, why you're not moving forward, why you are not where you want to be.

On the other hand, if you change locations and spend the majority of your time in a place you love (or even like a lot more), your attitude will become more positive and you will improve both your entire outlook and your life for the better. A world of possibilities really will open up for you because you will feel more alive. When you feel more alive, I would argue, you naturally say *yes* to more opportunities, you say *yes* to those things that bring you joy, you say *yes* to believing in hope and unlimited tries.

Keep in mind: running from one location to another will not magically fix your problems. No, it surely will not. Most of your problems will still be there. But if you find a place where you feel happier and more at ease, you'll come to find that many of your problems aren't as important or as big as they seemed before. Escaping from a vampire place will begin healing you in a way that makes the problems in your life more manageable. Escaping from a vampire place will give you a perspective that you just can't get when you feel stuck and unhappy by being somewhere that you just don't like, that makes you feel like you just don't belong there, and/or that sucks you back into a life you just don't want to be living. That last one—sucks you back in—is especially important if being in a certain place(s) where you used to abuse food and/or other substances/behaviors makes you want to resume abusing them whenever you return to that place. Escaping from a vampire place will also free you from dogma (which, again, is what other people wish you would do or how others think you should live your life) and help you figure out just who you are and what you want from your own life. I know all this because that's what happened for me.

Again, as *always*, listen to your body. Pay attention to how you feel and how your body reacts when you arrive in certain places, how you feel and react while you're there, and also how you feel and react when you leave. You'll know your vampire places easily if you'll just be mindful and honor your body as your guide. If you don't believe me, try an experiment and do this:

1. When you're in a calm emotional state, pick a place where you know you don't like to be.
2. Go there.
3. Hang out for a while.
4. Pay attention to how your body feels. (Does your chest constrict? Your throat tighten? Your muscles tense, ready to run? Your energy and/or excitement levels plummet? Do you feel more expansive and/or free when you finally leave? And the like.)
5. The answers (your body's reactions) will tell you everything you need to know.

Whatever the situation, you are not being true to yourself—and so not honoring/respecting yourself and thereby betraying yourself—by remaining in a place that's a vampire for you. Know this without a doubt: you will never be healthy and whole by steadfastly refusing to leave a place that drains the life from you.

This category includes places where you (a partial list):

LIVE

A vampire place to live is one that drains you instead of nourishes you. This one needs to be addressed first because, usually, you're in the place where you live the vast majority of the time. Maybe you love the city but you live in the country. Maybe you love the mountains but live where the terrain is as flat as a dinner plate. Maybe you love the ocean and the sound of waves crashing against the shore but you live in the dry, arid desert. Maybe it's not even that extreme: maybe you love having space and your own big yard and you live in a tiny housing development or in an apartment crammed right next to your neighbor. Maybe you like solitude and quiet and you're living with roommates who like to party. It could be, too, that you like neatness/order and you live in clutter/chaos. Or even the color scheme and/or decor of your home is simply not your taste or to your liking and you won't make the effort to do something (even a little something) about it.

WORK

A vampire place to work is one that diminishes you the longer you stay there. You shrivel with each day you show up at your job. You need to address this one next because it's likely the second place where you spend the most time. Maybe you work in a factory but you'd much rather be outdoors. Maybe you work in a competitive environment but you'd rather collaborate with your colleagues. Maybe you work in a simple, undemanding job but know you're capable of so much more if only you had more challenges. Maybe you're an introvert who'd rather be working alone somewhere in a back corner and you find yourself regularly working in partnership with others. Or maybe you're an extrovert who thrives around others and you find yourself working alone in a cubicle. Maybe you're in a job that plays to your weaknesses and not your strengths, and so you end up feeling overwhelmed and not-up-to-the-task every day that you show up to work. Or maybe you work at a job that gives you no fulfillment whatsoever and you drudge through every single day. Maybe you just plain don't like what you do and you'd rather make your passion into your profession instead.

VISIT

A vampire place to visit is usually one that either directly holds some kind of bad memories for you or it reminds you of a bad memory. When you go there, you relive events from your past. You feel smaller, stuck, less than, not good enough, powerless, and/or similar emotions. It's likely a place where something traumatic or with a lot of emotion attached happened to you. Maybe it's a house/community where you grew up. Or a place you once lived/stayed. Or a school you attended. Or a cemetery where someone you once cared about is buried. Or somewhere you were attacked, humiliated, shamed, bullied, and/or the like. It's also possible that the vampire place you visit has a good feeling attached to it, perhaps you felt happiness and joy as compared to your life today, and going back to that place makes you yearn and wish that you could go back to the way your life was in that moment of time.

The only requirement for the places you visit to be a vampire for you is that they cause you to get stuck emotionally so that you find it difficult if not impossible to let go of that place, move on, and move forward in your own life. It's likely that when you go that place, you will feel again however you felt at the moment you were there in the past. And it's the feelings that you're experiencing again along with the belief that you're stuck now that make you want to abuse food and/or other substances/behaviors for relief. Maybe you visit those places because you have to pass by them on the way to somewhere else. Or you return because you're going to visit someone who is there. Or you show up in those places again because you feel like something inside you got broken there and you're just trying to heal it. (Just know this: you won't be healed by going back. I know because I've tried. You will only be healed by going forward.)

PLAY

A vampire place to play seems like an oxymoron but it isn't. They are places where you're supposed to be having fun, letting loose, relaxing, rejuvenating, and being yourself, but instead you feel drained. Maybe you like rock-climbing but find yourself vacationing at the beach. Maybe you want to relax by going fishing but get talked into going to a nightclub instead. Maybe you love reading in a quiet nook but nobody will leave you alone long enough to get through a chapter so you give up and go do what they want. Maybe you love the outdoors and end up at the mall. Or maybe the opposite, you love shopping and find yourself hiking up a mountain instead. This also includes places that might seem like a way to play (or a way to relax and unwind) but actually end up sucking you back into abusing substances/behaviors and into a life you don't want to be living.

CREATE

A vampire place to create is one that zaps your creativity instead of nurturing it. You feel siphoned instead of energized, defeated instead of encouraged, doubt instead of excitement. All of us are creative. Period. You don't have to call yourself an artist to be a creator. You're creating a life for yourself every day with every choice you make. You're creating joy for yourself with the hobbies and interests you pursue. You're creating relationships with the people you hang out with. You're creating a vision for who you want to be and the kind of life you want to have every single day by the actions you take.

It's hard to be creative, I assure you, if you're in a place that doesn't support and nourish it. Maybe you're an extrovert and need to be around people to get your creative juices flowing but you won't step out to find a group where you belong. Maybe you're an introvert and need to be in a tucked-away space and left alone to be your most creative but you won't find the time and/or space to do that. Maybe you would love to have a little room of your own just for creative work but you won't make the space. Maybe you have a dark/dingy creative space and you love spaces to be bright/sunny but you won't make a change to get yourself what you need. Maybe your space is just crammed full of clutter, which simply exhausts you by its sheer volume, and you end up overwhelmed, don't know where to start, and so you don't ever start, you just avoid instead of taking the time to organize and throw things out.

What to do if you find yourself in a vampire place:

1. First and foremost, when you're in any vampire-place situation, honor yourself by listening to your body and trusting that your body would never lie to you.
2. Then respect yourself by meeting *your actual* preferences and *your actual* wants and *your actual* needs, NOT ones that you think, believe, and/or tell yourself that you should have or that others might choose for you.
3. Either use your voice to make your preferences known or take your own action so changes can occur in the place to make it more hospitable to you.
4. If changes don't occur, leave.
5. Don't force yourself to stay somewhere that drains you. Don't discount how your body feels or make excuses or talk yourself into remaining there or tell yourself it's not so bad or anything else that diminishes your trust in yourself. Simply choose to leave places that drain you, cause you to feel dead inside, and/or make you feel like you're living a life you don't want. Don't go back.

6. Then go to places that make you happier and more fulfilled. Hang out there instead.
7. If you're unhappy, drained, defeated, exhausted, stuck, and/or the like when you go to certain places, then choose differently. The choice is always (*always, always*) up to you.

A note about making excuses

I'm of the belief that you can either: 1. make excuses or 2. make it happen. So if you're justifying why you stay in vampire situations—perhaps, you argue, you don't have the money, time, resources, knowledge, skills, etc. to help yourself out of the situation you're in—then understand two things: 1. that is your choice, and 2. that is also an excuse. You will never be empowered by making excuses.

A note about fear

Fear of the unknown and/or of something new is not a legitimate excuse to stay trapped in a place that sucks the life from you. Like we talked about in Chapter Three, the only legitimate (real) fear is the one that actually endangers your life. If changing your location doesn't endanger your life, then the fear you feel, I say kindly, is just in your head. What that means to you is that you can experiment and change locations to see how your body reacts/feels. You can do that over and over until you find a place you love and/or one that feels like home to you. You will find the place where you most belong (oh yes, you will), and you will know it when you do.

And another important note: I would argue, from my own personal experience, that remaining in a vampire place too long actually does endanger your life or, at a bare minimum, the quality of your life both physically (ailments, immune dysfunctions, migraines, and the list goes on) and mentally (sadness, depression, powerlessness, and that list goes on, too).

A note about money and empowerment

Money, or lack thereof, can be a challenge but not an excuse. Maybe you can't afford to relocate or redecorate right now. That doesn't mean you can't hit a few thrift stores (yes, I am a fan!) for some new-to-you furnishings, or cut back on a few things that aren't necessities to buy things you love, or start saving a little every paycheck so that soon you'll be able to move to a place you really want to be. Once you start taking action, you'll see that: 1. you empower yourself, 2. your attitude will improve, and 3. I daresay, events in your life will start aligning to get you out of the place where you are and into a place where you will thrive. Here's the kicker though: you have to be the one to stop making excuses, take the first step, then be open and say *yes* to opportunities that come to you.

A note about creating hope and a vision

I'd suggest that you cut some pictures out of magazines of places you love and tack them to a corkboard and leave that board where you'll see it every day. Every time you look at that board (even if it's a glance as you walk past), you throw as much positive energy at it as you can (you think: *I'll get there, I'll have that, yes I will*) and get busy working toward visiting and/or living in the places pictured there. Why does this matter? Because hope and a vision—which we'll talk about in the next chapter—are the best motivators to change.

A note about situational depression

According to my family doctor, there's such a thing as situational depression. The fastest way to this kind of depression is to spend too much time in a place that you dislike.[1] The longer you choose to stay (and yes, I say kindly, it is a choice), the harder it will be to leave because that place will drain, exhaust, and/or demotivate you and leave you abusing food and/or other substances/behaviors in an attempt to combat the depression. You may even give up entirely and let the depression take over, which will leave you powerless while you wait for your situation, your (perceived) helplessness, and/or your life to just be over.

I know all this from personal experience because I chose to live in a place I hated, I stayed there for far too long, and that's what happened to me. Know this: the way out of situational depression is through taking action, at least it was for me. Change your location. Find places you love. Come alive again. It is quite possible that changing your geographical location is the main thing you need to do to help yourself heal.

THOUGHTS AND BELIEFS

We talked about this in-depth before, but it's so important that we're going to talk about it again because letting go of thoughts and beliefs that don't serve you will have an enormous impact on changing your life. Remember: beliefs are simply thoughts that you've repeated to yourself over and over again; they can be changed. Here are two of the truest things I know: 1. you are what you believe you are, and 2. you will live out what you believe.

If you're not sure what you believe about yourself, listen to the language you use when you talk about yourself. Do this:

- Finish this sentence right now: *I am [fill in the blank].*

Whatever follows the words *I am* is what you believe about yourself. Did you finish that sentence with words like: fat, ugly, unhappy, a failure, lost, worthless, useless, conforming, small, trapped, alone, not good enough, and on the negative list goes? Or did you finish it with words like: strong, powerful, courageous, growing, awesome, learning who I am, discovering my way, successful, hopeful, beautiful, gifted, talented, worthwhile, priceless, and on the positive list goes? Likewise, listen to the language you use when you talk about your life, your chances, your place in the world, and the like. I assure you that the answers matter because what you believe is exactly what you're going to live out in your life. It's all the negative things you believe that are the vampires, sucking the life right out of you.

In short, you will not be your authentic self in all those moments when you're living within the confines of thoughts and beliefs that no longer serve you. Instead, you'll be playing a role either for the benefit of others (because you hope to gain something from them) or for the benefit of yourself (you hide your real self behind the belief so you don't have to risk being vulnerable). You will also never rise above the belief to become who and what you most want to be, to become who you are meant to be, unless you challenge the truth of what you believe.

Remember: your subconscious is really what's running the show, making adjustments to your behaviors and influencing your choices all the time. What you think and believe resides in your subconscious, too. Beliefs, whether you are conscious of them or not, guide your brain. Your brain, in turn, guides your body, telling your muscles to perform movements (some even minuscule) that you may not even be aware of but that have a huge impact on the outcome of your life. Again, just like thoughts, beliefs are simply electrical impulses that travel through your brain, and those electrical impulses can be changed.

If you want to lose the weight and keep it off permanently, if you want to stop abusing food, you're going to have to remake yourself. You're going to have to become somebody new. The good news is that new person is the one you've always wanted to be, the one who isn't pretending to be someone they're not or striving to be someone else. You're going to grow comfortable in your own skin and thrive as who you are. You're going to learn that you are and always have been enough as-is. You're going to find the peace and contentment you've been searching for. And how do you go about remaking yourself? You start by changing what you believe, especially those beliefs that are vampires for you. You'll know a vampire belief because it narrows your prospects, categorizes you, and boxes you into a certain self-definition, and then you live out your life limited by the confines of that box. You cannot grow and expand if you have sides and a lid holding you back.

This category includes beliefs in the form of (a partial list):

LABELS

According to the dictionary, a label is either a single word or a phrase used to classify a person, particularly if it is untrue or constraining.[2] Labels have connotations (the moment you hear them, you know what they mean) and social norms (the moment you hear them, you have an opinion as to what's expected of them).

Negative labels often get hurled at you by others, pinning you to the spot like a spear. They also tend to stick, tacked in your memory like a notecard nailed to a wall. They are things like: fat, ugly, stupid, untalented, worthless, needy, moody, clingy, bossy, and on the list goes. They usually have their origins in things other people have said to/about you with words or you inferred about yourself from their actions. You end up mulling those labels over and over in your mind. Eventually, you start using them on yourself, and in that way, the labels drain you.

Labels can also have the air of being positive. Things like: cheerful, generous, sympathetic, outgoing, helpful, and the like. You might think the positive labels are better. While they are likely not as harmful to your emotional well-being, I'd argue that they still put you in the confines of a box. For example, if you believe yourself to be a cheerful person and you want others to see you that way, then it's entirely likely that when you feel lousy and grumpy, you will instead put on a cheerful front, tweak your actions and responses to make yourself come off as cheerful, and make sure that when you interact with anyone, you respond with a smile that you are *fine, just fine* as you cram yourself into the box that label requires.

You can also label yourself, seeing yourself not as a diverse person with a myriad of talents and skills but as a limited person confined to one thing or another. You, too, may label yourself with the diminishing/derogatory terms mentioned earlier and/or with the ones with the positive air. Or you may label yourself by your profession or by your family role or by something that means a great deal to you and the list goes on. The problem comes in when you allow that label to become your (sometimes sole) identity and then you limit yourself based on the connotations and social norms of that label.

In every case, you'll have to either choose to reject the label and believe something new (in the case of the negative ones) or choose to stop letting the labels confine you (in the case of the positive ones and the ones you use to identify yourself).

JUDGMENTS

According to the dictionary, a judgment is an opinion or evaluation about what someone believes or proclaims.[3] Know this: judgments are not always based on facts. An opinion, yours or someone else's, isn't necessarily the truth. Remember your limbic system from Chapter Three: *what you believe to be truth has more to do with what you feel about the statement rather than its actual veracity.* That means this: a judgment is only true for you if you feel that it is. So in short, judgments are conclusions that you've come to based on what you feel to be true and what you believe.

Judgments tend to come from an event that happened. They can come from others. Maybe someone once told you that you're not good at your profession and instead of questioning their opinion, you decided they were right. And the judgment became something like: *I am bad at what I do, I should find other work.* Or maybe someone rejected you and said they didn't like what you had to offer and you took that to heart. So the judgment became: *I am not worthwhile, I'll never amount to anything.* Maybe someone treated you badly and instead of deciding something was wrong with them, you decided something must be wrong with you. And the judgment became: *I am bad and I don't deserve to be treated well.*

Judgments can also come from yourself. Perhaps you cut yourself off from others then decided that nobody would ever want to be around you. Then the judgment became something along the lines of: *No one likes me, I am not lovable.* Or maybe you compared yourself and your life to someone else's and decided that you fell short. Then the judgment became: *I am less than and I will never be enough.* Or perhaps you stepped out to try something and you failed, possibly even publicly and/or humiliatingly. Then the judgment became: *See, I am a failure and I will never succeed.*

You internalize the judgment, repeat it on a regular basis, and let it be part of the story you tell yourself about who you are. Then because it's *your* story and what *you* believe, you live your life inside the confines of that judgment every day. You must reject, which is always your choice, any judgment that doesn't serve to help you heal, move forward, and/or grow.

THINGS YOU WERE TAUGHT

Things you were taught come from another person (either through repeated words or actions) whom you either loved or cared for a great deal and/or who was an authority figure to you. These people may or may not have had your best interests at heart when they were teaching you. They also may have taught you incorrectly because they, themselves, didn't know any better. Because you already had some emotional connection and/

or because you thought they knew more than you, you chose to internalize what they said and/or did. If you repeated those teachings to yourself, which you likely did, then those teachings became the beliefs that drive your choices and behavior.

These beliefs may have been meant to help you navigate your life because that's how whomever taught you understood the world themselves. But that does not make what they taught you true. Keep in mind: the person who taught you had fears and limitations of their own that colored both how they saw the world and also the knowledge that they passed along.

Vampire things you were taught may include beliefs like: life is suffering, everyone hates their job, money is an indicator of your self-worth and/or money is evil, certain classes of people are inferior to others, appearance and/or social status matters more than a person's character, gender roles and what's expected of a man and of a woman, a scarcity mentality where there's just not enough to go around, and on the list goes.

And if the beliefs you were taught aren't helping you take the action you need to in your life, aren't helping strengthen you, aren't helping you reach for and achieve a life you love, then the only thing those false beliefs are doing is keeping you tethered inside a box of someone else's making.

THINGS YOU WERE TOLD OR OVERHEARD

Things you were told or overhead are accepted as the truth because you were told with enough force, authority, and/or repetition that you didn't question what you were hearing. You didn't investigate and decide for yourself. These things might seem innocuous the first time you hear them. There might even be a little grain of truth inside the bigger lie. That's how these thoughts and beliefs suck you in and trap you. You recognize that little glimmer of truth and then, wrongly I'm sorry to say, apply that truth to the whole statement.

You may have heard and believed something like: *this is not what you're meant to be doing because it's hard for you.* Grain of truth: you are likely playing to your weaknesses instead of your strengths in some area, so yes, certain aspects of what you're choosing to do may be hard. Here's the lie: you're not good at any of it and it's all supposed to be easy (and then the next thought: so you should just quit). Or maybe you heard this one: *there's so much competition, how are you going to stand out, you should just give up now.* Grain of truth: there's a lot of competition in most areas of business. Here's the lie: there's not enough to go around (the scarcity mentality) and so you'll have to knock somebody else out of the running to get your share, and if you're not ready to dig in and start shoving your way through then you should just quit now. Or how about this: *you don't have what it takes to have/be/do/say what you want, that's for others and not for you.* Grain of truth: you will need courage and tenacity, you will have to work for what you want, and you won't be able to go it entirely alone. The big lie: others have some special quality that you don't possess and they have gifts, talents, skills, and/or good ideas whereas you don't, so you should just slink back into your comfort zone and stay there.

Always remember: when people (including me) say anything, that information is coming through a filter of their own experiences, including their own beliefs (which may or may not be accurate and true). You need to question, *always*, if what you're being told holds true for how you want to see the world or how you want to experience your life. It's vitally necessary, and also completely up to you, to reject those things that limit and confine you so that you can grow.

THINGS YOU CHOSE (AND STILL CHOOSE) TO BELIEVE

You decided (and continue to decide) that the thoughts you had were undeniably true. You replayed them over and over in your mind so they became your beliefs. Now, probably because you don't like change, you keep hanging on to these beliefs and letting them suck the life right out of you.

This category is especially important if the beliefs were ones that may have once been true at the time when you decided to believe them (just you accepting reality) but then you extrapolated them into the future so they became the limits you put on your life. You can recognize these beliefs because they often have *always* or *never* in them and they lead to a defeatist mentality, which makes you not even want to step out and try.

They include beliefs like (a partial list):

- I am overweight/bulimic/anorexic right now and always will be.
- This is the way it/I/life is right now and will always be. I will never overcome.
- I don't know how to do this right now and never will understand it.
- I am not skilled enough right now and never will be.
- I am not where I want to be right now and I will never get there.

These beliefs no longer serve you. They just don't. They are, instead, keeping you in a tiny little prison of your own making, one that you will never leave unless you use the key, which you already have. What's the key? You choose to stop believing those things that no longer serve you and instead you choose to believe something new that will actually help you. Remember: all you have to do to change your beliefs is to change the thoughts that you focus on and repeat. You always have choices, and those choices are always up to you. (Important note: *always* and *never* as part of empowering statements are great to believe).

What to do if you find yourself entertaining vampire thoughts and beliefs:

1. Remake yourself. You go from an overweight person to a thinner person or someone who abuses food to someone who uses food simply as fuel, by changing what you believe.
2. Know this: if you don't excise vampire thoughts and beliefs, you'll likely continue sabotaging yourself even if you don't necessarily realize why.
3. Change your mind. Simply make some edits if you don't like what you believe about yourself, about life, and/or about the world and your place in it.
4. Go somewhere quiet where you can be alone to focus and reflect. Listen for your intuition to guide your answers.
5. Write down beliefs you hold about yourself.
6. Add to that list as other beliefs come up.
7. Challenge each those beliefs. For every one, ask: *Is this true? Do I want it to be true for me?*
8. Reject beliefs that drain you. Accept beliefs that heal you. That choice is always up to you.
9. Then ask questions like these: *What do I want to believe about myself? What is true for me? What beliefs will help me move forward and grow?*
10. Write down a list of beliefs that you would rather believe instead.
11. Remember: you're creating neural pathways in your brain all the time. Your beliefs are simply neural pathways that you made by thinking the same thoughts over and over. Neuroplasticity (how your brain is malleable and can change) means you can form new and healthier beliefs any time you choose just by repeatedly thinking those new beliefs instead.
12. And remember this too: you're always in control of what you choose to believe.
13. Tack that list of new beliefs somewhere that you will read it daily.
14. Know this too: you may say/think/write new positive beliefs about yourself and tell yourself that you're full of it. But what you want to believe about yourself matters. Even if those beliefs don't feel true to you at all at this very moment.
15. Then think those new beliefs repeatedly, *especially when you feel drained.* Repeat, repeat, repeat because you turn a thought into a belief through repetition.
16. Now take action as if those new beliefs are already true for you.
17. Find your voice and use it. Repeat (*repeat, repeat*) those new thoughts and actions until that list becomes the beliefs that you hold about yourself. If you repeat a thought enough *and act it out in your life*, then that thought will become a belief that is true for you. I know because that's what happened for me. I assure you that if you keep repeating thoughts and reinforcing them with action, eventually those thoughts will become your beliefs.

18. Know this also: when your conscious and subconscious thoughts and beliefs are in sync, your life will move in the direction you want it to go with a whole lot less effort on your part. It may take some time to change what you believe, yes, but it will happen.

ADDICTIONS

Addictions, in whatever form, are dangerous and life-sucking vampires because your entire existence will eventually, if you don't do something to stop it, revolve around the addiction to the exclusion of everything else. Gone are your passions and hopes and dreams. Gone are your goals and wants. Gone are your relationships and genuine connection to other people. Gone is the connection to your own rational mind and intuition. Gone is everything that matters to you and in its place is the addiction.

It's entirely possible that the addiction you may find yourself trapped inside started innocently enough. Maybe it was just a bad habit that, left unchecked, grew into an addiction. Or maybe you decided to experiment, not fully understanding that you'd be physiologically hooked after the first or second hit. If you're addicted, you'll know it because whatever substance/behavior you use/do, you won't be able to stop or even slow down on your own terms. It's entirely possible that you may have convinced yourself that you are the master of your own life and you don't have an addiction at all. You may tell yourself that you just like to take the edge off. Or you can quit whenever you want. Or it can't be that bad because everybody does it. Or nobody is going to tell you how many beers, cigarettes, cupcakes, and/or [add your substance of choice here] you can consume. Or maybe your drug of choice is actually a behavior like abusing shopping, sex, dependency on others, and/ or [insert your out-of-control behavior here]. Make no mistake: when you are addicted, you are master of nothing. You are enslaved to the addiction. And in that way, the vampire of addiction sinks its fangs deep into your jugular while you close your eyes, go limp, and let it.

To start, addictions change the chemical makeup of your brain, specifically with regards to dopamine, which is the biochemical that makes you feel good. When someone has an addiction, that person's brain reduces the amount of dopamine it naturally produces on its own, which is why they end up craving whatever substance/behavior will produce dopamine and make them feel good. To add to that, the brain also changes by limiting the amount of nerve receptors that receive pleasure signals, which results in a person needing to abuse more of a substance to achieve the same effect as before (known as building up a tolerance).[4] From personal experience, I've found the same to be true of behaviors: it takes more food/shopping/sex/etc. to get that same high, escape, numbness, and/or the like. Next, addiction has been shown to activate the part of your brain that senses danger, which can cause you to feel anxiety when you're not abusing a substance/behavior. When that happens, you will end up abusing a substance/behavior not for the pleasurable experience of it but to stave off the feelings of stress and anxiousness you feel.[5] And finally, especially with substance abuse, the feedback loops (that we talked about earlier) are disrupted because some substances interfere with the electrical and chemical impulses cells use to communicate with each other and with the brain.[6] All that to say: that's how an addiction can start out innocently enough and turn into a raging vortex that swallows your entire life. And that's true whether you're ingesting a substance or abusing a behavior.

Eventually, you'll also get emotionally attached to the addiction and you end up claiming the addiction for yourself. You tell yourself a story that it is *your* addiction—it's part of you, just who you are—and you need it to prop you up, to make it through the day, to help you survive. And because you live out what you believe, and your beliefs come from the thoughts and the story you repeatedly tell yourself, the addiction has free reign over your life. At that point, the addiction has become your master; you answer to it. Period. I assure you that's true. Eventually, if you do nothing to help yourself, you'll reach a point where you'll care more about feeding the addiction than you will about your friends, family, neighbors, kids, spouse, job, finances, and/or yourself.

There are many people, including scientists and healthcare professionals, who believe addicted people have a disease. Brain science has shown that repeated substance abuse inhibits activity in the part of your brain used for making decisions, meaning you'll keep abusing the substance regardless of how bad the consequences are for you.[7] However, my opinion, which comes from decades of my own personal experience, is this: *I don't believe addicted people have a disease; I believe they have a choice.*

Like I said before, if you start believing it's not your fault that you're in the mess you're in, well, then you won't work real hard to get yourself out. If you tell yourself you have a disease, you'll get in the mindset that there's not much you can do about it. You won't be motivated to make the changes you need to make to stop the addiction and heal yourself of its cause. (And the cause, as you've been reading throughout this book, is *never* about the substance/behavior itself; the cause is *always* some underlying issue that you don't want to face.) The other problem, I've found, with believing that addiction is a disease is that you tend to just swap one addiction with another then justify that behavior because, well, you have a disease and you just can't help yourself. Again, that makes you a victim, and victim equals powerless, which is not what you ever want to be. Powerless means you'll end up waiting around for someone else to be an authority over you and come fix you and your life. And that's just wasted time because as you already know: *no one is coming to fix it.* To illustrate, this was me before: smoked nearly two packs of cigarettes a day, drank alcohol until I was drunk on a regular basis, bulimic and sometimes anorexic and binge eater who at one point weighed 304 pounds, shopping until I was in debt over my head, clinging to people to make myself feel better. Had I convinced myself that I had a disease and it just wasn't my fault, I'd probably still be doing most, if not all, of those things. Now, I don't do any of them.

Once again, as with every vampire, you will know an addiction by paying attention to how your body feels and reacts. Do you feel anxious, panicked, crazed, out of control, and the like at the thought of having to get rid of a substance/behavior? Do you feel anxious, panicked, crazed, out of control, and the like when you can't get enough of a substance/behavior? Do you have withdrawal symptoms when you stop the addictive substance/behavior (things like headaches, trembling, nausea, a tightening/pain in your chest, heart palpitations, sweating profusely, a feeling like your skin is just too tight or your skin is crawling, and the like)? And the biggest tell of them all: do you feel worse about your life, guilty, and/or ashamed after the effects of the substance/behavior have worn off (which also makes you want to run to abuse the substance/ behavior again)? If so, that behavior/substance is an addiction for you.

This category includes addictions in the form of (a partial list):

FOOD

Food, in and of itself, is not an addiction; it's simply fuel for your body, that's it. Food can only become an addiction when you start abusing it, using food not as fuel for your body but instead as a way to cope with your life, numb your feelings, give you courage/worth/value, or any other myriad of things that food was never designed to do. As we've been talking about, food can become an addiction when you're abusing it to make yourself feel better emotionally or to escape for a while or to give yourself the illusion that you're in control over something. The act of eating can also become an addiction when you're weighing and measuring everything you eat down to the ounce, writing down precisely every food you eat, spending hours reading labels for ingredients/calories, and/or like activities because you don't trust yourself enough to listen to your own body. You'll also know food is a vampire for you if you're bingeing, starving, purging, terrified of food and/or eating, fearful of getting fat and/or gaining more weight, and/or any other similar fear in which your life revolves around food and so the food controls you instead of you controlling the food.

SUBSTANCES

You can be addicted to illegal drugs, sure. You can also be addicted to prescription or over-the-counter drugs that you're abusing so that you don't have to feel. Alcohol is in here, too, if you're using it to numb/ avoid. Smoking falls in this category because honestly (and I can say this because I smoked nearly two packs of cigarettes a day before I quit), there are no (nope, not a one as far as I know) positive health benefits to lighting up nicotine cigarettes/cigars at all. Huffing makes this list, too, because again there's no benefit to your health and well-being to breathe in a bunch of chemicals. Other substances can be vampires, too: anything that you're using in a way that it was not originally intended because you're hoping to gain some temporary emotional and/or physiological benefit from it.

PEOPLE

Other people can become addictions in your life when you start using them to avoid dealing with your own self and your own life. You disempower yourself and run to them to fix it. You cling to others to soothe yourself. You focus on fixing others and/or their problems so that you can avoid facing yourself and fixing your own life. You hang on to relationships (even if they're extremely unhealthy) just so you won't have to feel what you're afraid to feel (lonely, inadequate, unlovable, incapable, or whatever feeling it is you're avoiding). In short, any behavior that causes you to be dependent on someone else for your own well-being, any behavior that leaves someone else in charge and you disempowered in your own life, and/or any behavior in which you're using others to make yourself feel better about yourself and/or your life falls into this vampire category.

BEHAVIORS

You'll know addictive behaviors if you find yourself chasing (and chasing and chasing, to the exclusion of other things) after a feeling, especially those behaviors that give you an adrenaline, dopamine, and/or serotonin reaction in your brain, which causes you to feel a kind of high when you do them. Behaviors, *any behaviors*, definitely can become an addiction when you use them repeatedly to numb yourself, avoid your life entirely, ease your fears, and/or give yourself a temporary emotional release that's easier than facing and dealing with whatever in your life is causing the problem. So shopping makes the list if you start using it in that way. So does sex. Overexercising. Watching television. Surfing the internet. Playing video games. Using a cell phone. Self-abuse like cutting yourself and berating yourself can also turn into an addiction.

Any behavior becomes a vampire if you're repeatedly using it not to nourish yourself or improve your well-being but instead you are using it as a way to distract yourself. In that way, you are busy going around in a circle with the behavior so you can avoid what you need to do to go in a straight line and move forward in your own life. Behaviors can also become addictive vampires if you're using them as a way to validate either your worth or value (so for example: shopping not to be kind to yourself but instead to prove that you're worth the cost of an item) or as a way for you to validate your own belief that you are worth very little (for instance: you harm yourself because you don't believe you're worth anything, so neither yourself nor your body matter).

ANYTHING ELSE YOU USE TO ESCAPE YOUR LIFE

I'm pretty convinced that *anything* can become an addictive vampire if you start using it in a way it wasn't originally intended so that you: 1. don't have to feel, 2. can escape and pretend what's happening really isn't happening, 3. use it as a kind of shield so you don't have to show anyone the real you, and/or 4. do it as a way to remain in the perceived safety of your comfort zone. You'll know if something has become an addiction for you if you use it whenever life gets challenging and you want to take the edge off or whenever you start to feel vulnerable/exposed and you want to feel safe/protected again and/or whenever you want to mentally check out.

What to do if you find yourself trapped in an addiction:

I know addiction has many facets/layers, especially if there are chemicals and a physiological craving involved. I know these short few paragraphs can't possibly address all of them. The best advice I can give you is this:

- the real you is the only person worth being in the world (I assure you this is true)
- and you don't owe the world your life (also true)
- and you most definitely owe it to yourself to show up in the world as the real you, meaning you are not addicted to anything (absolutely true)
- and the real you is enough as-is (true without a doubt)
- so do yourself a kindness and stop sabotaging and betraying yourself (because that is what you're doing every time you choose the addiction over yourself)
- because you won't ever get to be the person you want to be and to create the life you most want to have if you're tethered by an addiction (and make no mistake: that tether is short, limited by the demands of the addiction)
- so you need to be the one to release and free yourself to go in a straight line toward what you most want (because again and always: *no one is coming to fix it*).

My guess is that you're in a situation you don't want to be in. You probably feel something that you don't want to feel like: lonely, trapped, scared, powerless, disappointed, worthless, that you don't belong, and/or [insert your desperate feeling here]. Maybe you don't see a way out or maybe you do but you're afraid to take it. Maybe you've been playing the victim for so long that being powerless and helpless has become its own addiction. I know, all too well, how it's easier to just use some substance/behavior to escape your life than it is to be raw and real. I know how terrifying it can be to show the real you—*this is me, take it or leave it, I'm fine with myself either way*—to the world and all the risk that involves because the world just may leave it. But you're not doing this for them. You're not getting rid of the weight and/or ceasing to abuse food for them. You're not living your life for them. You're not being who you most want to be for them. You're not going after your own hopes and dreams for them. *You are doing all this for you. Always remember that.* Here's the truth as best as I can tell it: the only way out of an addiction (or pretty much anything else) is through.

So do this:
1. Stop waiting for someone to come fix it. Like I keep saying: *no one is coming to fix it.* So you fix it.
2. Decide that your own healing matters deeply *to you.* Give yourself permission to do whatever you need to do to reach your goal of being healthy and feeling whole again.
3. Befriend yourself. Speak strength to yourself. Look yourself in the eyes in a mirror and smile. Then tell yourself words you most need to hear. Repeat to yourself that you're worth the effort (because you are) and the real you is valuable as-is (also true) and that your passions, gifts, and talents matter because you matter (truest thing there is) until that becomes the story that you believe and so live out in your life.
4. Let go of anyone else's expectations. Your life belongs to you and *you alone.* You don't owe anyone your life. No, you certainly do not.
5. Use your voice and speak the truth. Start by admitting to yourself that what you're dealing with is not some little problem you can control. Admit to yourself that you've got an addiction.
6. Write down what substance(s)/behavior(s) you're addicted to. Write down why you're abusing them, what you're trying to numb/avoid/feel/control/etc. Write down the truth about how you feel and the truth about anyone/anything in your life that needs to be addressed. This is just for you so be honest. Lay it all out so you can see exactly what you're dealing with.
7. Then find *someone you trust* and tell them the truth about the addiction(s) you're determined to overcome.
8. Then answer this: *What do I most need to help me?* Maybe it's a support group, counseling, a treatment center, and/or some kind of medical therapy from your doctor. Or it could be, too, that you need to replace the addiction with something healthy that brings you joy and makes you come alive, which is my personal choice (more on this in Chapter Six).

9. Don't wait. Take action *now* and do whatever you need to do to take care of yourself. *You be actively involved and determined in your own healing.* This includes giving yourself permission to release any of the vampires mentioned in this chapter (people, places, things, and the list goes on) or any other vampires you've fallen prey to. It's vital that you get any and all vampires out of your life (or severely limit your time with them if you aren't able to excise them entirely) because they are, in my experience, a major part of the reason you choose to have an addiction. Once you get rid of the vampires, you'll come to find the want/need to abuse substance(s)/behavior(s) will likely ease if not vanish altogether.

10. And remember: you'll know your vampires by the way your body feels and reacts, so always listen to your intuition, which again includes both your mind and body.

11. Be careful not to simply swap one addiction for another. You want to free yourself from any and all substance(s)/behavior(s) that are an addiction for you.

12. Persevere. Don't stop until you're free. You're worth the effort, I assure you that you are.

ARMOR

Armor is a deceptive vampire. It doesn't feel like it's latched on and sucking the life out of you. Instead, it feels protective, like it's keeping you safe and secure from threats and harm. What it's doing instead, though, is keeping you invisible. According to my layman's understanding of both psychology and a human being's hierarchy of needs, every person—you, me, everybody—is hardwired to connect with other people. It's in our basic nature to seek out others for companionship, protection, and belonging.

Armor prevents all of that. Armor, in whatever form you use it, is all about hiding the real you and keeping that real you hidden. It forms a barrier between you and everyone else. It says you can come this close to the real me and no closer, and in that way, it prevents anyone from entirely experiencing the authentic you. When you use armor, you're the one who ends up encased in a shell. Armor doesn't let others in, true, but it doesn't let you out either.

Keep in mind that the most convincing lies/schemes start out with a kernel of truth. Here's the truth: you began using armor as a way to protect yourself, and protecting yourself, we can all agree, is a good thing. At some point, you got hurt physically, mentally, emotionally, and/or spiritually. You didn't want to be hurt again. The best way to make sure of that was to load yourself up with some kind of barrier/shield. So that was what you did. Except that you got hurt again. Then you decided the problem wasn't whomever or whatever hurt you, the problem was that you needed more armor. So you piled on some more. And that pattern kept repeating. Hurt then more armor. Hurt then more armor. And that's how it happened that you came to the conclusion you won't be safe, happy, fulfilled, able to live, and the list goes on without having your armor on at all times.

But here's the truth. Armor is an illusion. It gives the appearance of safety. But it's like a magician's sleight of hand: it looks real, it may even feel real, but in the end, armor is just a parlor trick that takes something (your sense of worth, your ability to be secure in your own self, your power, your happiness, your connection to others, and on the list goes) from you. Armor is heavy, especially if you have years of it piled on top of your real self. It weighs you down. It exhausts you as you haul it around wherever you go. It keeps you small and confined inside it. Often, it includes a chain that stakes you to a spot and keeps you there, unable to explore anything beyond the length of that tether.

Like with every vampire, both your body and your mind will reveal what you're using to armor yourself up. So do yourself a kindness and listen to your intuition. Do you rarely/never feel like your authentic self? Do you feel a separation/distance from others even when you're with them? Or smaller, contracted into yourself when you're with others? Or a mental numbness when you're with others? Or not in your body, physically there but mentally not there (like you're watching/interacting with others from a distance)? Do you feel like you've been cocooned? Or a longing to break free (that you don't act upon)? Do you stiffen around other people? Does the tone/pitch of your voice change when you talk to others? Do you behave one way when you're alone and a different way around others? Those kind of reactions from your mind and body signal that you're using armor and that you've got a vampire that's feeding on you.

This category includes armor in the form of (a partial list):

PHYSICAL DISTANCE

I'm an introvert; I often need to be by myself for my own health and well-being. Some people need a break from the stimulation of being around others, and that's perfectly fine. When physical distance becomes a vampire is when you use it to consciously withdraw from and avoid people because you don't want them to see the real you for whatever reason. It's armor when you retreat into your house, room, cubicle, favorite place, and the like so you can hide yourself. It's armor when you stand in the back of rooms and behind objects and/or people so as not to be seen.

Physical distance includes preferring the lights to be off so that no one can see you. Or not wanting to have your picture taken because you don't want a record of what you actually look like. Or not looking into anyone else's eyes when you meet them or talk with them. It also includes keeping the extra flesh on your body because that creates a barrier that keeps some people away. It's wearing baggy, shapeless clothes that don't feel true to who you are just so you can hide yourself.

You will know you're in the grip of this vampire when you're doing any behavior that limits your physical interaction with others and/or with the world in an attempt to hide who you really are.

MENTAL DISTANCE

If you're an introvert like me, you may tend to need a lot of mental distance for your own health and well-being. I would argue that everyone regardless of whether introverted or extroverted, at some point, needs a mental break to be their best selves.

Mental distance becomes armor, and therefore a vampire, when you consciously choose to not let anyone get emotionally close to you. It may not feel like a conscious choice right now (maybe you feel like you've always been that way, that's just who you are), but at some point in the past, you made a conscious decision not to let anyone fully know the real you. Mental distance is about not telling the truth about how you honest-to-goodness really think/feel, it's about editing and sanitizing what you really think/feel, it's about swallowing back the words you want/need to say aloud, all in an effort to hide your true self and give yourself the illusion of safety.

Mental distance is also checking out, so that you're physically somewhere but mentally, you're not in that same place at all. You detach yourself from your body, as if you're observing and not experiencing, so that whatever's happening to/around your body isn't really happening to you. Or it's being in the present moment with your body, but letting your mind wander into your past history or a future that hasn't happened yet so you're not often in the actual now.

Mental distance also includes abusing substances/behaviors to either numb yourself or give yourself the illusion of being brave, strong, fearless, unstoppable, and/or [insert the feeling you're hoping to achieve here]. It's any substance/behavior that takes you out of feeling inside your body, right where you are in this very moment and right where you are the most powerful, and weakens you by separating or even severing the connection between your mind and your body.

You will know you're in the grip of this vampire when your body is doing one thing but you are having thoughts/feelings of *this is not who I am, this is not who I want to be, this is not the path I want to be on, this is not what I want to be doing, this is not where I belong*, and the like. You are also in its grip during any moments in your life where you are retreating away from the reality of where your body is so that you can hide the real you in some fantasy in a corner of your mind. You are *always* in its grip when there's any kind of disconnect between your body and your mind.

BUSYNESS

Busyness as armor is about using constant motion as a way to avoid. It's anything you do as a way to stay distracted much if not all of the time so you don't have to interact with people or really ponder your life and/or your choices. Busyness is about doing and doing and doing (sometimes into exhaustion) just so you can hide the real you, both from others and also from yourself.

You'll know if busyness is a vampire for you if you feel fear at the thought of coming to a stop or even slowing down to pause because then you'll have to deal with others, feel your feelings, and/or face reality. Again, listen to your intuition, both your body and mind. Does your heart start racing at the thought of not constantly having something to do? Do you feel panicked if you don't have a distraction at all times? Do you feel a tightness in your throat, chest, and/or belly when you come to a stop and just stand there with nothing to do? Or maybe you fall into sadness/melancholy when you aren't busy? Or you find yourself somewhere on the spectrum between the extremes of panic and depression, and you just feel uncomfortable/restless when you slow down?

Busyness as a vampire is also about believing that how much you do and/or accomplish is the only reflection of who you are. It's believing that your resume is your entire life. It's believing that you are not enough as-is, that you have to prove your worth through your achievements, and so you just do and do and do more in an endless cycle.

MATERIAL THINGS

Material things become armor when you use them not for their intended purpose or to bring yourself true happiness/joy/fulfillment but instead you use them to hide your authentic self and/or attempt to gain your self-worth and value from what you own. The whole keeping-up-with-the-Jones's thing is all about armor. You wrap yourself in material things to prop up your own self-esteem, create a facade with your stuff, then show that to the world as the real you. When you do that, you are looking for validation, approval, accolades, and/or the like from others. Using material things as armor is not about sitting with yourself as you are and with what you have—be that a little amount of stuff or a lot—and being okay no matter what.

Your material things should bring you joy and fulfill a want/need; they shouldn't suck the life out of you. And that's exactly what they're doing if you're using them as a barrier between you and others or even as a barrier between you and dealing with your own self. Your focus becomes not what you honestly feel, truly want, personally need, and/or creating a life you'd love to have, but instead your focus becomes about keeping your material things intact (and even growing) so that you can cultivate a sense of safety. But, as we've already talked about, there are no guarantees of either comfort or safety in nature; material things, I assure you, cannot offer you an ironclad guarantee that everything will always be well.

You'll know if material things have become armor if you'll simply pay attention to your body. Do you feel stressed, anxious, overwhelmed, and the like by trying to keep up appearances? Or do you feel stressed and anxious about the need to accumulate more stuff in order to feel good about yourself and your life? Do you feel drained, tired, swamped, and the like by the sheer amount of stuff you have (possibly, even likely, stuff you don't even want and/or is not your taste)? Do you feel dread (even a little) or feel yourself shrinking back in any way at the thought of having to deal with others without your stuff? Does your pulse quicken or your stomach feel queasy or your body tremble at the thought of presenting yourself to the world without hiding behind your material things? And, as always with any vampire, the biggest tell there is: do the material things you use as armor create a desire to abuse food just so you can make the feelings of not being true to yourself (also known as self-betrayal) go away?

SAYING NO TO OPPORTUNITIES

Saying *no* to opportunities when you actually don't want or have time to do them is an excellent way to defend your own boundaries and protect your well-being. Saying *no*, however, becomes a vampire when those opportunities are something that you're interested in doing (even if you're just a little interested), but you say *no*: 1. because you are feeling head fear and/or 2. so you can keep yourself hidden. It's when you say *no* to opportunities so you can keep yourself small and keep yourself in your comfort zone and give yourself the illusion of safety. It's when you say *no* so you don't have to step out and try, which involves risks and would also expose the real you.

Saying *no* to opportunities is also about saying *no* to your own growth. You keep yourself small to distance yourself from others, to steer clear of your own feelings, to manage risk, and to avoid doing what you feel drawn and/or called to do. You say *no* in an effort to hide or suppress your own gifts, talents, and passions (hiding/suppressing both that you have gifts, talents, and passions, as well as the depth and breadth of them).

As always, pay attention to your body and your mind. Do you feel a yearning to say *yes* that you suppress? Do you feel your power being drained from you when you say *no*? Does saying *no* feel like a self-betrayal? When you say *no*, do you feel a tightness/constriction/hollowed-out feeling in your chest? Or do you feel a kind of dropping sensation (like a trapdoor opening and you falling) in your belly when you say *no*? You'll know that saying *no* to opportunities has become a vampire for you because the motivation behind your refusal will not be about you and fulfilling yourself but instead will be about risk management, protecting yourself, and/or the wants of other people.

What to do if you find yourself encased in armor:

1. Say *yes*. To life. To opportunities. To doing the things you want to do. To having the things you want to have. To being the person you want to be. You have to say *yes*. And you have to keep saying *yes* because the moment you say *no*, your journey down that particular path ends.
2. Know you are strong enough to handle whatever comes. Look yourself in the eyes in a mirror and say: *I am strong enough as myself to handle whatever comes my way*. Repeat that to yourself over and over—*I am strong enough as myself to handle whatever comes my way*—until it becomes the story you believe and so live out in your life.
3. Take this to heart: you are not living your life for anyone else. *You're living it for you.* Hold that in your heart and keep it at the top of your mind *every time* you make a choice.
4. Take this to heart, too: your worth and value are *always* intact no matter what happens.
5. Now go through. Show up for yourself. Show up for life. Show up without your armor. Even if you only shed it a little at a time. You just have to keep showing up and shedding it. Showing up and shedding it. Until one glorious day, you'll show up without any armor at all.
6. And relax into the process. Going without your armor is sometimes terrifying. So take a deep breath in through your nose, hold it three seconds, let it out slowly through your mouth. Repeat, repeat, repeat. Keep moving onward and upward. Keep growing.
7. Then let go. Of the outcome. Of expectations. Of others' opinions. Of anything that's hampering your growth.
8. Take this to heart, too: you cannot rise above until you let go of the stuff that holds you down (see Chapter Four if you need pointers on how to do that).
9. Always remember: 1. you free yourself by being yourself, and 2. there's only one life you can really save, and that's your own.
10. So give yourself permission to be yourself. Let others see you as you really are. That's the only way you'll ever truly be free. (Again, let the people who like you for who you really are gravitate toward you; those are the people you want in your life.) Give yourself permission over and over again, as many times as it takes. And then one fabulous day, you won't need your own permission anymore; you'll just show up as yourself from that point on.

11. Then pursue your own gifts, talents, passions, wants, hopes, and/or dreams. It is your job to find out what you love, what lights a spark in you, what makes you feel the most alive. It's also your job to go do it (a how-to is coming up in Chapter Six). The easiest way to foster real connection with others without your armor on is to do what you love. You are your truest and most unguarded self when you're immersed in something that makes you come alive.

OH, SOME SCIENCE

So your body runs on a system of feedback loops, which we've talked about before. As a refresher, chemicals and electrical impulses get released from the brain. Your cells react. Chemicals and electrical impulses go back to the brain. Your brain then reacts by releasing more chemicals and electrical impulses. And on and on it goes in a loop. The most important things to note: there is a specific movement to feedback loops and they run nonstop.[8] So you can see that if something in the loop isn't working correctly (say, because the information that's passed on is faulty), the whole feedback loop won't be working correctly.

When you let a vampire latch on, let it feed on you, and do nothing to stop it, you compromise the healthy functioning of your body's feedback loops. Vampires are toxic to the running of feedback loops. That toxicity (in the form of stress, anxiety, depression, sadness, fear, tension, panic and the like—whatever reaction it is you're having to the vampire) changes the electrical and chemical makeup of the impulses coursing from your brain to your cells and also from one cell to another.[9] In turn, your brain and cells form their responses based on that toxic information. Often, that toxicity can disrupt communication between cells. Cells can start to behave erratically. Your body doesn't run as efficiently. The systems of your body (like your immune system, for example) can become weakened and less healthy. According to Dr. Caroline Leaf, feedback loops that are compromised eventually manifest as physical symptoms, like illness and disease.[10] Again, your brain and cells communicate in fractions of seconds, meaning it doesn't take long for corrupted feedback loops to spiral out of control.

If you needed a solid reason to excise the vampires and make some positive changes in your life, there it is. It's all about the science: you simply care enough about yourself and your well-being to make sure your feedback loops and your body don't spiral out of control.

THIS IS A PRACTICE AND A PROCESS

Lest you forget, here's another reminder that you won't get this right the first time (or necessarily the fourth, tenth, eighty-fifth . . . sigh) and that's okay. Vampires tend to latch on, and sometimes it's hard to break their grip. Cut yourself some slack and *take really good care of yourself*, that's imperative and nonnegotiable because you matter and you are worth the effort. And if you don't believe that, then change the story you're telling yourself *right now*. There is no perfection when it comes to banishing the vampires. It may be messy and get ugly. You may get scared and go running back to them. Eventually, though, when you see how they really are draining the life from you, you'll be able to let them go. And remember: every mistake is simply a brand new chance to do it better the next time.

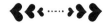

CHAPTER SIX

BE AUTHENTIC

OR

**Find what makes
you feel alive
and go do it.**

Chapter Six

**"Let yourself be silently drawn by the strange pull
of what you really love. It will not lead you astray."
—Jalaluddin Rumi**

I PINCH A razor blade between my thumb and index finger. I turn it this way and that. The top edge catches a glint of light coming through the window and holds it.

The emotional pain is immense. I just want it to stop. But it doesn't ever stop. I go to bed with it at night. I wake up to it in the morning. I live with it through the day. It's pressing, swamping, suffocating. It makes me want to claw at my throat.

Crazy. Evil. Rotten to the core. No ones else likes her either. Fat. Ugly. Stupid.

The pain of it crushes.

And I just want it to stop.

I slice the blade high up on my left forearm. There's a sharp sting, almost a burning. Bubbles of blood well up in a line. They catch in the fine downy hairs as they slide down, zigzagging toward my wrist. Not deep enough. Just the skin opening. No muscle tissue. No arteries or veins. Just a hesitant first try. I wanted to see if I could do *it, if I had the nerve. And I have. But if I really want to die, I mean really want to, then I'm going to have to cut deeper.*

A cartoon plays on the television. A coyote chases a roadrunner toward a cliff. The bird stops at the edge in a flurry of dust. The coyote hangs in midair for a second then falls into the chasm. The bird beeps then takes off running again. Blood drips down my arm and onto a wad of paper towels in my lap. I hold up the razor blade and catch a sliver of my reflection. A corner of my right eye. The bridge of my nose. Blood is smeared along the bottom edge. I slice into myself again, sideways across my arm, this cut closer to my wrist. Still shallow, not much pressure. A question circles my mind like water does a drain: You sure you want to do this?

I'm afraid to kill myself.

What will happen to my soul? Will I go to hell like I've heard? What if I don't die and have to live with the shame of trying and failing? More pointing fingers. More whispers following behind my back. What if I don't die but end up damaged because not enough blood and oxygen make it to my brain? And will dying actually fix it? What if the place I end up after I'm dead is worse than here?

I look up at the ceiling. Stippled plaster. A yellowed water stain in the corner by the window. I say, "Will you help me?" I wait a beat then two. No answer. So I make another cut, crisscrossing the one near my wrist, making the shape of an X. Blood runs down across the meat of my thumb and hangs at the edge of the knuckle. Drops fall and stain dark ovals onto the paper towels. Suddenly, there's a release of all that pain. There's just the heat and the sting and a kind of numbness. I glance up at the ceiling again. Then to the window. The high blue sky. White clouds scudding by. I cock my head to the left. I wait. I listen. But heaven doesn't answer. There's never an answer, is there? There's just silence where there ought to be some words.

On the television, a bumbling hunter chases a talking bunny through a forest. The volume is low, barely audible. The hunter fires his shotgun, the blast missing the rabbit and taking out a tree in a shower of splinters. He rants and raves. The rabbit munches on a carrot. I drag the blade just left of the blue vein snaking from my wrist toward my elbow, just enough pressure to dent the skin but not break it.

Are you sure?

I just want the pain to stop.

There's no going back.

No one else will help.

A teacher's voice from health class lands in my head: suicide is a permanent solution . . .

I have to do something.

. . . to a temporary problem . . .

But who else will come to help me?

. . . suicide attempts . . .

I make a fist.

. . . are a cry . . .

The tendons go taut.

. . . for help . . .

I slice the blade alongside those tendons for an inch or so. Still shallow, more like a scratch. Tiny bubbles of blood. No permanent damage. Maybe not even a scar. The razor edge drips. So does my arm. The paper towels are dotted with blood, creating patterns that make me think of an inkblot test. This one's a cat. That one's a horse's head. Another one a person lying on the grass looking up at the stars.

Time to choose. What's it gonna be?

An animated duck is on the television screen now, his beak blasted off his face and lying on the ground. The hunter grips the shotgun, both barrels smoking. I wipe the razor blade clean on the towels and set it on my knee. I wrap my arm in the paper towels, holding pressure until the cuts stop bleeding. The sting remains. So does the heat. And the numbness. But there's an aliveness to the way I feel too, right here and right now, nothing else matters.

I push the knob and the television shuts off. A pop and a tiny white cloud there in the middle of a greenish screen and then it winks out into blackness. I wash my arm in the bathroom sink down the hall. I wrap a gauze bandage around the cuts then pull my shirt sleeve down to hide my arm. I bury the paper towels in the bottom of the garbage can then rearrange the trash on top to cover them. I hold the razor blade under the faucet, dry it with the hand towel, then tuck it back into the small box of others inside Father's shaving kit. I glance at the mirror above the sink.

I wasn't courageous enough. Not tenacious enough. I didn't have the intestinal fortitude, as Father would say, to go through with it. I can't even manage to help myself.

I say, "Coward."

I say, "You are fat and ugly and weak."

I say, "They are right about you."

After that, I can't hold my own gaze, so I turn away.

Nobody will ever know. I will never tell. The cuts will heal. They'll leave tiny white scars for a time but even those will fade, and it'll be like it never happened. Except that the want for it—the strength and the guts to make the deep cut—will stay with me for a long, long time to come.

I am fourteen years old.

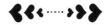

YOU ARE ALIVE FOR A REASON: YOU HAVE BOTH A GIFT & A PURPOSE

Well, we've come to the part of the book where you're going to have to be the bravest of all. You're going to do the sometimes challenging but always completely fulfilling work of becoming yourself. You're going to have to let go of all the armor that you use to protect yourself because it's actually harming you. You're going to have to fully take to heart that limiting yourself and keeping yourself in the background and small (no matter how much you might weigh) serves no one, least of all yourself. You're going to have to stop keeping yourself contained in a body that doesn't suit you or dimming your own light so people won't be intimidated by you or being one person when you're out in the world while you're a different person when you're alone. It's the incongruence—knowing you are one kind of person but denying it while attempting to pass yourself off as another—that causes you pain and suffering.

Hear me: *you are here for a reason; you have both a gift (or more than one) and a purpose.* As Pablo Picasso once said, "The meaning of life is to find your gift. The purpose of life is to give it away." Finding your gift is as simple as discovering what makes *you* come alive, what brings *you* joy and happiness and fulfillment, and then doing that. Giving it away is sharing what makes you come alive with others, whether that's through things you create, knowledge and teaching, or just encouraging others by giving them implied permission to find what makes them come alive themselves (meaning: because you came alive, others will see that they can come alive, too). If you do nothing else with your life other than those two things—finding your gift and giving it away—you'll have done enough. I didn't used to believe that; now, having lived it, I believe that wholeheartedly.

I also know you will never truly find your gift(s) by hiding yourself in a body (overweight or underweight) that doesn't feel like you, abusing food and/or other substances/behaviors to keep yourself numb and unchallenged in your comfort zone, and/or remaining compliant and nonthreatening to other people. It takes courage and strength and faith to venture out and find the real you, especially in a world where people who are sad, frightened, lonely, unfulfilled, disgruntled, and on the list goes tend to attack those who have let themselves and their inner lights shine bright. Just know this: *you are only responsible for saving your own life.* Other people's insecurities are their problem, not yours. Other people's opinions don't belong to you. And anyone who prefers you weak and small and manageable is a vampire who will suck you dry and not someone you ever want in your life (see Chapter Five).

Once you do the work of becoming who you truly are, people may decide they don't like the real you, which means they liked the facade you portrayed but they never really liked *you* at all. People may feel threatened or intimidated by the real you, which, unless you are in some way violent/demeaning to them, has nothing, I repeat *nothing*, to do with you. People may not like the real you simply because you've changed, and change, *any* kind of change, is scary to them. It's entirely possible that you will become yourself and people—peers, relatives, lovers, friends, mentors, and on the list goes—will leave your life and never come back. Or it may be you who decides that people need to leave your life because they no longer fit with who you truly are, and you'll be the one to leave the relationship, never to return. You may lose some, most, or even all the people you care about, and that'll be really tough on you. I know because it happened to me. But like every other task/suggestion mentioned in this book, there's no going around becoming yourself, there's only going through.

Know this going in: people will *always* come into and go out of your life. There are never any guarantees that they will stay. Even people who promised you they would stay. Even people whose responsibility it is to stay. Even people whom you don't think you can live without. Do yourself a kindness: say what you need to say (*always!*), wish them well, and then let them go. When they leave and it's just you, the real you, you'll learn many good and invaluable things about yourself. For one: you won't be diminished by loneliness; being lonely is simply a feeling and if you just sit with it for a little while, you'll see that loneliness doesn't make you less of a person, that loneliness (like all feelings) won't destroy you either. For another: people or events won't crush you if you refuse to let them. And most important of all: you are strong, you are a survivor, and you don't need anyone (or anything) else to make you whole.

Once you stop pretending you're someone else and let go of all the selves that don't ring true to you—the imitator, the kiss-up, the better-than-you, the perfectionist, the unworthy, and on the list goes—that's when you'll finally be comfortable in your own skin. That's when you'll be able to fully discover and cultivate your own unique gifts and talents. That's when you'll have something truly original to offer in this world. The real you is worth the effort it takes to uncover, I assure you that it is.

Again, it doesn't matter if anyone else likes the real you; what matters—the *only* thing that ever matters—is that *you* like the real you (read Chapter Three on befriending yourself if you need a reminder). And the best news of all is this: once you start excavating the real you, the need to abuse food and/or other substances/behaviors to hide, escape, numb, and the like from the pain and suffering caused by incongruence (again, presenting a facade—read: lie—to both yourself and to the world) will fade down to a pinprick then wink out altogether. And that, I assure you, is worth more than your body weight in gold.

SO STOP HIDING YOUR LIGHT

Your inner light is that spark of life inside you that burns brightly when you are fully and truly yourself. It's when you're at your happiest and most authentic. It's when you feel the most connected to yourself, to others, to the environment around you, and to a purpose bigger than yourself. It's when you are offering what you have instead of trying to be someone else. Your light shines through when you're not guarding and protecting yourself but instead are projecting to the world who you really are. It's when you let go of fear and expectations and worry and proving and beating yourself up, and instead you choose to let yourself simply be yourself, as-is, in the moment. It's an incredibly empowering place to be. *Shining your own light is when you're at your most powerful.*

Your light is made up of your gifts, talents, passions, and those things that make you feel the most alive when you do them. You have gifts, talents, and passions (oh yes, you do!) even if you don't know exactly what they are yet. You have something to offer in a way that only you can, and there's someone in the world who needs it. You were born with a kernel of those gifts, talents, and passions inside you, and your job in this life is simply this: to figure out what your gifts, talents, and passions are, to nourish them and help them grow, and then to share them with the world. And if you're unsure as to what your gifts, talents, and passions are, well, hang tight because we'll be talking about uncovering all those things shortly.

Shining your light is using your gifts, talents, and passions to bring yourself fulfillment and joy as well as to give your life deeper meaning. Shining your light is also sharing your gifts, talents, and passions with others. Shining your light happens when you actively seek out and cultivate those things that make you come alive instead of hiding or dimming them. You have something that you are brilliant at, I assure you. You may not know what that something is just yet, and that's okay. Just know that it's inside you, simply waiting for you to discover it, and you'll figure it out as you go along. And always keep in mind that the motivation behind doing that brilliant something needs to be this: *you are doing it for you.* Not for anyone or anything else. Not to prove your own worth and value. Not to get people to like you. Not for money. Not for accolades. Not to gain someone/something. Not for any other motivation except your own well-being and happiness. You won't ever feel fully alive and inside your body and excited to wake up every morning, I would argue, until you do, *wholeheartedly*, what you're brilliant at. You won't ever stop abusing food and/or other substances/behaviors, I would also argue, until you let yourself do, without constraints, what you're brilliant at. Those constraints could be things like you'll only do what you're brilliant at if: the outcome is *this specific thing*, or you get what you want by *this date*, or the end product is something others would buy in *this quantity*, and on the list goes.

Here's another true thing you need to take to heart: *hiding your light serves no one, least of all yourself.* Your gifts, talents, and passions, if you pursue them, will bring joy and healing most importantly to yourself and secondarily possibly to others. But if you refuse to cultivate them, all that unused potential, all that unexpressed creativity, all those unfulfilled wants, wishes, and dreams will turn toxic inside you. You will steep in a stew of frustration, wanting, bitterness, regret, envy, fear, resentment, and/or on the list goes. If you think I'm being melodramatic, I'd ask you this: *Why do you think you're in so much pain? Why do you think you're trying to numb yourself? Why do you think the cycle of abusing substances/behaviors continues over and over and over again?* I'd argue it's because you actively choose to dim your own light and hide the *real* you. And when you do that, you cause a rift (the hole/wound we've been talking about throughout this entire book) inside yourself. On one side of the rift is who you know yourself to be. On the other is the persona that you project to the world. They can't pleasantly coexist inside you. As I said before, you can't be healthy and whole when you're fighting a battle with yourself. You know the truth plus you don't speak it equals a war inside you. And so it's the rift (the being at constant odds with yourself, the incongruence) that's tearing you apart and fueling the numbing activities you do.

When you fail to shine your own light, you risk many things but here are the two biggest: 1. you shrink your life down to the size and shape of those who would dim you and 2. (even more damaging) you never get to realize your own potential.

Reasons you may choose to hide your light (a partial list):

YOU ARE AFRAID

I get that it's scary to shine your light because that makes you a beacon. Beacons are meant to help guide. And beacons are also meant to be noticed. The haters seem to be everywhere, and they tend to sling stones at beacons, trying to shatter their lights. And you've likely been hurt enough. So to keep yourself from getting hurt again, you dim yourself to the level of those around you so you can blend in. Keep this in mind though: every time you dim yourself for other people so as not to intimidate, anger, offend, risk rejection, and the like, you betray yourself and widen that rift inside you, the one that's tearing you apart and causing the pain you're desperately trying to numb/avoid by abusing food.

You may think you're safer in the shadows. Keep yourself small and in the dimness and maybe you can squeak by unnoticed. You likely believe you're minimizing risk. But what you're really doing is making living your life about others instead of about saving yourself and getting yourself to where you most want to be. Keep in mind, too: there really are no guarantees of comfort or safety in nature. There are no guarantees, none whatsoever, that keeping yourself minimized and in the background is going to save you from pain. The only thing doing that *is* going to guarantee is that you live in a constant state of unease and don't ever grow into the person you were meant to be.

YOU DON'T RECEIVE WHAT YOU HOPED YOU WOULD IN THE TIME FRAME THAT YOU THOUGHT YOU SHOULD

Maybe you were mistakenly taught that if your gifts, talents, and passions don't earn you something tangible in the end (money, accolades, fame, and the like), well, then they are not worth pursuing. If you believe that, one of two things will likely happen: 1. you won't even bother to try to discover your gifts, talents, and passions or 2. you quit as soon as whatever it is you were hoping to gain from them doesn't materialize. But pursuing what makes you come alive is what you need to do to heal the rift inside you. The easiest way to give yourself permission to pursue your gifts, talents, and passions is to make your well-being your sole motivation and to let go of the outcome.

YOU ARE PLAGUED BY SELF-DOUBT

You don't trust yourself to know what shines a light in you. You refuse to trust your intuition to guide you toward your gifts, talents, and/or passions. You don't trust your ability to achieve your own hopes, wants, dreams, and/or desires. Again, self-doubt tends to be a self-worth issue. Maybe you don't trust or believe that you're worthy of doing what you love, and so you convince yourself that you are not deserving of doing what shines a light in you. Just know this: it's the urge to shine your light versus the act of stopping yourself from doing it that is at the heart of that rift we've been talking about.

YOUR DEFINITION OF SUCCESS DOES NOT INCLUDE USING YOUR GIFTS, TALENTS, AND PASSIONS

Somewhere in you how you define success for yourself, it doesn't include doing what shines a light in you. That could be because your light doesn't earn you something tangible, like we just talked about, and your definition of success is all about tangible gain. Or it could be that somewhere along the line, you defined success by someone else's standards, which didn't include what shines a light in you. Or maybe you made a definition of success without your gifts, talents, and passions in it because you simply didn't know better. I'm here to tell you that any definition of success that does not include using your gifts, talents, and passions only widens that rift inside you.

YOU PUT THE NEEDS OF OTHERS BEFORE YOUR OWN

Using your gifts, talents, and passions is a need (oh yes, it is!) if you want to be healthy and whole. If you don't believe me, look back in Chapter Two to *Meet Your Own Needs* and the hierarchy of needs defined by Abraham Maslow: *esteem*, which includes the sense that you have a purpose in the world and the belief that you have unique gifts and talents; and *aesthetic*, which includes being creative to bring yourself fulfillment and happiness. You may argue that you have many people in your life who need you, and so you don't have time to prioritize yourself. But remember: you're exchanging your life for what you choose to do with your time. So answer this: *Do I want to spend my time abusing substances/behaviors or do I want to spend it fulfilling myself?* That choice is always up to you. To heal the rift inside you, you need to write your own name in the top spot on your priority list, learn what sparks a light in you, and take action to pursue it.

A QUICK EXERCISE TO EXCAVATE THE REAL YOU

1. Turn to a new page in your journal.
2. Make two columns.
3. On the left side, write: WHAT MAKES ME FEEL THE MOST ALIVE.
4. On the right side, write: WHY I DON'T DO IT.
5. Now write, quickly, whatever comes to you. Don't overthink and especially don't edit. Just answer those questions. Be honest because telling yourself the truth is the only way you're going to heal yourself. You don't have to show this to anyone, *ever*, so tell the truth.
6. Now you know: a.) some of the things that make a light shine in you and b.) why you don't pursue them. You are now armed with self-knowledge.
7. Keep that list handy because you're going to use it shortly to learn just how to let your light shine bright.

So how do you let go of hiding your light?

1. Choose to believe that your gifts, talents, and passions matter deeply to you. Choose that actively pursuing them also deeply matters to you. Those are choices that are squarely up to you. Then stand by those choices no matter what.

2. Once your gifts, talents, and passions deeply matter to you and pursuing them also deeply matters to you, what anyone else thinks of your choices won't be all that important anymore. And when you start to shine, you'll come to find that the people who sling stones won't be all that important to you either.

3. You remind yourself (*daily if necessary*) that hiding your light is: 1. widening that rift inside you and 2. part of the reason you continue abusing food to cope with the pain. Hiding your own light, in no uncertain terms, is self-betrayal. And we already talked about how detrimental it is to your well-being when you betray yourself.

4. Give yourself permission (*as often as necessary*) to let your light shine bright. You were given gifts, talents, and passions for a reason, and I assure you that it wasn't to hide them in the dark. It was to let them shine out into the light. So be the beacon you were meant to be. Let your own light guide you all the way home.

A SEVEN-STEP PLAN TO GET YOU TO THE LIFE YOU MOST WANT

STEP ONE

DISCOVER YOUR GIFTS, TALENTS, AND PASSIONS

There is something you love to do. Yes, there is.

Something that makes you feel in the present moment like nothing else does. You lose time when you do it. You feel electrified and incredibly grateful that you get to do this thing when you're doing it. You feel excited at the thought of doing it. You can't wait to get up in the morning to do it or get back to it when you're busy doing other things. That's what it means to come alive, and that something you love to do is what makes you come alive. It's your job in this world, the most important job there is, I'd argue, to find out what makes you feel the most alive and then to go do it.

The problem comes in when your head belief slams into your heart belief and takes it out. Your head belief says something like: *I need to spend my time doing things that bring me money, power, status, prestige, fame, and/or [insert a fleeting definition of success here].* Your heart belief says something along the lines of: *I want to be a teacher, baker, artist, writer, healer, and/or [insert what would fulfill you here].* Your head belief tends to be about fear and risk management and the perception of safety, all of which we've already talked about.

Pursuing your head belief at the exclusion of your heart belief is what's widening that rift inside you, crushing you emotionally, and keeping you running to abuse food to numb yourself. Abusing food or any substance/behavior is the opposite of coming alive, it's pinning yourself down while you slowly die inside, and that's all it is. Your heart belief, on the other hand, is about personal fulfillment and it tells you in which direction you most want to be headed, even if you feel scared to pursue it. Pursuing your heart belief, and therefore coming alive, is what will heal you from abusing food and/or any other substance/behavior.

It's also entirely possible you've convinced yourself that you don't actually know what your gifts, talents, and passions are. Maybe you believe you have nothing special to offer. Or you believe you don't have anything you love to do and/or are brilliant at doing. But I'm here to tell you that you do. And not only that, I'd argue that you already know what those gifts, talents, and passions are. That information is inside you, I assure you that it is. Your life speaks to you all the time; all you have to do is a little listening.

Some action steps to Discover Your Gifts, Talents, and Passions:

STEP 1A
LISTEN TO YOUR LIFE

1. Take some time to be alone in a quiet place.
2. Read through the list you recently wrote about what makes you feel the most alive and why you don't do it.
3. Now add to that list anything else that interests you (even a little), activities you naturally gravitate toward and/or things you find yourself doing without even thinking about them, what you're doing when you're at your happiest, your preferences if I asked you to describe your perfect day.
4. Then take a look back at your history and write down what you loved to do when you were a kid, when you didn't limit yourself and were full of hope and anything was possible, what your dreams were back then, what you most wanted to be when you grew up.
5. Now add to that list anything (and everything) you would love to do if only it weren't for the fear.

238 | Start Where You Are Weight Loss

STEP 1B
PAY ATTENTION

1. Simply be aware of your own day-to-day life. You don't even necessarily have to slow down, although going a bit slower might make it easier for you.
2. Pay attention to what:
   - activities make you lose track of time when you do them.
   - piques your interest when you see, hear, smell, feel, and/or touch it.
   - makes you stop and look, maybe catch your breath, and/or perhaps makes your heart beat faster.
   - feels like it causes a little spark to flare inside of you at the thought of it.
   - makes you, when you do it, feel like you're finally home, this is where you belong.

STEP 1C
FIND WHAT MAKES YOU COME ALIVE BY FINDING OUT WHAT DOESN'T

1. Pay attention to what you hate doing or at least dislike a whole lot.
2. Know this: when Michelangelo did the statue of David, he said he sculpted it out of a block of marble by chipping away at everything that wasn't David until the only thing left was David. You can do the same, chipping away at what you hate until all that's left is what you love, and then the only thing left will be the real you.
3. So write down a list of all the stuff in your life that you don't like:
   - activities you don't care for
   - people you don't enjoy being around
   - work you don't like to do
   - any lifestyle you don't want to be living
   - or anything else that leaves you feeling drained (see Chapter Five on discovering your vampires if you need some further guidance).
4. Once you chip away at all the stuff you don't like, eventually the only things that remain are the ones that make you come alive.

STEP 1D
NARROW YOUR FOCUS

1. Do yourself a kindness and don't overwhelm yourself with too many *well-it-could-be-this* or *maybe-it's-that* or *it-could-be-this-other-thing that makes me come alive*. When that happens, you grind to a halt.
2. Simply figure out what you, personally, love about the things that make you come alive.
3. So with the list of things you love in hand (from Step 1A, *Listen To Your Life*), pick the one *you're most drawn to*.
4. Then write an answer to this: *What matters to <u>me</u> in this?* Write down the first answers that come to you (so no overthinking or editing).
   - To illustrate: when I decided to get into photography, I started with what kind of pictures I like to take—mostly portraits—then what color palette I gravitated toward—earth tones—then I paid attention to the light I prefer—natural—and how I like to frame shots—close-up and off-center. I started with a narrow focus (just photography) then fine-tuned that narrow focus into something specific & unique to me: what makes me come alive when I'm taking pictures.
5. Simply pay attention to and follow your own personal preferences, that's all you have to do to find out what *specifically* matters to you about the things that make you come alive.
6. It may take some experimenting and a lot of tries, and that's okay. You're working to tailor your life so it suits you and that's how you'll find the real honest-to-goodness you.

STEP 1E
TRUST YOURSELF

1. Remember: self-trust is the first secret of success. So trust that you know what's best for you. You have been with you for your entire life. You know yourself better than anyone else. Yes, you do. Sometimes others can point you in the right general direction, but nobody else can tell you what makes you come alive.
2. Let yourself be vulnerable during this process, which will likely throw you out of your comfort zone. So know going in that there will likely be some discomfort but, in the end, there'll be something completely worthwhile because of it.
3. Be open to *whatever* answers come up in you (because all the answers you really need to guide your life are already inside of you; it's just a matter of excavating them).

4. Be okay with being a beginner. Be okay with not knowing everything right now in this moment. Be okay with learning as you go along.
5. Be okay with making some errors along the way, because you will. Every mistake will simply get you closer to the real you.
6. Know that some days you will feel like you're fumbling around in the dark. That's a normal part of the process of finding what makes you come alive. So be patient, kind, and gentle with yourself. And whatever you do, don't go running for someone else to tell you what your gifts, talents, and passions are or might be. You just keep moving forward and trusting, *just trusting*, that you will discover those things for yourself, because you will.

STEP 1F
LET GO OF OUTSIDE EXPECTATIONS

1. Choose to let go of what others want/wish/hope for your life.
2. Choose to let go of what and/or where society says your life should be by now.
3. Choose to let go of putting yourself on someone else's timetable and so believing either there's not enough time left or it's too late for you.
4. Choose to let go of anything that's adding pressure to you as you discover who you are and what you love.
5. Choose to do what you do, with every action you take and every choice you make, to save your own life.
6. Remember this: you won't ever figure out who you are and what makes you come alive by proxy or via committee or with a majority vote. The only thing that's important in discovering who you are is what truly and deeply matters to you.
7. So give yourself *unlimited tries*.
8. And forgive yourself *as many times as it takes*.
9. Then keep going—trial and error and trial again—until you find what it is that makes you come alive.

STEP 1G
TAKE BABY STEPS IF THAT MAKES IT EASIER FOR YOU

1. Know this: you don't have to quit everything else (including your job) and jump headfirst into what makes you come alive, not if you don't feel comfortable doing that.
2. So start small.

3. Pick one of the activities you love to do (from Step 1A, *Listen To Your Life*) and pour some of your energy into just that one.
4. Narrow your focus to figure out what specifically appeals to you about that one activity.
5. Stick with that one activity for a time, *even if you don't have immediate results*. See where it leads. No pressure. Just let yourself experiment.
6. Be open to letting yourself and what makes you come alive simply unfold and grow.
7. Remember: it's okay to grow slowly. Truly, it is. Coming alive is the goal; it doesn't matter when you get there. As long as you are *actively* moving toward that goal, the overwhelming need to abuse substances/behaviors will ease.

STEP 1H
HANG ON TO HOPE AND KEEP ON GOING

1. See what you've started all the way through to the end.
2. Know this: you may lose faith in yourself and/or in the process along the way; it happens to all of us.
3. But see what you've started through anyway, *all the way to the end.*
4. Don't stop until you discover what makes you come alive.
5. Then go do it.
6. Know this too: when all is said and done, it's likely that you may—with your gifts, talents, and passions—end up creating something completely astounding and phenomenal.
7. So hang on to hope. You can and will accomplish amazing things if you'll just have a little faith in yourself, if you'll just make your well-being your sole motivation, if you'll just keep going, if you'll see whatever you've chosen to do all the way through to the end. You will get there. You will.
8. And once you do that, you'll *never* have to go back to stumbling around that confusing, dark, shadowy place of not knowing.
9. So do yourself a kindness: keep going—maybe slow but always steady, a little bit at a time—and see what you've started all the way through to the end.

STEP 1I
IF YOU STILL DON'T KNOW, TRY THIS

1. Go online and search for *Survey of Character Strengths*. It's a quiz you can take that will help you pinpoint your particular strengths so you can accentuate and nourish those.

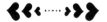

STEP TWO

DEFINE YOUR DEEPEST HOPES AND DESIRES

We all want to manifest something in our lives. Maybe you want something grand and extravagant and impressive (not to prove anything, mind you, but as a personal preference). Maybe you want something simple and homey and comforting (not limiting yourself, mind you, but as a personal preference). Maybe you want a sense of accomplishment or fulfillment or belonging. Maybe you want to win awards or travel the world or finish that project you started a decade ago. Whatever it is, defining your deepest hopes and desires is about *defining what a successful life looks like to you*, it's about having a life that is as big or as small as you want it to be. It's about having a life in synchronicity with what is at the core of who you are.

It's incredibly important, when defining your deepest hopes and desires, to know your own gifts, talents, and passions. You need to ask yourself: *How can my gifts, talents, and passions help me realize my deepest hopes and desires? How can I incorporate my gifts, talents, and passions into my life so I can do more of them every day?* By weaving what a successful life looks like to you into your daily schedule and combining it with your own gifts, talents, and passions, you will end up creating a life that's fulfilling and meaningful to you.

The definition of your deepest hopes and desires needs to be *specific to you*. Again, it's often easy to get caught up in and chase after what your friends, family, and/or society deems important. But living out someone else's deepest hopes and desires will only serve to deepen the rift/hole inside you because you're not being true to yourself (so betraying yourself) and you know it. And deepening that hole, as you've read throughout this entire book, also causes you psychological pain, which you then want to numb/avoid by abusing substances/ behaviors. But if you define your deepest hopes and desires by being specific to yourself—*what you most want for your life, what deeply matters to you*—well, you'll feel an empowerment and an excitement that will act as a springboard to launch you into a life that feels full of possibility, into a life that makes you come alive.

And finally, I've said this before but it bears repeating here lest you forget: *you are worth having your deepest hopes and desires*. You are worth having a life that matters to you. You are worth doing the work, spending the money, taking the time, and leveraging the risk it will take to make those hopes and desires come true. You are worth doing/having whatever it is that makes you feel alive because that's how you'll find happiness, fulfillment, and peace.

Some action steps to Define Your Deepest Hopes And Desires:

STEP 2A
OPEN YOURSELF UP TO POSSIBILITY

1. Always remember: you create the life you're living with every choice you make and every action you take.
2. Remember this, too: the path you're currently on is the one you've chosen. If you don't like the path you're on, simply choose differently.
3. So choose (again, it's your choice) to be open and willing.
4. Ask yourself this: *Just what if I could have all my hopes and desires come true?*
5. And this: *What if I could have/be/do/say what makes me feel the most alive?*
6. And this: *What if every day I woke up excited about my life? What if every day I woke up happy to have another day to pursue what I love? What if every day I woke up curious to see what amazing thing is going to happen next?*
7. Remember: the only difference between impossible and I'm possible is commitment. So ask yourself this: *What if I truly believed in I'm possible no matter what?*

STEP 2B
LET YOUR FEAR POINT YOU IN THE RIGHT DIRECTION

1. Know this: sometimes, okay often, what you're really scared of is what you want the most. It's entirely possible that your deepest hopes and desires terrify you. But as long as those deepest hopes and desires don't result in bodily harm or your death, then the fear you feel about pursuing them is only head fear. And again, head fear is simply a story in your mind.
2. So write an answer to these: *If I wasn't afraid, what would I most want to have/be/do/say? If fear didn't stop me, where would I most want to go from here?*
3. Be honest. You're not showing this to anyone, so tell the truth.
4. Then remember: there are no absolute guarantees of either comfort or safety in nature. Avoiding head fears may make you *feel* safe but will not actually *keep* you safe.
5. Now write this then say it aloud: *Not pursuing my head fear(s) will not guarantee that I will be safe.*
6. So change how you look at fear and risk. Since there are no guarantees of either comfort or safety, you might as well pursue those things that are head fears *even if you have to do them afraid.*

7. Choose to believe that your head fears about your deepest hopes and desires are actually a way for you to know in which direction you're supposed to be going. Those head fears can become a road map to the life you most want if you'll just let them.

STEP 2C
PRIORITIZE

1. Start with your answers from Step 2B, *Let Your Fear Point You In The Right Direction*.
2. Rewrite that list, ranking them by how much they matter to you from the most important to the least important.
3. Know this: you can have *as many* deepest hopes and desires as you like. This exercise just helps you so you don't overwhelm yourself with where to start first.

STEP 2D
DEFINE YOUR DEEPEST HOPES AND DESIRES
BY TAILORING THEM TO FIT ONLY YOU

1. Start with your prioritized list (from Step 2C, *Prioritize*).
2. Make sure that list includes only what *you* most want. So read through it now and cross off anything that is a hope/desire belonging to someone else that you somehow felt obligated to add to your own list.
3. Now for each item that's not crossed off, customize it by adding as many *specific* details as possible so that you get what you most want. Think of this step like this: you're happiest when you special order a meal and get to eat *exactly* what you want—extra pickles, no onions, heavy on the mayonnaise, and the like—so you don't feel like you're settling or compromising or being deprived.
4. When you've finished customizing, read through your list.
5. Then for each, answer this: *Does this hope and desire fit me like a second skin, excite me at the thought of it, represent the real me?*
6. If the answer is *yes*, great. If the answer is *no*, either add more specifics until you can answer with an honest *yes* or cross it off your list.
7. Know this: once you have a list of hopes and desires that feels true to you, you'll find yourself: 1. filled with a sense of purpose, and 2. fueled by your desire to achieve your deepest hopes and desires.

STEP 2E
WRITE THEM DOWN

1. Make sure you've written down your hopes and desires (as opposed to answering all these questions in your head) because the simple act of having a written list you can refer back to will increase your odds of success. Science has shown that the act of writing things down has significant effects on your brain. You'll be better able to remember for four reasons: 1. the paper you've written on will be a visual reminder to you every time you look at it, and repetition helps solidify that memory in your brain, 2. writing in your own words is more effective for memory creation than reading the words of others (known as the generation effect)[1], 3. writing increases the odds (also through the generation effect) that whatever you write will be encoded in your brain and stored as memory (brain encoding begins through the body's senses and is the first step in the process of memory creation)[2], and 4. writing will also let you process the information at least twice because you first think the thought then write it down, again using repetition to solidify that memory in your brain.

2. Keep that list where you can easily get to it but others cannot (so a drawer, a wallet, tucked inside a book, and the like).

3. Reread that list, even if you just scan it, often (daily, if that will help you the most) because repetition will solidify that list in your memory.

4. Use that list as a roadmap to get you to where you most want to go, to a life that matters to you. Now you know in which direction you need to be headed.

5. Use that list to help you refocus if you get distracted and/or discouraged.

STEP 2F
KEEP IT TO YOURSELF

1. Do yourself a kindness and don't tell anyone about your deepest hopes and desires just yet.

2. Know this: you're just getting started, and you might feel insecure or struggle with self-doubt or maybe you're even teetering on the edge of giving up because of fear. That's only natural.

3. Know this, too: if you share your deepest hopes and desires with the wrong person—someone with their own limits and fears, even if that happens to be someone you love, respect, and/or admire—they may either sow seeds of new doubt in you or increase the level of self-doubt that was already there. Imagine if they laugh at you or criticize you or say it's not a good idea or ask if you actually think you can have/be/do/say what you want. You're likely to shrink back, question your own hopes and desires, and maybe

even altogether abandon your endeavors to achieve the life you most want. You may even start repeating to yourself whatever it is they said to you, making their story into your own. And then you'll really get stuck, because not only will you quit but you're unlikely to try again anytime soon.

4. So even if you're excited about your deepest hopes and desires, keep quiet about them until you're *well on your way* working toward achieving them.

STEP THREE

IMAGINE YOUR IDEAL LIFE

Right now, your deepest hopes and desires are intangible, just thoughts and ideas and what-you-wished-your-life-looked-like in your head. The next step is to realize that your mind, as we've already discussed, is your greatest ally. It's a powerful tool that you need to use to your advantage. Every single thing that you have done or currently do had its origins as a thought in your mind at some point. Again, you thought about something and your brain, in turn, guided your body, telling your muscles to perform movements (some even minuscule) that you may not even have been aware of but that had a huge impact on the outcome of your life.

So how do you get your brain working for you and not against you? How do you harness the power of your brain to steer you to where you most want to be? Well, you start by imagining/daydreaming/envisioning your ideal life in your mind. The ability to imagine plays a key role in your being able to achieve that ideal life. Why? Because achieving your ideal life will take action on your part and your brain, according to neuroscience, doesn't distinguish between real and imaginary movements. Studies have shown that the same regions of the brain will be activated to the same degree whether a person is actually physically performing an action or just mentally imagining he/she is.[3] What that means to you is this: imagined actions are processed the same as real actions in your brain; your brain, in turn, sends out electrical impulses based on that input, which causes voluntary *and also involuntary* movements in your body.

The voluntary movements you are aware of, of course. But it's your subconscious mind that guides you without you knowing it through those tiny involuntary movements. Those tiny involuntary movements are the ones that will do the most, unbeknownst to you, to steer you toward what you think about and/or imagine. Buckling down isn't involved. Neither is working harder, faster, and/or smarter. Nor are massive amounts of willpower. Just thoughts and imagination, that's it. So, you see, you don't have to clench your jaw or give it everything you've got or put a lot of sweat, blood, and tears into your weight-loss efforts and/or your efforts to stop abusing food. You do, however, have to *actively and daily* imagine your ideal life.

When you imagine your ideal life, you are creating a picture in your mind of your end destination, of where you ultimately want to be. Right now, you are on a path to somewhere. Oh yes, you are. Why not choose to make that somewhere the place where you'd most like to be? Imagining your ideal life will give you something to aim for. It will give you direction. And most importantly, it will give you a sense of purpose.

Since you're reading this particular book, *part* of your ideal life is going to include eating only when you're hungry and stopping when you're comfortably full (or whatever way of eating you come to find works best for you). Part of your ideal life will also be the cessation of abusing food, which may mean a thinner you if you're overweight or a heavier you if you're underweight, but no matter your current size, always a healthier you. An important note: weight loss and/or overcoming food abuse *cannot* be all you envision for your ideal life; your life has so much more to offer than just your weight and what you choose to eat.

Some action steps to Imagine Your Ideal Life:

STEP 3A
SAY YES

1. Know this: you will more than likely have to actively push yourself out of your comfort zone to realize your deepest hopes and desires.
2. Know this, too: you'll never really know how much you're capable of, how strong you really are, and how fulfilling your life can really be until you leave the confines of the box you've put yourself in (or the confines of the body size you've trapped yourself in). Your life can be as grand or as simple as you want it to be, just make sure that it's not simple because you're afraid to leave your little zone of familiarity and safety (even though, remember, safety is just an illusion).
3. Choose to stretch and reach and grow.
4. And to do that you need to say *yes* to your ideal life.
5. Because if you say *no* at any point, well, your journey down that particular path ends (unless and until you say *yes* to it again).
6. So say *yes* and keep saying *yes* to any people, places, things, opportunities, and the like that will help you realize your deepest hopes and desires, which in turn will lead you to your ideal life.

STEP 3B
BEGIN WITH YOUR HOPES AND DESIRES

1. Take at least fifteen minutes to be alone somewhere quiet.
2. Read through your list of deepest hopes and desires (from Step Two, *Define Your Deepest Hopes And Desires*, then Step 2E, *Write Them Down*).
3. Now close your eyes and picture your ideal life in your mind, incorporating those hopes and desires.
4. Set the scene as if you were right in the middle of it. Let your mind wander to any and every possibility. Take note of where you are, what you're doing, what you look like, how old you are, the things and people you surround yourself with. Add in how things feel, smell, taste, and sound in your ideal life. Let the image in your mind feel vibrant and alive to you.
5. Then immediately afterward, with all that still fresh in your mind, write down what you envisioned for your ideal life using the present tense (so *I am*, not *I was* or *I will be*). Be as specific as possible with the details. Or you may want, especially if you're a visual person, to find images of your ideal life that correspond with what you saw in your mind's eye and arrange them in a collage. Again, be as specific as possible with the details.

STEP 3C
ADD IN YOUR GIFTS, TALENTS, AND PASSIONS

1. Read through what you wrote or look at the collage you created after you envisioned your ideal life (from Step 3B, *Begin With Your Hopes And Desires*).
2. Now *in relation to reaching that ideal life*, take some time to reflect and write *honest* answers to these:
   - *What are my strengths?* (so you're going to empower yourself and emphasize those)
   - *What are my weaknesses?* (so you know what not to emphasize nor spend a lot of your time on)
   - *Where is it necessary for me to strengthen my weaknesses?* (perhaps it's intellectual: so take a class and learn something new; maybe it's financial: so find more work or apply for grants; maybe it's psychological: so seek out a therapist/support group; maybe it's time: so look at where can you rearrange your schedule; you get the idea)
   - *Where is it necessary for me to let go of my weaknesses and ask for help and/or delegate?* (yes, you're going to need some help from others to reach your ideal life; nobody can do it all)

STEP 3D
CHANGE THE STORY YOU TELL YOURSELF

1. Pick one of your deepest hopes or desires (from Step 3B, *Begin With Your Hopes And Desires*), preferably the one you're most drawn to doing.
2. Now take a deep breath in through your nose, hold it for three seconds, then let it out slowly through your mouth with an audible sound.
3. Then write what bad things you believe could come to pass if you pursued that hope/desire. Write the most horrible thing you can imagine would happen if you moved in the direction of that hope/desire. Write the worst possible outcome you can think of if you pursued that hope/desire all the way to its end.
4. Now take a deep breath in through your nose, hold it for three seconds, then let it out slowly through your mouth with an audible sound.
5. Now write the most amazing things that could come to pass in your life if you pursued that hope/desire. Write the most phenomenal thing that you can imagine happening if you went in the direction of that hope/desire. Write the best possible outcome you can think of if you pursued that hope/desire all the way to its end.
6. Now take a deep breath in through your nose, hold it for three seconds, then let it out slowly through your mouth with an audible sound.
7. Know this: the worst or best outcome is the story that you're telling yourself. You will believe (and so live out) whatever story you tell yourself over and over.
8. So stop telling yourself that worst-possible-outcome story.
9. And start telling yourself that best-possible-outcome story instead.

STEP 3E
KEEP YOUR FOCUS

1. Keep your ideal life in the forefront of your mind.
2. Refer back to the vision of it (from Step 3B, *Begin With Your Hopes And Desires*) often, especially if you get distracted and/or discouraged.
3. Know this: keeping your ideal life as your focus will help you stay on track and will prevent you from winding up on detours that don't get you to where you most want to be.

STEP 3F
KEEP YOUR IDEAL LIFE TO YOURSELF FOR NOW

1. Know this: your ideal life is solely about *you* and what *you* want to see come to pass. So no need for anyone else's input or approval.
2. Be cautious when sharing your ideal life with others (so you don't get derailed by any negativity before you hardly even start). Again, it might be wise for you to wait until you're *well on your way* to achieving your ideal life before you tell others what you're striving toward.

STEP FOUR

MAKE AN UNBREAKABLE PROMISE TO YOURSELF

There's no way around this step. Making an unbreakable promise to yourself, without a doubt, is what will make or break your aspirations to reach your ideal life.

An unbreakable promise is the understanding and agreement with yourself, a kind of personal contract, that you are all-in. It means that you know and accept what you're getting into, and you'll keep taking action toward your ideal life no matter what challenges get thrown at you. It also shows that you are willing to do whatever it takes, through whatever means necessary (including shoving yourself clean out of your comfort zone) to reach that ideal life. An unbreakable promise to yourself signifies that reaching your ideal life matters deeply to you and you are striving to reach it for *your own self and your own well-being* regardless of what anyone else says/does. It's also a solemn vow to yourself that you'll press on and keep going, that you won't give up and quit. Remember: no matter what you choose, unbreakable promise to yourself or not, you're going to get hit with challenges in life, that's not a matter of *if* but of *when*. The great news is that you already decided way back in Chapter One to keep going until you reached the goal(s) you set for yourself; otherwise, you would've quit reading this book by now. Now, in this step, you just need to go a bit further and make that promise unbreakable.

Just to be perfectly clear: an unbreakable promise is one that you *fully intend to keep*. You'll just be wasting your time and energy if you off-the-cuff say, *sure I promise*, only to back out later when obstacles pop up or people leave your life or uncomfortable emotions hit you (and on the list goes) because you didn't fully understand the depth and breadth of what you were agreeing to. You need to know your level of commitment to yourself and at what point that commitment to yourself stops (meaning: *you'll go this far and no further.*) Being all-in means that you'll go as far as you have to, as far as it takes—even if you're so far out of your comfort zone that you can no longer see the edges of it—to save your own life. If that's not you, right now, just know this: 1. you're in your body and with yourself for the whole of your life, 2. you're worth the effort, and 3. all you have to do to raise your level of self-commitment is change your mind.

And finally, once you make an unbreakable promise to yourself, once you are *fully* all-in (meaning: *you will reach your ideal life. Period.*) and start taking action to move yourself toward your ideal life, I can tell you from personal experience that seemingly miraculous things will likely start to happen for you. Call it the universe, God, providence, the force, whatever works for you. But you'll likely be provided with all kinds of help. For example, people with the perfect expertise coming into your life right when you need them, money appearing almost out of nowhere to finance you on your way, words of encouragement when you most need to hear them, events lining up with perfect timing to take you on to the next step where you need to go, and the synchronicity list goes on. I'm a believer because I've seen it happen too many times in my own life not to be. I have no doubt that, when you make an unbreakable promise to yourself, you'll become a believer, too.

Some action steps to Make An Unbreakable Promise To Yourself:

STEP 4A
TURN YOUR DEEPEST HOPES AND DESIRES INTO DOABLE STEPS

1. Now write your best possible outcome (from Step Three, *Imagine Your Ideal Life*, then Step 3D, *Change The Story You Tell Yourself*) at the top of a new page.
2. Write (in broad terms) all the steps/actions you can think of that you'll have to take to get yourself from where you are now to that best outcome.
3. Repeat this process (writing a best possible outcome, then write in broad terms all the steps/actions you can think of) for each hope/desire on your list (from Step Two, *Define Your Deepest Hopes And Desires*, then Step 2E, *Write Them Down*).

STEP 4B
CHECK YOUR MOTIVATION, ALWAYS

1. Read through your list of doable steps (from Step 4A, *Turn Your Deepest Hopes And Desires Into Doable Steps*).
2. Then answer this: *Are these all about me and what I want for my life?*
3. Know this: creating doable steps based on what others want (people pleasing) or what others have (competition/comparison) is setting yourself up for failure. In the end, you either won't finish (because they don't deeply matter to you and so you'll quit) or you'll have no personal fulfillment when you do finish (because they weren't really your true wants to begin with).
4. So choose doable steps that deeply matter to you, that you deeply want.
5. Now answer these: *Will achieving these doable steps give me self-fulfillment and personal satisfaction? Will achieving these doable steps make me feel like I'm having a successful life?*
6. And if the answer is *no*, well, then that doable step needs to be adjusted/rewritten so it will give you those things or it needs to be removed from your list. (If you made a collage of images (from Step Three, *Imagine Your Ideal Life*, then Step 3B, *Begin With Your Hopes And Desires*), add or remove any images based on your newly-revised doable steps. Keep that collage somewhere you can see it often, preferably daily.)

STEP 4C
LET THAT DOABLE-STEP LIST HELP YOU PRIORITIZE

1. For each action that remains on your doable step list (from Step 4A, *Turn Your Deepest Hopes And Desires Into Doable Steps*), answer this: *Does this need to be done by me or can I delegate it to someone else?*
2. Circle/Highlight anything that can be delegated to someone else so you can lighten your load.

STEP 4D
ANSWER PROBING QUESTIONS HONESTLY

1. Answer these:
   - *Am I willing to believe in my own worth and value no matter what?*

- *Am I willing to decide right now that reaching my ideal life matters deeply to me and that's reason enough to strive for it?*
- *Am I willing to believe I am strong, courageous, tenacious, intelligent, and fully capable of doing whatever needs to be done so I can have a life I love?*
- *Am I willing to learn and experience new things?*
- *Am I willing to stick with it even if it takes a long time (longer than I ever imagined it could)?*
- *Am I willing to spend time, money, energy, resources, or whatever it takes on myself to facilitate my own growth and healing?*
- *Am I willing to leave my comfort zone?*
- *Am I willing to be open to growth and healing even if it's painful and/or requires me to do things that scare me?*
- *Am I willing to face whatever obstacles/challenges arise? Or carry on even through setbacks? Or do whatever it is I need to do to thrive and flourish?*
- *Am I willing to tell myself the whole truth and also face the whole truth?*
- *Am I willing to let go of everyone/everything that doesn't serve me so that I can become who I want and am meant to be?*

STEP 4E
COUNT THE COSTS OF CHANGE

1. Know this: moving forward will require you to change. There's no way around it.
2. Know this, too: you will have to sacrifice some things. There's no way around that either.
3. So answer these:
   - *Am I willing to sacrifice my time?*
   - *Am I willing to sacrifice my money?*
   - *Am I willing to sacrifice my current lifestyle?*
   - *Am I willing to sacrifice my social activities?*
   - *Am I willing to sacrifice my family and/or other significant relationships?*
   - *Am I willing to sacrifice whatever is necessary for my growth and healing?*
4. Know this also: your journey to your ideal life will likely take you down paths that you would have never originally thought you'd be going. It's entirely possible that you will have to sacrifice people, places, and/or things that you may never have foreseen coming.

5. So do yourself a kindness: *right now*, count the costs to the best of your ability and be clear on what you're willing to sacrifice so you aren't surprised and/or derailed later.

STEP 4F
GET RID OF ANY ESCAPE CLAUSE

1. Answer this: *Am I all-in no matter what?*
2. If your answer is *yes*, write your unbreakable promise: *I am fully all-in. I will reach my ideal life. Period.*
3. If your answer is *no*, answer these:
    *   *Why don't I want to be all-in?*
    *   *What am I afraid will happen if I commit to my own best health and well-being?*
4. Know this: You won't succeed in reaching your ideal life (or in much of anything, I would argue) if you're entertaining some kind of escape clause, even if that escape clause is just a thought (maybe even subconscious) in your mind. Why? Because when you have an escape option/plan, you give yourself permission to quit when the going gets tough.
5. So choose, *right now*, to be all-in and remove any kind of escape clause from your life.

STEP 4G
RESPECT YOURSELF

1. Choose (yes, it's your choice) to *always* trust yourself and treat yourself with respect.
2. So stop, *right now*, looking for external validation and/or permission from others.
3. Answer these:
    *   *Will I press on even if no one approves of my decisions/choices?*
    *   *Will I keep going even if no one else gives their stamp of approval to my ideal life?*
    *   *Will I carry on if there is no permission other than my own?*
4. So choose to respect yourself and validate your own ideal life.

STEP 4H
HONOR YOURSELF

1. Choose (yes, it's your choice) to *always* have integrity with yourself.

2. Know this: you're making this unbreakable promise *to yourself and no one else*. You are promising that you will start (and not procrastinate), you will carry on (through whatever life brings your way), and you will finish to see what you started through all the way to the end (reaching your ideal life, achieving whatever matters to you). That's what you're agreeing to.

3. So choose to honor yourself and keep your word to yourself.

STEP 4I
CHOOSE TO PERSEVERE

1. Decide, *right now*, that you will persevere, that your ideal life matters deeply to you and needs to be achieved by you, that you'll keep going until you reach your destination.

2. Know this: you may not see immediate results, you may not see results in the time frame you had in mind, and/or you may not get the results you were expecting.

3. Decide anyway, *right now*, that you will persist in the direction of your ideal life and that you will persevere until you reach a life that is true to you.

STEP 4J
BE WILLING TO GROW SLOWLY

1. Know this: crushing yourself (through unrealistic deadlines, by working a ridiculous amount of hours, with stringent guidelines, skipping doing things you enjoy, and the like) to force something to happen will only leave you burned out, miserable, and more likely to give up.

2. So cultivate and practice patience *every day*.

3. Be willing to grow slowly, even if you don't like it.

4. Know this, too: it's likely going to take some time to get where you want to be. It may even take a lot longer than you think. People (myself included) tend to *vastly* underestimate the time it takes to reach their destination.

5. Know this also: the good news is that you've got your whole life to get there. It doesn't matter *in the least* how slowly you're moving as long as you keep moving in the direction you most want to go and you don't stop.

6. Write this and add it to your unbreakable promise (from Step 4F, *Get Rid Of Any Escape Clause* (short version of promise) and also Step 4H, *Honor Yourself* (long version of promise): *I may go slowly, but I won't stop.*

7. And finally, know this: you're more likely to get to your ideal life by going slowly because you'll keep plodding along and moving in the direction of that ideal life instead of quitting in fear, frustration, anger, burnout, misery, and the like.

STEP 4K
BE HOPEFUL

1. Take hope to heart.
2. Know this: the quickest way to defeat is to lose hope, which causes you to lose heart, and so you give up.
3. So always believe there's hope, even if it's just a tiny sliver. Hang on to that hope no matter what.
4. Know this, too: if you keep taking action and moving forward, if you refuse to let anything derail you, then you will get to your ideal life. Oh yes, you will.

STEP FIVE

DESIGN YOUR TINY TARGETS

So this is the step that definitively separates those who reach their ideal lives from those who don't. It's here at designing your tiny targets, where you're going to need to accept some truths in order to move through. I call them targets because a target is something you aim at with the sole focus of hitting it.

First, the truth is that achieving your ideal life is not about sitting around hoping it comes to pass. Instead, designing your targets is about effort, taking steps *daily* to reach your ideal life, and keeping *every* unbreakable promise you make to yourself.

Second, this step is about moving forward and making measurable progress. So this is where you need to choose to stop wishing, discussing, dreaming, and the like about your ideal life, all of which do not actually yield any results. You'll need to choose to stop procrastinating and instead start taking action to move in the direction of your ideal life. Here is where you'll also have to choose to stop keeping yourself busy or distracted doing things that don't produce growth and movement toward what you most want, which also includes beginning lots of projects that move you toward your ideal life but never finishing them.

Third, and maybe the most challenging aspect of this step, is that *right here and now* is where you're going to have to accept that *you, and you alone,* are fully responsible for whether or not you reach your ideal life. That task falls squarely on your own shoulders because, remember, there's only one life you can truly save in this world and that's your own.

Your targets are those actions you wrote in Step Four, *Make An Unbreakable Promise To Yourself,* the ones where you started with the best possible outcome and wrote (in broad terms) all the steps/actions you'd have to take to get yourself from where you are now to that best outcome (from Step 4A, *Turn Your Deepest Hopes And Desires Into Doable Steps*). Your targets will serve as your road map. As any traveler can tell you, the easiest way to get from point A to point B is to follow a map. This step, designing your tiny targets, is about fleshing out each of those steps and drawing a roadmap with *as much detail as possible* so you can, easily and without too many detours or getting lost along the way, make it to your ideal life. It's also about making each of your targets smaller (tiny, if need be) so they aren't so frightening to do because the less scared you are, the more likely you are to take action and move forward.

Some action steps to Design Your Tiny Targets:

STEP 5A
SAY YES

1. Say *yes* to moving in the direction of your ideal life because if you say *no,* your journey down that particular path ends.
2. Keep saying *yes* to every step you're going to take to get there because, again and always, the moment you say *no,* well, your journey in that particular direction stops.

STEP 5B
CREATE YOUR TINY TARGETS

1. Read through your edited doable step list (from Step Four, *Make An Unbreakable Promise To Yourself,* then Step 4A, *Turn Your Deepest Hopes And Desires Into Doable Steps*).
2. Know this: you will be breaking down each doable step into smaller (tiny, if need be) steps, making them small enough that the thought of doing them doesn't make you anxious. Each one of those smaller steps is a tiny target (aim, focus, hit). It doesn't matter at all how big or small those targets are.

3. Know this, too: your best course of action is to make each target small, smaller, smallest. If you break each step down into the smallest possible increments, this is what'll happen: 1. they'll be so much easier to follow and achieve, which will encourage you and give you momentum to keep going, and 2. you're less likely to scare yourself and/or feel overwhelmed, confused, floundering, lost, and the like.

4. So start with just the first doable step you wrote (from Step Four, *Make An Unbreakable Promise To Yourself*, then Step 4A, *Turn Your Deepest Hopes And Desires Into Doable Steps*). That's now your big target, the one you aim to hit.

5. Write down all the smaller steps/actions you will have to take to reach the end result of just that first doable step.

6. Make each step small enough (again tiny, if need be) that the thought of completing it doesn't scare you or at least scares you much, much less. Those are now your tiny targets, the ones you aim to hit. (An example: one of my tiny targets was to click a button on a website to approve a proof. That was the only task I had that day. Click a button on the computer. That's it. And because I did that one simple thing: 1. I was done working toward my ideal life for the day, and 2. I got a reward, which we'll talk about more in a bit).

7. Know this also: tiny steps might be slower, true, but, in the end, they'll still get you where you want to be and usually with a lot less fear and stress.

STEP 5C
CREATE SPECIFIC TINY TARGETS

1. For each tiny target, add any specific details you'd like to hone that target so you get *exactly* what you want. Just like you eat exactly what you want so you feel sated, you're going to make tiny targets that are *as specific as possible* so you feel fulfilled. Add as many or as few details as you like.

2. Know this: you likely won't know every specific detail now. You will learn things as you grow and know yourself better.

3. So revisit your tiny target list and add (or subtract if you change your mind) more specific details as you move forward toward your ideal life.

4. Know this, too: the more specific you are, the easier it'll be for you to decide whether or not you're on track.

5. Keep your tiny target list somewhere you can see it often, preferably daily.

STEP 5D
RECOGNIZE YOUR SUCCESSES

1. Each time you finish and/or achieve an image in your collage (if you made one during Step Three, *Imagine Your Ideal Life*, then Step 3B, *Begin With Your Hopes And Desires*) or an item on your tiny target list, put a check mark, gold star, favorite sticker, and/or whatever makes you happy on it.
2. Know this: it's vital to give yourself visual cues that will serve as a reminder of all the progress you're making, the successes you're having, and how far you've come, which in turn will motivate you to keep going. (See *Oh, Some Science (Part Three)* at the end of this chapter to understand why recognizing your successes is so important.)

STEP 5E
LET THAT TINY TARGET LIST GUIDE ALL YOUR ACTIONS AND DECISIONS

1. Let your tiny target list be the roadmap you follow to get to where you most want to be. So refer back to that list when making decisions.
2. When faced with a choice/decision, ask this: *Does this choice help me get to my ideal life or hinder me from getting to my ideal life?*
3. If you answer honestly, you'll find decisions/choices will become easier to make and you will increase your chances of success exponentially.

STEP 5F
DEFINE MEASURABLE PROGRESS FOR YOURSELF

1. Pick a measurement that *works for you* (which might be: total number of pounds lost or blocking out half an hour every day for yourself or finishing a project every month).
2. Know this: you need to know what constitutes progress *for you* so you'll know for certain if you're making any.
3. Know this, too: no one is policing you. You are defining and making progress because doing so matters deeply to you.

STEP 5G
GIVE YOURSELF DEADLINES

1. Pick a deadline (date or time) that *works for you*, that both pushes/motivates you and is also realistic and achievable.
2. Let that deadline spur you to keep moving, reaching, and growing.
3. Do your best to reach that deadline.
4. But also cut yourself some slack and don't beat yourself up if you don't make it. Just practice self-compassion and keep working toward your tiny targets, your doable steps, and your ideal life until you do make it.
5. Know this: no one is policing you on this one either. Deadlines are *for you and you alone* to help you keep going and to help you measure your progress.
6. Always remember: you're doing all this to save your own life.

STEP 5H
DON'T SHARE YOUR TINY TARGETS WITH THE PUBLIC

1. Know this: you may think that broadcasting your tiny targets will motivate you by making you accountable to others.
2. But check your motivation as to why you feel the need to tell others.
3. Then know this, too: public declarations tend to make achieving your targets about them (whoever they are) and not about you. Making your targets about others only adds stress (you made a declaration, so pressure's on to reach it) and increase your fear of failing (all eyes are on you, after all).
4. Now answer this honestly: *What will happen if someone gives me a snarky little comment about my tiny target?* (Comments like: Just who do you think you are? You can't possibly do that. You really think you have what it takes? That's a stupid goal. And, sigh, sadly the list goes on.) *Will I use those comments as fuel and keep going? Or will I take them personally and give up?*
5. You'll be doing yourself a kindness if you keep your tiny targets to yourself for now (and for as long as you need or want to). Or if you feel like you need some support, then you find a person and/or a small group of people *you trust* to encourage you and you tell only that person/group.

STEP 5I
TAKE ACTION

1. Take a deep breath in through your nose, hold it for three seconds, let it out slowly through your mouth. Repeat (*repeat, repeat*) often and breathe your way through.
2. Do the first tiny target today.
3. Repeat *daily*—that's hugely important, every day do a little something, get yourself into a habit of moving forward—one tiny target after the next after the next until you reach your ideal life.

STEP 5J
CELEBRATE AND REWARD YOURSELF

1. Incentivize yourself and motivate yourself with something you really want. Give yourself a reward *every single time* you reach a tiny target. Yes. *Every. Single. Time.*
2. Know this: tiny targets are awesome because they are easy and you get a lot more prizes. You are worth the effort, time, and money to give yourself a little (or big) something that would bring you joy. (Three caveats: 1. not any food/beverage item nor any behavior/substance you abuse, 2. stay within your budget so as not to add stress to your life, and 3. only give yourself prizes that nourish you and make you feel good about yourself.)
3. Prizes don't have to cost much or even anything at all—the only thing that matters with prizes is that they will bring you happiness when you receive them and they'll feel like a little celebration for a job well done.
4. *Plan the rewards in advance.* So pick something you'd really like to have/do and make that your reward once you've hit your tiny target.
5. Be sure to have integrity with yourself and give yourself the prize. You did the work, you get the reward. Period.
6. Remember: you're training your brain all the time. So promising yourself a reward for doing the work then giving it to yourself equals trust yourself more (and motivate yourself more). And promising yourself a reward then refusing to give it to yourself equals trust yourself less (and demotivate yourself, too).
7. So every time you hit a tiny target, you go do something nice for you. (See *Oh, Some Science (Part Three)* at the end of this chapter to understand why giving yourself rewards is so important.)
8. Repeat. Reach a target, celebrate, give yourself a reward. Over and over.

STEP SIX

CREATE YOUR LIFEWORK

As you already know, your time alive is limited. All of us exchange our time on this earth for something. Wouldn't you rather it be for working toward and achieving your ideal life (the things that you most want, the things that you love, the things that make you feel the most alive)?

You create your lifework by doing this: 1. you make reaching your ideal life your focus and 2. you make your gifts, talents, and passions your purpose for being alive. Once you do that, your lifework gives you a reason to get up in the morning, targets to aim for, and a destination to reach. Creating your lifework, if you let it, will change your thinking and how you view the importance of your life. You let go of everything that's not serving you and everything that's not helping you in your quest toward your ideal life. You realize that you matter. You realize that your lifework matters because it matters to you. You finally understand that the simple fact that something matters to you is reason enough to pursue it and see it through to the end. Creating your lifework will also change the choices/decisions you make, how you treat yourself and others, and your overall behavior because now you *know* where you're going (so no more confusion), you are *determined* to get there (so no more procrastinating, waffling, hoping, wishing, and the like), and you'll *change* what you have/are/do/say in order to get yourself there (so you can finally be free to live a life that's true to who you are).

When your ideal life and your tiny targets become your lifework, well, that's when the magic truly happens. Your daily life, and also your overall life, will take on new and deeper meaning. You'll no longer feel like you're stumbling around in the dark, trying to find your way in your own life. You'll no longer be rudderless and adrift in any way, wondering why you're here. Instead, you'll know exactly in which direction you need to be headed and you'll also know the steps you need to take to get yourself there. The other great thing about creating your lifework is that it streamlines the process of making choices and decisions: so a *yes* to those things that help you reach your lifework and/or bring you joy/nourish you and a *no* to those things that don't. Creating your lifework will also prove to you (in case, for some reason, you didn't believe it) that you are responsible for your own life and how it turns out because you're the one who imagined your ideal life and designed your tiny targets to get there. Your ideal life is what *you* determined that you most deeply wanted, so you're accountable to yourself for the outcome and the results that you achieve.

And finally, you need to create your lifework because doing so will: 1. help you grow into the person you want to be and are meant to be and 2. increase your strength, perseverance, and persistence. You are more likely to stick with the process (and it is a process) and tough out the journey (and it is a journey, from now until you are gone) and keep going in the face of wanting to quit (because at some point, you will want to give up) if you believe that what you're doing matters deeply and is your lifework. It's imperative that you create your lifework—having it written down where you can reread it or having a collage of images you can see—that will remind you what most deeply matters to *you*, what *you* are working toward, and that *you are your sole motivation* to finish what you started. Your lifework, if you'll just let it, will act like an anchor during the turbulent times of your life, holding you steady so you don't stray off course, keeping you from capsizing when challenges hit you, and giving you something to hold on to when you don't yet see the blue skies at the end of the storm.

Some action steps to Create Your Lifework:

STEP 6A
COMBINE YOUR IDEAL LIFE AND UNBREAKABLE PROMISE WITH YOUR TINY TARGETS

1. Read through your answers from Step Three, *Imagine Your Ideal Life*, Step Four, *Make An Unbreakable Promise To Yourself*, and Step Five, *Design Your Tiny Targets*.
2. Organize those (including your measurable outcomes, deadlines, and rewards) by putting them together in a single notebook, computer file, poster board, or whatever works for you.
3. Revisit that compilation often (preferably daily) so: 1. your lifework can become your focus, 2. you will know which tiny target you need to hit that day, and 3. you will see your progress and know how far you've come.

STEP 6B
DECIDE YOUR LIFEWORK IS BOTH VITAL TO YOU AND A NECESSITY FOR YOUR HAPPINESS

1. Believe that your lifework needs to be accomplished by you in order for you to feel like you are having a successful life.

2. *Be your sole motivation.*
3. Disregard what anyone else says/thinks/does about your lifework because this is your life you're working to save.
4. Know this: when your ideal life is important enough to you that you'll achieve it no matter what, then it becomes your lifework.
5. Know this, too: once you see your lifework as a *necessity* in your life, as a *necessity* for your happiness, you will be willing to persevere regardless of what obstacles (growth being painful at times, self-doubt that you'll have to overcome, others who may shake your confidence, financial challenges, and the list goes on) that you encounter along the way.

STEP 6C
TAKE ACTION

1. Take a deep breath in through your nose, hold it for three seconds, let it out slowly through your mouth. Repeat (*repeat, repeat*) often and breathe your way through.
2. Do the next tiny target on your list today.
3. Repeat *daily*. Yes, one tiny target *every day*, one after the next after the next until you reach your ideal life.
4. Taking action daily will cement in your mind that your ideal life deeply matters to you and is your lifework. It will also train your brain and make a habit out of forward progress.

STEP 6D
CELEBRATE AND REWARD YOURSELF

1. Again, give yourself a reward (something you really want that nourishes you) *every single time* you reach a tiny target. Yes. *Every. Single. Time.*
2. Have integrity with yourself and give yourself the prize. You did the work, you get the reward. Period.
3. Repeat. Reach a target, celebrate, give yourself a reward.
4. Giving yourself rewards will also reinforce for you the importance of your lifework.

STEP 6E
ASSESS AND MONITOR YOUR PROGRESS

1. First, give yourself credit for how far you've come and write a list of all your victories and successes (no matter how big or small).
2. Then ask yourself the following questions:
   - *Am I on track, making progress and meeting my deadlines?* (If so, fantastic; celebrate, reward yourself, and keep going! If not, what changes do you need to make?)
   - *Am I growing and moving forward?* (If so, rock on! If not, what do you need to address so you can grow and move forward?)
   - *Am I productive (getting things finished) or just busy (lots of work but nothing completed)?*
   - *Am I stalled?* (If so, why?)
   - *Am I making excuses?* (If so, why?)
   - *Am I afraid?* (If so, that simply means your tiny target is too big. How can you make it smaller to the point where it doesn't scare you anymore?)
3. Make yourself accountable and keep an *honest* eye on how you're doing.
4. Know this: if you wind up off track, which sometimes happens, you'll be best served to know it sooner than later so you can make a few adjustments now and get yourself right back on track to where you need to be.
5. So just be honest about where you're currently at in your journey. Then make your tiny target as small as need be so you can start moving forward again.

STEP 6F
CUT YOURSELF SOME SLACK

1. Take the pressure off yourself, *right now.*
2. Remember: your aim is progress, not perfection.
3. Remember, too, to do yourself a kindness and look at your life like a game or an experiment.
4. So celebrate your successes and learn from your mistakes. Remember also: *there is only success or learning.*
5. If what you tried doesn't work, simply come back at your tiny targets with more wisdom and perspective on the next try.
6. Practice self-compassion. Be kind, gentle, and patient with yourself *always*, and just start again right where you are.

STEP 6G
REMEMBER YOU'RE ON A JOURNEY

1. So enjoy yourself along the way.
2. Take excellent care of yourself and take some breaks. Rest. Relax. Rejuvenate.
3. Allocate some time (even if it's just fifteen minutes) during your day to play and take your mind off everything.
4. Go on excursions for your mental health and well-being.
5. Do things that bring you joy *now* and choose to be happy *now*, not when you reach your goal weight and/or your ideal life.
6. Be open to opportunities that come your way. Try something new just for the exhilaration of it. Remember: you need to keep saying *yes* if you want your journey down that particular path to continue.
7. Give yourself permission to bring yourself happiness as you work your way from one tiny target to the next, however that happiness looks for you.
8. Embrace and enjoy the process of getting to your ideal life.

STEP 6H
LET YOUR LIFEWORK FUEL YOU

1. Again, it may take some time to get where you're going.
2. So let your lifework be a source of encouragement, motivation, inspiration, and joy in your life. Let it fuel you to keep going.
3. Let your lifework befriend you, too. Let it keep pulling you upward and forward, especially on the days when you're tired and you just want to stop. Let it remind you that this is where you're headed and, yes, you're going to get there.

STEP 6I
FINISH

1. Don't stop until you have seen what you've started all the way through to the end.
2. Remember: you won't be finished until you reach your ideal life and the final result of your purpose.
3. Remember, too: it doesn't matter *in the least* how slowly you go as long as you don't stop.

STEP SEVEN

LIVE WITH PURPOSE

By now, I hope you understand that you're choosing the life that you're living. And I hope, too, that by now you know the only way to have a different life, one that you love and is true to who you are, is to make different choices. Again, that means being thoughtful and purposeful in your decisions and your actions. All the work you've done so far has been to get you to consciously think about what you most deeply want so: 1. you'll know in which direction you need to be headed, and 2. you'll start taking action and moving forward in that direction. When you live with purpose, you say *yes* to head fears, regardless of how much they scare you, because you know they'll help you grow into the person you want and are meant to be, and you say *no* to those people, places, and/or things that don't move you toward your ideal life.

Living with purpose also requires that you deeply believe both that you matter and that what you're doing matters. You need to strengthen your belief that you're on a mission (which you are, your mission is your lifework, and now you just need to believe that *every day*). You also need to cultivate a sense of urgency: *you need to be doing your lifework now and it needs to be completed by you soon* (because, I'm sorry to say, your life is finite and there are no guarantees as to how long you'll be around).

Why do both those things matter? Because you'll only be willing to sacrifice and do whatever it takes when you deeply believe both in yourself and in your lifework. To save your own life, you need to deeply believe that you're worth saving, that what you have to offer matters, and that you have something in your lifetime that needs to be completed by you. Once you *truly* believe that—deep down where it matters most and where that belief won't be swayed by anyone or anything—you'll accept that your lifework is your mission, you'll work hard toward achieving it regardless of challenges that may come, and you will ultimately succeed because you just will not quit until you see your lifework through all the way to the end.

And finally, living with purpose includes not holding on to your history (*well, I've done it this way for years and I'm not changing* or *I made a crushing mistake and I blew my only chance* or *I've failed too many times and I'll never succeed* or *nothing works out for me because I'm not worth it* or [*insert whatever it is you tell yourself about your past here*]) and sacrificing yourself and your future in the process. You let go of your history so you can move forward unencumbered. That means you learn what you can from what's happened in your past (what worked and what didn't work, what you did and what you failed to do) then you start fresh today, right where you are, from a more wise and informed perspective.

And once you learn, you teach others so you can bring them up along with you. From this point on, you fully accept as one of your core driving principles: *more life for all*. You understand that you're not in competition with others, trying to get your fair share; instead, you're in collaboration with others, trying to help them realize their potential while you are busy realizing your own. You save yourself, yes, and in doing so you give permission, by your example and by your teachings, for others to save themselves. And in that way, by your own coming alive, you give the world at large what it most needs: more people who have come alive.

Some action steps to Live With Purpose:

STEP 7A
COACH YOURSELF

1. You act toward yourself just like any good (team or life) coach would.
2. Living with purpose means you don't wait around for motivation, inspiration, or encouragement to come from the outside.
3. You encourage yourself with reassuring words you most need to hear when you're feeling down. You holler at yourself to keep going when you're ready to quit. You give yourself whatever tools you need. You tell yourself you can do this when succeeding or failing at reaching your ideal life is on the line. You do whatever it is you need to do to handle obstacles and/or learn from setbacks so you can pick yourself back up, dust yourself off, and carry on.
4. Use your own name when you encourage yourself. (Example: *You do beautiful work, YOUR NAME; You got this, YOUR NAME; You are capable/strong/intelligent/tenacious, YOUR NAME.*)
5. Know this: you know yourself better than anyone, so you know best what you need at any given moment. Yes, you do. So in those moments when you desperately need someone to give or say or do something that will help you, well, you just coach yourself.
6. Know this, too: feel-good biochemical levels rise in your brain when you hear words of encouragement; that's true whether those words of encouragement come from someone else or from yourself. (See *Oh, Some Science (Part Two)* at the end of this chapter to understand why encouraging yourself is so important.)

STEP 7B
ALWAYS LOOK FOR THE OPEN PATH

1. Know this: some paths you may really, really want to walk down are blocked to you. Maybe the timing is off and you're not meant to go down them yet. Or maybe there's something dangerous for you that way so you're actually being protected. Or maybe you're just not meant to go down that particular path at all. That's true even if you don't feel that way, don't believe it, and/or don't want to accept it. It's also true that in some cases, paths you go down may not look the way you thought they would/should and so they just plain aren't what you envisioned/wanted at all.

2. Know this, too: you probably don't see all the other paths that are open to you because you're so focused on the ones that are blocked.

3. Now write a list of paths that you really want to go down that seem to be blocked to you.

4. Living with purpose means that you choose to be flexible and open to other options. It means you look away from those blocked paths and instead look around for other opportunities. So write answers to these:
   - *What other paths are open to me that will still get me to where I want to be?*
   - *What other choices do I have?*
   - *What other decisions do I need to make that will move me forward?*
   - *What other actions can I take that will make me feel alive?*

5. Let go of any blocked path(s). Do yourself a kindness and stop wasting time that you cannot get back. And make no mistake that staring down a blocked path, hoping and wishing and yearning, is just a waste of your time.

6. Now find a way that's open to you. Choose to go down that path instead.

7. Know this also: it's entirely possible, and even quite likely, that the path of least resistance is the one you're meant to be on.

STEP 7C
HAVE AN ABUNDANCE MENTALITY

1. Believe that there's always enough for you (because there absolutely is).

2. Believe that you're not in competition with others for scarce resources; instead believe there is enough to go around for everybody (because there absolutely is).

3. Believe deep down in your core that you want more life for all.

4. Be genuinely grateful for all the good things already in your life.
5. Believe that you will always get everything you need and more.
6. Living with purpose means you practice all of those things (numbers 1-5 above), thinking them repeatedly until they become beliefs or doing them repeatedly until they become habits.
7. Know this: once you *genuinely* change your mentality, seemingly miraculous things—money, relationships, perfect timing, stuff you most want—will likely start coming into your life without a whole lot of effort on your part.
8. Remember: levels of dopamine (the feel-good chemical) rise in your brain when you're consciously grateful for what you have, which in turn makes you feel happier and more content.

STEP 7D
TAKE A LEAP OF FAITH

1. You must get out of your comfort zone and step into the unknown.
2. Take heart because you're in excellent company with the rest of us hanging out beyond the confines of our comfort zones who aren't necessarily happy about it and/or don't necessarily like it either.
3. Know this: you may, even now, have only the vaguest of notions as to where you're supposed to be headed. Or maybe you know exactly where you want to be but you're not quite sure of all the steps you need to take to get you there. Or maybe you're just too scared to even try. But you must take the first step, even if you have to hold your breath and your heart is a jackhammer in your chest and you're trembling like a sapling in a hard wind.
4. So take the leap of faith no matter what.
5. Prove to yourself just how much courage you have. Then the next step and the one after that and the one after that (and on and on) will get easier.
6. Know this, too: your comfort zone will expand and grow with every step you take, and you will amaze yourself at just how much you are truly capable of.

STEP 7E
CHANGE YOUR FOCUS

1. Take your focus off food and/or other substances/behaviors that you're abusing and put it squarely on reaching your ideal life.
2. So focus on what *you* truly want, who *you* truly want to be, and where *your* ideal life will take you.

3. And it will be those things that you focus on that will grow and expand in your life.

STEP 7F
PRIORITIZE

1. Remember: your life, as a whole, is what you choose to do in exchange with your time.
2. So put yourself as *number one* on your daily to-do list. Take excellent care of yourself. Meet your own needs. Make your well-being your first priority. Make completing your lifework your mission.
3. Then, with yourself firmly at number one, you choose and prioritize what's most important to you: those people, places, and/or things that matter most deeply to you, those activities/actions that will help you reach your ideal life sooner.
4. Know this: you make the schedule you keep and you also choose the people, places, things, and/or activities that will help you or hinder you.
5. So do yourself a kindness and choose wisely.

STEP 7G
SURRENDER THE OUTCOME

1. Let go of trying to control the outcome.
2. Relax into the process and the journey.
3. Breathe (deeply in through your nose, hold three seconds, let it out slowly through your mouth) your way through.
4. Know this: once you let go of controlling the outcome, absolutely surrender it, there is space available for truly miraculous things to happen in your life that will likely surpass your wildest dreams.
5. Know this, too: the caveat to reaching that place of miraculous things is that you have to let go of controlling the outcome to get there.

STEP 7H
BE PATIENT

1. Practice (*practice, practice*) patience.
2. Be kind and gentle with yourself as you wait.

3. And accept, *right now*, that there's a reason you're not *yet* where you want to be:
    *   Maybe you need to build your character or learn to accept rejection or be more humble.
    *   Maybe you need to learn perseverance or to trust yourself or to negotiate confrontation.
    *   Maybe you are lost and need to find yourself first.
    *   Maybe you've given up and need to believe in yourself again.
    *   Maybe you're overwhelmed and overstressed so you need to learn how to have fun and enjoy life first.
    *   Maybe you need to stop seeking approval from others and start trusting your own intuition.
    *   Maybe you need to strengthen your mental health so you are ready for wild success when it comes.
    *   Maybe you need to conquer your fears.
4. So stop fighting against what currently is and instead look for the lesson(s) in whatever you're going through. The sooner you learn whatever it is you need to learn from the happenings in your life, the sooner you will move forward toward the place you want to be.

STEP 71
REMEMBER YOU'RE STILL GROWING

1. Every day, remain open so that you can learn what works and what doesn't, what you want from life and what you don't, what actions you need to take and when you need to let go.
2. Know this: maybe you're not where you want to be, but the fabulous news is that you're still breathing and still growing and still learning, all of which means that you still have time to take action in the direction of your ideal life and your lifework.

OH, SOME SCIENCE (PART ONE)

So by now you know that what you say about yourself has power, what you believe is what you will live out in your life, and what you do is always a choice you are making. You create the world you're living in.

Now we need to talk about the psychological term congruence again. Congruence is when how you act and what you say and the things you do in the outside world are in alignment with what you think and believe inside of you.[4] We already talked about honestly and integrity with yourself before, and this, congruence, is why it's vital that you do your best to not only express yourself but also take actions that are in line with what you believe. Why? Because an absence of congruence (where you believe one thing but act/say/do another) leads to:

- an increase in stress (which increases levels of various biochemicals in your body that, left unchecked, weaken your immune system and make it more difficult to lose weight, among other detrimental things)
- some difficulty in your brain building/maintaining memory pathways (because you beat one path with your thoughts and another with your actions).[5]

Always remember: creating new and lasting beliefs or behaviors starts in the brain, and you are training your brain all the time. If you act/say/do things that don't match your thoughts and beliefs, you're providing conflicting information. Well, you believe this, but you're doing/saying something different. Your brain, in turn, won't know which beliefs/behaviors are supposed to dominate so neither will, which causes problems in the way neural pathways are formed.[6] *That's why positive thinking, by itself, doesn't work to change your brain.* Congruence—positive thinking in line with positive actions—is what will work to change your brain and, in turn, change your life.

OH, SOME SCIENCE (PART TWO)

Serotonin is a biochemical that, among other things, is involved in creating feelings of self-worth, self-confidence, and happiness. Speaking words of encouragement to yourself starts with uplifting thoughts in your mind. Those thoughts have been shown to positively influence serotonin production.[7] Likewise, talking about yourself (including self-introspection) has been shown to activate the mesolimbic dopamine pathway, which is part of the pleasure/reward center of your brain (meaning: it releases the biochemical dopamine that makes you feel good).[8] To add to that, research has shown that when you use your own name while speaking strength to yourself (*Nice work, YOUR NAME*; *Keep going, YOUR NAME*; *You can do this, yes you can, YOUR NAME*), you are involuntarily activating several parts of your brain, including those responsible for self-reflective behaviors that are the core of who you are as a person [9] (which is a powerful way to get your own attention).

OH, SOME SCIENCE (PART THREE)

Rewards come in two types: intrinsic, which are pleasurable by nature (you like them), and 2. extrinsic, which are not inherently pleasurable but at some point you learned that they bring you pleasure much like an intrinsic reward (you want them). Incentive salience, which is how much you want a particular extrinsic reward, is what causes the degree of intensity with which you go after that particular reward. It is a cognitive process that occurs in your brain's hypothalamus, is mostly regulated by the transmission of dopamine, and contains both a wanting (which drives motivation) and a liking (which creates pleasure when you achieve) component.[10]

The mesolimbic dopamine pathway in your brain is what activates when you receive a reward. Dopamine, again, is the biochemical that makes you feel good. When you receive any reward, dopamine levels spike in your body. In particular with extrinsic rewards (the ones you choose for yourself), the amount of that dopamine spike is significantly correlated to how much you want that particular reward (so the more you want it, the more dopamine will be released in your body when you get it). Your brain doesn't distinguish whether that reward is coming from someone else or from yourself; the dopamine spike happens either way.[11]

That same mesolimbic dopamine pathway also activates when you recognize your successes due, in part, to the liking component of incentive salience (because you achieved something you wanted). Every time you set and reach a target (even if they are tiny targets), your brain gets a spike of dopamine. In the same way, each time you acknowledge your progress and see how far you've come, your brain also gets a burst of dopamine. To best reap the pleasurable feelings that dopamine produces, you need to take a moment to savor those successes (and let the dopamine circulate in your brain) instead of rushing on to the next thing.[12]

OH, SOME SCIENCE (PART FOUR)

Why all this talk about dopamine? Well, John Salamone, a researcher at the University of Connecticut, has shown that dopamine production is positively correlated with motivation. That study has shown that low levels of dopamine cause people to be less willing to work for what they want, which means they tend to choose the easiest way even if that way has little personal reward for them. On the other hand, higher levels of dopamine in the body do the opposite, motivating people to make an effort to reach for what they want, even if the task is difficult, because the reward has great value to them.[13]

So what does this mean to you? If you want to be more motivated to reach for what deeply matters to you, you need to get your body producing more dopamine. How do you get your body to do that? Well, it's stuff we've already talked about, all of which causes dopamine levels to increase naturally (a partial list):

- Make tiny targets for yourself and reach them.
- Recognize your successes.
- Talk with someone you trust and get positive feedback.
- Envision your ideal life.
- Play to your strengths and delegate your weaknesses to others.

THIS IS A PRACTICE AND A PROCESS

Just another friendly reminder to not beat yourself up if you don't get this right. The whole process of finding what makes you feel alive and then doing it is about getting it right more often than you get it wrong. Be extra kind to yourself when you make mistakes. Channel the kindest person you know when you talk to yourself after you screw up, because you will screw up *and that's okay*. Don't use your mistakes as an excuse to abuse food or numb yourself with some other substance/behavior or throw in the towel or turn your back on yourself. All you have to do is start again, right where you are.

Don't make yourself crazy trying to follow the rules. If you want to make rules/guidelines (and I use those terms loosely), then make ones that work for you and follow those (and still don't make yourself crazy trying to follow them). Release yourself from the slavery of perfection so that you can be yourself, which is all you want anyway, because yourself is awesome and amazing as-is. And remember: every mistake is simply a brand new chance to do it better the next time.

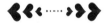

CHAPTER SEVEN

LET FEAR BE YOUR GUIDE

OR

**How to be
the hero of
your own story.**

Chapter Seven

"You gain strength, courage, and confidence by every experience in which you really stop to look fear in the face. You are able to say to yourself, 'I have lived through this horror. I can take the next thing that comes along.' You must do the thing you think you cannot do."
—Eleanor Roosevelt

THE THERAPIST'S OFFICE *is a small room, space enough for a desk and a chair and a small couch against the far wall. There's a long narrow window in the corner that lets in a slant of afternoon light. It falls in a rectangle near my feet. I poke my toe into the light then pull it back. The desk is mostly neat. A calendar blotter with tiny doodles in the corners, puffy clouds and lopsided stars, a phone number scrawled in smeared blue ink near the bottom, and a half dozen overlapping coffee rings. Pencils and pens, tips down, in a red ceramic cup on the right corner. A stack of Manila folders in a metal tray. A swivel chair on rollers with a plastic mat underneath to protect the baby-blue carpeting. Potpourri in a crystal bowl on the left corner, giving off just the faintest of scents, the rose petals covered in a thin layer of dust. A fern in the window, the tips brown and the soil cracked and dry.*

The lady does not have a green thumb, I think.

I stare out the long window at the parking lot. A man stands next to a green Toyota and fumbles in his coat pocket for his keys. His arm is slung around a brown paper grocery bag and two fingers from that same hand hold a dangling briefcase. He's yanking and pulling at his pocket. The car window reflects his face: horn-rimmed glasses and a receding hairline and his mouth slung open, probably cursing at the stuck keys. The clock above the desk ticks, the second hand jerking its way around the face. I fiddle with my hands, weave the fingers together, crack the knuckles, press the tips into the couch arm until they blanche, then smooth them along my thighs.

The counselor is in her forties, I guess. Short dark hair cut in a bob with a hint of gray where the color didn't cover. A silver barrette holds the left side like a schoolgirl. The barrette has a blue jewel near the clasp that sparkles as it catches the light. Wrinkles at the edges of her eyes. She wears a tracksuit, navy with silver piping down the legs and cuffed around the wrists. The top is too small, the fabric stretched and straining across her bust. She rolls forward on her swivel chair so the desk is no longer between us and she says, "Do you know why you're here, Shelli?"

I look at the counselor then at the cream-colored mug clasped between her hands. There's a red lipstick imprint on the rim. The lipstick on her mouth, though, has faded through the day, mostly rubbed down to a washed-out pink. Her lip is cracked underneath, bloodied at one time and now crusted over. She leans forward on her chair. Her thighs are thick and they spread across the cushion. The chair creaks. "Your parents," she says, "are concerned about your weight gain."

I turn to the window again. My mother's old Ford sits in the parking lot, low-angled sunlight glinting off the windshield. Mother is in the waiting room right now, a few doors and a short hallway away, licking the tips of her fingers and leafing through a Good Housekeeping magazine. Just fifteen minutes before, we'd been together in the station wagon, Mother with her hand on the gearshift, pushing it into park, me staring at the office building with its pinkish windows reflecting the shopping mall in the background. Mother turned the key and the engine sputtered a few times then clacked once and went silent. She turned to me and said, "This appointment is for you, Shelli. You don't talk about us, me and your father. Don't you air our dirty laundry. You understand? Our dirty laundry's nobody else's business, especially to some stranger."

"What am I supposed to talk about then?"

"You just talk about what's wrong with you."

And then we were in the elevator, the silence thick between us. Then we were in the empty waiting room, where I stood looking at a half-dozen magazines, none of them for teenaged girls, fanned across a coffee table in the center. The cloudy receptionist's window slid back. Mother's voice came high and friendly, giving first her name and then mine.

In the counselor's office, I just stare out the window. The green Toyota is gone, a fresh oil spot on the ground where it had been. I think: Someday, I'll write my story and call it, Dirty Laundry Hanging on the Line. Out there flapping in the breeze, snapping away for everyone to see, how about that Mother?

"Shelli?" the counselor says.

It's hot, stuffy in the room. I am big. I suffer in the heat. Sweat blooms on my forehead, around the collar of my shirt, bumps down my back, gathers between my thighs so when I stand up there will be a damp spot on the cushion where my crotch had been. I glance at the clock, white round face with green hands that give off a luminous glow when it gets dark. 6:10 p.m. Fifty more minutes to go.

"They say you yell a lot at home. There's a lot of fighting. Can you tell me why you're so angry? Why are you lashing out at your family?"

Father walked past me that morning, frowning, a look on his face like he bit into a lemon. He scrounged in the refrigerator, pulled out a carton of half-and-half and set it on the counter. He poured himself a cup of coffee, spooned in sugar, tipped in a dollop of cream, then stirred, the spoon clinking against the sides of the mug. The refrigerator whirred on and birds on the deck chattered at the feeder and the floor creaked as he shifted his weight to put the creamer back. He tossed the spoon into the sink and blew on the coffee, steam rising in a swirl. He took a single sip then looked at me over the rim. He averted his eyes just as quick, like somehow it hurt to even see me. Then he shuffled back out of the kitchen without a word, leaving me there at the table alone. Six months since he last spoke directly to me. Six months since that day when he pinned me on the bed. If he needs to say anything, he says it to Mother, who then says it to me. He won't speak to me, even if I speak to him first, standing there looking up at him, waiting for an answer. If Mother isn't there, he'll just walk away. Or if Mother isn't there, and I am in the way, he will just shove me hard. Not a single word directly to me. Not one. Six months and a clear message: you don't exist, you don't matter, no one wants to hear what you have to say. I do not know this yet, but this silence between he and I will last for over a year. The message will be hammered home.

Outside, dandelions dot the narrow strip of grass between the parking lot and the sidewalk. They're swollen with white fuzz. Tufts of those spores scatter on the breeze, catching on silver car antennas and the boxwood bushes lining the walkway and the blue awning of the building. A single skinny maple, surrounded by all that concrete and blacktop, tosses in a gust of wind. The tree makes me think of a lonesome finger, stabbing toward the sky. A line of dark birds sway on the low arc of a telephone wire until something startles them. They rise in a group, bank to the south, and vanish over the top of the mall.

"Shelli," the counselor says, "your parents wouldn't bring you here if they didn't care about you."

6:17. Forty-three more minutes.

"We're good parents," Mother had said just two days before. "Some kids are just born bad."

She'd been angry when she said it. The soft dark holes of her nostrils flared, her face a lovely shade of crimson. The flat of her hand slammed against the table to emphasize and give a kind of texture to her words so that every time I hear that same sound—the flat thwack of a palm against wood—I'll think: some kids are just born bad.

What if Mother is right? What if I was just born bad? What if it's inherent? Part of my nature? What if there's no fixing it? Broken. Busted beyond repair. Toss me out. Get a new one.

My chin trembles. I clench my teeth to make it stop. I blink a half dozen times. I press back the cuticles on the fingers of my left hand; the one on the ring finger is red and inflamed. The thumbnail's been bitten down to the quick. There are scratches near the meat of my thumb where the outdoor cat got me when I tried to corral it into the garage. A stray thread snakes out from the hem of my shirt, and I wrap it around my index finger, unwrap it, wrap it again, then let it go. The white thread holds the curl.

"Shelli, your mom is paying me to help you. I can't help you if you won't talk."

6:28. Thirty-two minutes left.

In my head, I'm laughing. Ha, ha. What is there to say? Another lie? I've lied enough. I live a lie every day. Smile, Shelli, smile. Say everything is fine. Okey-dokey. A-okay. Roger that. I'm fine, we're fine, everything's great, nothing to see here. Move along. All of it a lie. Doesn't this woman understand that the screaming, my screaming, is just a release? Like a pressure cooker venting steam because otherwise it would explode and take out everything around it. It's also a way to feel alive, because when I'm not screaming, I feel dead.

The therapist sighs. She sips at her drink, long since gone cold. The lipstick print smudges. A drop of tea rolls down the side, hangs there for just a second at the bottom of the mug, then falls and dots the polyester fabric on the woman's thigh. "Okay, Shelli. I can't make you speak. You want to talk, I'm right here."

Maybe, I think, it is me. Maybe, somehow, it's all my fault. Maybe there's a reason they don't like me, that other people don't like me. Maybe I was born with it. Maybe I was born bad like Mother said. Why can't I be somebody else? Why? Why?

Sometime in the last ten minutes, the sun dropped a notch in the sky and now hangs just over the top of that skinny maple. It slides into the office in a long sheer and hits me in the stomach. I poke my fingers through the buttonhole of my shirt, feel the warm spongy flesh below my navel. Honestly, what is there to say? To admit the dirty laundry is to admit there's something wrong with me. And what would people think then? That I'm unlovable? Unwanted? Unworthy? Un—what? Just un—.

I curl that stray thread again, pull it gently until it bunches the cotton near the hem. Outside, two teenagers walk hand-in-hand along the sidewalk. I make up a story about them: the blonde girl riding shotgun in a rusted Chevy pickup truck, cruising down an empty dirt road, gravel pinging up against the undercarriage, only the headlights to illuminate the trees on either side, flowing past like water in a stream, and the girl's bare feet crossed at the ankle and hanging out the window, leaning against the boy's shoulder, her face washed in the dashboard lights, on their way to a bonfire where they'll dance slow, taking tiny steps across a hayfield, twirling through the dewy grass and the mist coming up off the pond, the cows lowing in the field beyond a barbed-wire fence. Then a little red-headed girl in a yellow sundress dress skips past, holding the hand of a man in a rumpled business suit. Another story: the red-headed girl in pink bunny pajamas, standing in a bathroom doorway with her teddy bear clutched to her chest, wiping the sleep from her eyes, and the man, her father, leaning over the sink, washing blood from his hands, saying, "It's just paint, Rosie. That's all. Just paint. You remember Homer from down the road? We was just painting his barn."

The clock chimes softly. 7:00 p.m.

I heave myself standing and head for the door.

"Take a seat in the waiting room, Shelli. I want to talk to your mom."

I know I'll get an earful in the car on the way home about how much money the counselor costs. I hear it every time we go. This is the first time I haven't spoken a word. Maybe I won't ever have to come back. How can the woman possibly help me if I can't tell her the truth? "What a waste," Mother will say later, her hands tight on the steering wheel, and that last word will cut through me like a blade. What I'll hear: Shelli, you're not worth the money. Shelli, you are a waste.

I am fifteen years old.

THE HERO'S JOURNEY

Most stories follow a predictable path, an arc that the main character must go through from the beginning of the story to the end. This same essential pattern can be found in different stories from around the world, where the hero must go through a series of stages of adventure before she comes out victorious. "The Hero's Journey" is an explanation of this pattern described by Joseph Campbell, who studied myths and archetypes, in his book, *The Hero with a Thousand Faces*. What follows in this chapter is my telling of the hero's journey in my own way, leaning on Campbell's structure. (Hero in this context refers to females as well.)

Essentially, a common person becomes a hero when she ventures out of her comfort zone and into the unknown, she encounters then defeats the obstacles and enemies that try to block her way, and then she returns to her normal life with a newfound wisdom that she then passes on to others. Well, I'd argue that it's not just fictional stories and myths that follow this pattern. As I've been saying throughout this entire book, you've been telling yourself a story your entire life (about who you are, what you're capable of, what your chances are, who you want to become, and the like). You are living your story right now. You are the main character, the protagonist. I'd argue that you, too, are on a hero's journey, whether you realize it or not. And my guess is that you want to be victorious.

So no matter where you are in your life, if you feel stuck (which you likely do with your weight, abusing food, self-image, or whatever it is for you), just remember this: your life is *your* story, you can *always* (even right now) make some edits, you can *always* (even right now) rewrite the ending.

STAGE ONE
THE CALLING AND SAYING NO TO IT

Definition: The hero starts out as a normal person just living her life within her comfort zone when a catalyst happens, something that calls her to action and makes her trek out into the unknown.[1] The normal person who isn't yet a hero often refuses the calling. The refusal can come from any number of reasons that keep the potential hero safe in her comfort zone. The refusal changes her journey: the person goes from being empowered through action to disempowered through waiting for another to come save her.[2]

This is the part where you know/feel/believe that your life has a calling on it, something that you're supposed to do, some adventure that you're supposed to embark on. I'm a firm believer that everyone has a reason for being alive. I'm also a firm believer that everyone has gifts, talents, and passions to offer regardless of whether you earn a living off them or not (see Chapter Six to discover yours). The calling will upset the status quo, which is often scary. You won't be able to live the same way you've been living or look at life the same way as you have been, which can also be scary. You will have to change and grow, which is scary too, but also what we've been talking about this entire book.

Sometimes the calling is overt and you know it without a doubt. Other times, it's a nagging sensation that just won't go away. Either way, the calling is there. I know it is. It was for me; it is for you. You may be ignoring the call on your life. You may be one of those people plugging their ears with their fingers, thinking that'll stop you from hearing it. You may keep yourself ridiculously busy, trying to ignore it. Or maybe you start moving in the opposite direction, trying to outrun it. Or, as was true for me so maybe it is for you too, you eat and eat (and eat some more and/or purge and/or starve, abusing food in some way) to numb yourself because you're afraid to say *yes* to the calling. But no matter your reaction, the calling is still there, whether you want to heed it or not.

You may have lots of little callings, which tend to lead you to the bigger one. Those little callings are also knowings in your heart, head, and/or gut (your voice of wisdom or intuition) that you're supposed to go in a certain direction and do/say certain things. Maybe those little callings ask things of you like: change careers, stop eating wildly, go back to school, create something brand new, move to another country. The little callings are sometimes easy but not always.

Weight loss and the cessation of abusing food is a little calling. While you may think that getting rid of the excess weight then keeping it off and/or no longer abusing food is the journey of a lifetime, it's not the end destination. It's a stepping stone toward having a life that fulfills you. We talked in Chapter Six about your gifts, talents, passions, and who, deep down, you most want to be. Knowing those things about yourself matters because both the weight (overweight and underweight) and food abuse (in general) are just barometers. They are just there to tell you that something's wrong, to point out that you're not happy or satisfied with your life in some way. Right now, you may feel that your life revolves around: trying not to binge on food, numbers on a scale, diet after diet after diet, crazy amounts of exercise, purging after you eat, refusing to eat at all, and the like. But your life, I hope you've come to see, is so much bigger and more important than all of that.

Here's something that's absolutely true: *You'll know the calling on your life when you hear it. You may not want to know it, but you will.*

Three of my little callings:
- Getting rid of the excess weight.
- Learning to be absolutely secure in my own self.
- Writing this book.

If you want to be the hero of your own story, you're going to have to accept the calling. There's just no way around it. If you were writing the story of your life and your hero (that's you) said *no*, well, you're done writing a couple of paragraphs in. Say *no*, and that's the end of your hero's journey. If you want to be the hero of your own life, you're going to have to say *yes*. No one's going to force you, and no one else can do it for you. You are going to have to be the one to say *yes*. *Yes*, you want your life to be different, better, grander. *Yes*, you want to grow. *Yes*, you want to change. *Yes*, you are willing to take action and keep moving in the direction of the call no matter how scared you may be, no matter what challenges get thrown at you. *Yes*, you want to live a life that is true to who you are.

Here's what I truly believe from having lived through it: *it's the refusal of the calling that leads you to abuse food*. Refusal of the calling amounts to self-betrayal. Saying *no* to what you feel/know in your head, heart, and/or gut that you're supposed to be doing throws you into being at odds with yourself. For as long as you refuse, you'll have an interior war going on. And like we already talked about, that war within yourself (incongruence) is what leads you to abuse food as a coping mechanism. Every single time you abuse food and/or any other substances/behaviors, you shout a loud *NO* to your calling.

The good news is that if you've refused your calling, even for years, you can still change your mind. Oh yes, you surely can. You can accept the calling, *right now*, and you can start your journey right where you are. One caveat: once you say *yes*, you're going to have to keep on saying *yes*. *Yes* through the obstacles. *Yes* through the head fears. *Yes* to relationships changing and people leaving your life or opening yourself up for others to see the real you or holding your ground when the onslaught of criticism comes or pressing forward no matter how scared you might be. *Yes* to whatever steps it may take to heed the calling. If you choose to say *no* again, your journey comes to a stop *until you change your mind*. And remember, you can *always* change your mind.

My saying *no* to the calling:

- About getting rid of the excess weight: All the weeks when the scale didn't move downward. All the weeks the scale moved upward. All the days when life got hard. Every single time I stood in front of the refrigerator, wanting to overeat just to numb myself. Each time I chose to abuse food because of those events, I said: *F*ck it. I quit.*
- About being secure in my own self: Some ten months after I said *yes* to the calling when all my friends seemingly vanished out of my life and someone I loved deeply broke my trust completely and my support system just up and disappeared, leaving me alone with nobody else to turn to. I said: *Wait, I was just kidding. Please make it stop. No. No. No. I take the yes back. I take it back. The answer's no.*
- About this book, right off the bat when the calling came: *No f*cking way.*

STAGE TWO
COSMIC HELP

Definition: Once the hero says yes to her calling, someone or something (other people or unseen forces) comes into her life to support, guide, and help her along her journey. The hero will be given exactly what she needs along the way so that she can complete her quest.[3]

First and foremost: you're going to have to commit to being the hero of your own story (which you did back in Chapter Six, during Step Four, *Make An Unbreakable Promise To Yourself*). You must commit *for you*, not because someone else wants you to. So check your motivation (see Chapter One). Saying *yes* is a commitment. Commitment means you need to accept that achieving your weight-loss goals (or any goal for that matter) is not about theories and discussions. It's about taking action and putting forth some effort and *producing results*. It's about having strength and perseverance and persistence and courage. All of which, I know for sure, you have.

Second, you alone are fully responsible for the success or failure of your efforts. Remember: *no one is coming to fix it*. So if something's not working, you need to be the one to change it. There's no making excuses or assigning blame or settling for anything less than what you want.

Third, you need to *fully* commit to being the hero, which means you take the escape clause out of the realm of possibility. No matter what you have to go through to get to where you want to be, you won't give up and quit. You are on a mission and you will keep going until you achieve it.

And finally, once you *fully* commit and start taking steps in the direction of the call (even if they're itty-bitty tiny steps), well, that's when the real magic happens. I mentioned this in Chapter Six and I'm saying it again here because it really is like magic. You will find that cosmic help comes to you frequently, quickly, and many times without you even asking. Money right when you need it most. Encouragement just before you want to give up. Lessons you most need to learn. Aid from unlikely places. People, oftentimes strangers, who provide knowledge, guidance, and other kinds of support. Things you need dropped right into your lap. And the list goes on and on. I have seen it over and over in my own life. All you have to do is commit. *Truly and fully commit.* Then believe and trust (even if trusting feels like you're walking a high wire without a net) that you'll get what you need right when you need it.

My cosmic help:
- About getting rid of the excess weight: one person after another (friends, acquaintances, strangers) who had lost weight then gained it all back plus more. Every one of those people was a daily reminder that traditional diets don't work, every one a reminder that I *always* need to find what works for me and do that.
- About being secure in my own self: a yoga instructor who taught me, through holding different poses *while alone and accountable to no one but myself* on my mat, about the importance of pushing beyond the discomfort (physical, yes, but also emotional), breathing through it, relaxing into it, and holding on all the way until I finish (because finishing what you start is always personal—it's about you and you alone).
- About this book: another writer, who was also struggling to complete her own work, came into my life; we now have a writer's group with just the two of us. Together, we help each other push through self-doubt and fear and encourage each other to finish our own work.

STAGE THREE
CROSSING INTO THE UNKNOWN AND A DARK NIGHT OF THE SOUL

Definition: The hero actually leaves her comfort zone and everything familiar to her behind. She crosses the boundary of what is safe and known to venture out into what's beyond, which is unknown, full of risk, potentially dangerous, and usually filled with what the hero imagines will happen there (which may or may not be what

286 | Start Where You Are Weight Loss

actually happens there).[4] *Out in the unknown, the hero realizes she cannot move forward without separating from her former self. She turns her focus inward. She becomes willing to let go of her former life and who she once was, which is a kind of death. The hero then becomes willing to change into who she is meant to be, which is a rebirth.*[5]

The fact is that if you want to be the hero of your own story, if you want to have heart-pounding and miraculous things happen in your life, if you want to get the weight off and keep it off, if you want to stop abusing food and fighting with your body, you are going to have to step out of your comfortable, safe routine and into the wild journey without a guarantee of what the outcome will be.

This step is often where people get stuck. They think they are safe in their comfort zone. They keep their gifts, talents, and passions hidden. They abuse food rather than change to make their lives fulfilling and exciting and what they want them to be. But, remember, there are no absolute guarantees of either comfort or safety in nature. *There is no sure thing, even in your comfort zone.* Again, as I keep saying, life happens and rarely asks for your permission first.

There's no way around this step either. You'll have to choose to be brave and courageous, which I know you are. And if you don't believe you are brave, all you need to do is change your mind. I once overheard someone say that bravery is simply starting and not quitting until you see whatever you started all the way through. So bravery is just a matter of perseverance. And perseverance is just a matter of plodding along, no matter how slowly you go, and refusing to quit.

Yes, there will be risk involved. You'll have to let go of control. You'll have to have some faith that you're alive for a reason, that you have a purpose. You'll have to trust yourself. But know this: you are trustworthy and strong enough to handle whatever comes your way. Yes, you are, or you wouldn't still be here. So take a deep breath, believe that in the end everything works out for your good to get you to where you're meant to be, then take that first step into the unknown.

My crossing into the unknown:
- About getting rid of the excess weight: stopping all the bingeing and purging and starving, changing what I believed about weight loss and food, giving up all the diets, choosing to listen to and trust myself, deciding to create a way of eating and living that works for me.
- About being secure in my own self: letting people leave my life and not chasing after them, forcing myself to stop looking to others for answers that I needed to find out for myself, sitting with myself and feeling whatever I was feeling and breathing my way through without numbing/avoiding no matter how hard it was.
- About this book: the cursor blinking at the start of a blank page, me taking a deep breath and holding it, then typing the first sentence.

The dark night of the soul is where you end up emotionally broken, where you've lost all your faith, where you think about quitting, where you maybe even consider dying rather than having to go on. Here is where you realize that you can't keep fighting your journey, where you finally and fully realize that to continue on you have to be all-in. Here's where you realize that you can no longer run away from your weaknesses (including fear), that you only have two choices left, either fight it out and become someone new or go back to your old self and perish.

This is also where you understand that the journey is bigger than you are, that your gifts, talents, passions, and purpose were given to you to share for a greater good, that who you're meant to be serves a larger whole, and you're humbled by the fact that you won't be able to (nor do you have to) go it alone. Here is where you finally, in utter desperation and out of pure need and because maybe you don't know what else to do, call on divine or supernatural help.

It's at this stage where many people (on weight-loss journeys and otherwise) quit. It's here that there will be no more abusing food (or any substances/behaviors) to numb yourself or make yourself feel brave or be your crutch or distract yourself or for any other reason. You will have to feel everything coming at you. You will have to deal with whatever is going on in your life. You will have to move forward even though you're scared. You will have to stand on your own two feet and make choices that are best for you, even if those choices are uncomfortable or scare you. You will have to be fully responsible for taking action and fixing your own life. That's what it will take to move through this stage. And you are more than capable of doing all that, I assure you that you are. All you have to do is: 1. keep moving toward the life that you want to have (one *tiny* step at a time if that's what it takes), and 2. refuse to stop.

It's at this stage too where you can be pointed in the right direction, if you'll have the wisdom and courage to let that happen. Know this: sometimes what you want and what's best for you are two different things. I know, I don't like it either, but that's the truth. Know this, too: you will get guidance. It may come from the world outside you. It may come from your own inner voice. Either way, you need to be open to the possibility that your life can be so much greater than you envisioned. You also need to be open to the possibility that what will make your life greater is not what you originally had planned. So this is also the stage where you finally let go of who you thought you would be so you can become who you're meant to be.

My dark night of the soul:
- About getting rid of the excess weight: Nearly a hundred pounds gone and standing in front of the opened refrigerator, staring at the shelves, trying to decide if I was going to binge. I wanted to numb the loneliness and sadness. I wanted to ease the fear. I wanted to be someone else. I called for divine help (which admittedly doesn't seem like much of a call for help): *Why would you make someone like me?* The answer that popped into my head: *You never had to be fat. You just never did. It was a lie you*

got told and a lie you believed. You lived it out. But you don't have to believe it anymore. And it was in that moment, too, that I got the call to write this book.

- About being secure in my own self: Finding out someone that I loved deeply and trusted implicitly, who was also the very last crutch in my life, lied to me. Not some small white fib but a real whopper; a lie so big you could call it a scheme, which was what my best friend did when I told her. A lie said as this person looked me in the eyes. Repeatedly. Convincingly. And then, as these things usually go, I got blindsided by the truth like a sucker punch to the skull. I slumped back in a stuffed chair, holding my head in my hands, trying to catch my breath. I didn't move for nearly an hour. I called on divine help: *What do I do?* The answer that popped into my head: *You don't go running back. You stand up and be strong in yourself. You're the only person you can one hundred percent count on. It's just you and me now.*

- About this book: Sitting at the coffee shop, looking at my first draft and all my notes, feeling overwhelmed. I asked myself who would even want to read it and what difference would it make anyway. I also thought that I'd rather die than continue to struggle writing it, rather die than open myself up and be vulnerable, rather die than put myself out in the world and risk being rejected again, rather die than tell the truth. I called on divine help: *I can't write this. I just can't do it.* The answer that popped into my head: *Oh yes, you can. You already have. I'll be here to help. I'll get you everything you need right when you need it. Keep going. You're writing it to heal yourself.*

STAGE FOUR
TRIALS, TRIBULATIONS, AND TEMPTATION'S TRAP

Definition: The hero must overcome a series of obstacles/challenges in order to begin her transformation. Here she grows and become stronger, rising above whatever immature beliefs she held in her past. Little by little, her resistance (to change, to letting go of what no longer serves her, to protecting her ego, etc.) is conquered. The hero learns what she must do to save herself.[6] The hero admits that what she thought life should be is not what her life really is, and it was her choices and decisions that got her where she is. She will at this point or some point in the future be tempted to detour from her journey or quit her journey entirely.[7]

Again, like we've already talked about, know going in that you're going to get hit with some obstacles, challenges, and/or tests, some kind of adversity that seems difficult, if not impossible, to overcome. That's inevitable. You may tremble and start looking around for the nearest exit. You may tense up, ready to bolt. You may go running back to abusing food in an attempt to make it all stop or go away. Your actions may yell

NO to the call without you actually saying a word. You may tell yourself: *there's no way, I can't*. You may even start to believe it.

But know this: defeat is *always* optional.

Remember: whatever it is, *food will not fix it*.

Then take this to heart: one small step (tiny, if need be) at a time, you can. *Oh yes, you can*. And if you'll just keep saying *yes* and taking action and moving forward, you will.

Trials and tribulations will teach you if you'll let them. They will show you just how strong, courageous, tenacious, intelligent, persevering, and on the list goes that you are. Success in those trials will inspire you to keep going, sure. But it's the failures in your tribulations that'll shape you and strengthen you and help you grow. What do you do when you're faced with failure? Do you slide into self-pity? Do you hunker down and decide to learn something so you can do it better the next time? Do you start looking around for someone to blame? Do you throw your hands in the air and quit? Do you walk through the situation and feel how much it hurts? Do you turn to abusing food or fall back into abusing other substances/behaviors to numb the pain? Do you make yourself a solid promise that you're never going back to the way things were, and so you choose to move forward instead?

The answers matter. Again, the answers are your character. The answers show you just who (deep down) you are right now. The great news is that who you are now is not who you have to be forever. That's especially true if you're one of the people assigning blame or quitting or turning back to abusing food and/or other substances/behaviors. You can always (*always, always*) change your mind. You can *always* choose and behave differently.

So answer this: *What kind of person do I want to be?* Because that's the question that the trials and tribulations will ask and the one that you'll have to answer.

My trials and tribulations:
- About getting rid of the excess weight: Every time something happened that made me want to turn to abusing food. Regrets, memories, rejections, betrayal, loneliness, writer's block, depression, physical pain, and all the wasted time. Every one was a trial and a choice: overeat and numb myself or sit with whatever I was feeling until it was over. I failed a lot until I decided: 1. I didn't want to live like that anymore, and 2. the food wasn't fixing anything; all it was doing was making me gain weight. Now, I fail a lot less. And when I do fail (because there's just no doing this perfectly), I no longer spiral out of control for days/weeks/months at a time. I just wait until I'm hungry again to eat and move on, simple as that.
- About being secure in my own self: Where to start on this one? Abandonment, betrayal, humiliation, loneliness, financial strain, learning to listen and trust my own intuition *every single time*, letting go

of everything out of my control (the outcome, the future, other people, and the list goes on), finding out what *exactly* deeply mattered to me, being one hundred percent responsible for my choices, not waiting around anymore for someone to fix it or to give me permission, being absolutely okay on my own. I failed a lot. I fell back into old patterns, let people treat me badly because I didn't believe I deserved better, chased after things/people/substances to distract/numb me. But eventually, I started succeeding, too. Sitting with myself through one thing after another. Staying in the present moment and handling whatever life sent my way. Not worrying. Trusting that I would get everything I needed right when I needed it. Being calm in the midst of chaos and just breathing my way through.

- About this book: Self-doubt, hands down, was the hardest test. Believing my story matters and someone, somewhere, needs to hear it (and eventually realizing that someone includes me). Fear of rejection and having no control over how the book would be received. Fear of showing the real me to anyone because I almost never, before now, talked about my struggles with weight. Fear of being bullied and ridiculed again. The failure was this: I wrote lots of notes on scraps of paper and the backs of receipts and unused but wrinkled napkins then put them in a box and left them. Seven months of thinking about it but not organizing it. I talked myself out of writing the book because: 1. it won't be any good, 2. no one will read it, 3. I can't open myself up like that, and 4. what will people think. Fear won. The success was: I kept showing up, even those scribbled notes were still a step forward. Eventually, I put myself on a schedule and met my own deadlines and decided to write it to heal myself (like my voice of wisdom told me to) whether anyone else ever read it or not.

As we've already talked about, you will, at some point, be tempted to pause, veer off in another direction, and/or quit altogether. That's not a matter of *if* but of *when*. Something or someone is going to come around that seems a lot better than struggling through. You may feel like you've been through enough already and you deserve to cave to this one temptation. Or maybe you feel like there's nothing else good in your life and so you say *yes* to the temptation. Or perhaps you just want a break and you tell yourself it'll just be temporary, so you invite the temptation right into your life.

Whatever the reason: *if you choose the temptation, your quest ends.*

Of course, all hope is not lost because you can start your quest again, but only after you abandon the temptation. Thing is: sometimes it's hard to give up the temptation; that's especially true the longer you say *yes* to it and allow that temptation to remain in your life. Remember: you're training your brain all the time. Whether you give in to or push through a temptation, you're teaching your brain to make the same choice that much easier the next time. So keep that in mind when you choose to do what's best for you. Like we talked about earlier, you need to decide what you're going to do long before the temptation arrives, you need to choose *right now* that you're going to say *no* when temptation comes your way.

Even if you've given in to temptation lots of times (yes, my hand is raised too), you can still retrain your brain (neuroplasticity, remember) by staying strong and steadfast the next time temptation comes. When you do that over and over—look temptation in the eye, holler *no*, and keep carrying on with what you know you need to do to get to where you most want to be—you'll make a new neural pathway in your brain. Eventually what was such an enormous temptation for you—one that stopped you in your tracks and made you sweat and forced you to wrestle with yourself—will, if you keep saying *no* to it, become something that you just shrug at, say *nope not gonna happen*, and move away from without even batting an eye.

My temptation's trap:
- About getting rid of the excess weight: Temptation came in the form of food, of course. This was especially true when I was emotional, exhausted, stressed, feeling trapped, and on the list goes. Temptation also showed up as falling back into traditional-diet thinking (eat only "healthy foods", never be able to eat this or that ever again, go back to weighing and measuring everything I ate, count calories, exercise like a maniac, be enslaved to the food/charts/measurements) not because it worked but because it was familiar and less scary than the unknown of forging my own path.
- About being secure in my own self: Temptation came in the form of distraction, anything to keep from sitting with myself and feeling what I was feeling and/or anything that kept me going in a circle/cycle instead of moving straight forward in my life. So shopping (buying stuff I didn't need), busyness (just being in constant motion), causing tension with other people (creating drama), excessively watching television and losing myself in books and surfing the Internet for hours on end and anything, really, that I used not for joy or relaxation but instead used to avoid being with myself and/or to avoid doing what I knew I needed to do.
- About this book: Temptation came in the form of anything (a hammock in the backyard, new recipes to spend an afternoon making, housework, washing the car, seriously I do mean anything) that I used as an excuse to keep my butt out of my writing chair. Temptation also showed up in the form of self-doubt with thoughts like: *I'm no good at this, no one is going to read it, I don't have it in me to write this, why am I wasting my time writing it*, and on the list goes. You wouldn't think of self-doubt as a temptation, it's not exactly seductive, but it made me want to stop and quit all the same.

STAGE FIVE
EXPERIENCING UNCONDITIONAL LOVE AND
THE RESTORATION OF THE POWER BALANCE

Definition: The hero fully experiences nourishing, comforting, protective, unconditional love. She rests easy knowing she is encompassed and supported by this love, which transcends whatever challenges she may be going through. This love also helps bring into balance the fantasy she has created in her mind of what the world should be with what the world before her actually is. And finally, this love opens the mind of the hero to the constant presence of the life-giving Universe which surrounds her.[8] The hero humbles herself and detaches from her ego. She has faith in herself. She also trusts in something greater than herself that's nurturing and wants to see her succeed. The hero changes her emotional response to whatever it is she believes holds the most power over her life so she can become the authority and power in her own life.[9]

While it's entirely possible that you'll find (or have already found) a person in your life that may be this step for you, may let you experience love in that powerful way, I've found that every person I've ever known in my life, at some point, has failed me. That's true because people (yes, all people) are fallible. It's been my experience that this, too, is where people get stuck; they spend time looking and waiting for someone else to provide that kind of transcendent love. And, as I keep saying: *no one is coming.*

I would argue that believing in your own worth and value, befriending yourself and learning to completely trust yourself (like we talked about in Chapter Three), giving yourself unconditional love regardless of how others treat you, and taking responsibility for your own happiness and how you treat yourself in the good times and the bad, is the cornerstone to your hero's journey. It really is imperative that you choose to love yourself through whatever may come your way. When you choose to love yourself, you will defend your boundaries, you won't allow others to hurt you, and you will get yourself out of situations that are causing you harm. You will also stop having/saying/doing things that hurt you. The more you love yourself as-is, the more willing you are to do whatever it takes to live authentically as yourself.

I would also argue that the Universe is a supportive, nurturing place. Remember: you will live out what you believe. So do you believe the Universe is a friendly place? The answer matters. Why? Because what you believe about the Universe and your place in it colors every choice and decision you make. If you believe there is no force out there in the Universe, well, that means you're on your own and, in the end, none of this matters anyway. If you believe there is some force in the Universe and it's out to get you, you will believe (and live out) that life is stacked against you and you can never succeed. If you believe the force in the Universe wants to see you succeed and thrive, well, you will get help and resources and guidance right when you need them the most. I'm not telling you that you need to believe in any particular religion or deity. That's a choice for you to make. What I'm saying is this: start believing the Universe is a friendly place that wants to help you. (And even if you think I'm crazy, still give it an honest try. It won't cost you anything but a little bit of your time. Repeat this daily for at least 66 days: *I believe the Universe is a friendly place that wants to see me succeed*. See what happens.)

And last, I would also argue that when you combine trusting and befriending yourself with believing the Universe is a friendly place, you will come to find that all-powerful, all-encompassing, unconditional love that you (and all of us, really) seek.

My experiencing unconditional love:
- About getting rid of the excess weight: The day I finally decided to get rid of the weight solely for me because it was a goal that deeply mattered to me and I was worth the effort no matter what it took. That was the moment that the yo-yo dieting and crazy-making eating rules and the fear of food stopped. (I befriended and trusted myself.)
- About being secure in my own self: I took a long, hard look at my life and realized that everything that had happened to me had needed to happen to get me to where I was. It also turned out that everything that had seemed so horribly bad had really worked out for my good. (So the Universe really was trying to help me.)
- About this book: I wrote myself a note telling myself the book was important, my story was important, the world was hurting, I was in a unique position to help, and somebody somewhere desperately needed to hear what I had to say so they could save their own lives. I also told myself I would still love me whether I finished the book or not, whether I ever wrote anything again or not. I told myself every single day that I didn't have to fear, that I would get everything I needed right when I needed it, that everything would fall into place. All I had to do was just keep showing up and writing. And that's what happened. (So I befriended and trusted myself and experienced that the Universe really is a friendly place.)

My educated guess, because you're using food not as fuel but as some kind of crutch, is that there's something in your life that you believe holds all the power over you, someone or something you feel powerless against. It may be a person you can't seem to break free from and includes any relationship in which you feel less than or unequal. It may be a place that when you go there, you feel small and get sucked back into a life you don't want. It may be a thing that makes you feel trapped, stuck, overwhelmed, suffocated, dead inside, and the like. And when you feel powerless, you likely react by abusing food to cope. So take a look at the answers you came up with in Chapter Five (the vampires) to find out what you believe is holding the most power over your life.

I would argue that food or any other substance/behavior you are abusing is *not* what holds the most power over you. You may think it does. It may feel that way to you. But it's been my experience that anything used to numb/avoid is a symptom, it's not the cause. The cause is what you've given your own power to. So first you need to discern what, ultimately, is draining your power. Then second, you need to take steps to rid yourself of those things that make you feel powerless. (Again, see Chapter Five for how to do that.)

It's possible that you don't like change or confrontation. It's also likely you don't trust yourself to take care of your own needs. So you stay in places/situations that diminish you and/or with people who make you feel small and unimportant. I say this kindly: that's a choice you're making. You don't have to make that same choice anymore. You can choose differently, starting *right now*. This truly is the turning point of your journey to lose weight and/or stop abusing food, I assure you of that. You won't ever be able to move forward and be the hero in your own life, to get the weight off and keep it off, to stop abusing food and instead use it for fuel, until you confront and then defeat whoever or whatever you believe holds the ultimate power over you. As I've said before: the only way to get your power back is to take it. Here, in this step, is where you take it back.

My restoration of the power balance:
- About getting rid of the excess weight: My father, it turns out, is the person who held the power over me as I spent decades trying to prove myself to him, trying to get him to love me the way I wanted him to, trying to be the person he wanted me to be. I struggled and struggled and struggled to drop the weight when he was alive. Because of social norms and characteristics I'd been taught—like loyalty, obedience, family comes first, among other such things that were warped in a way they never should have been—I didn't understand that I had a choice not to let him have all that power over my life. I didn't know that I could just cut all ties and end the relationship forever and move on without him. After he died and the connection (albeit not a healthy one) was severed, the majority of the excess weight (honestly) seemed to fall right off without all that much effort from me.
- About being secure in my own self: Once every last crutch left my life, my motivation became myself and not others. I finally determined what I wanted for my life, made goals based on those wants then reached them solely for myself, and was positive that whatever I chose to pursue deeply mattered to me. I decided without a doubt that I had worth and value just as I am. I became a lot more selective on the people who I let into my life. I chose to follow my own passions and cultivate my own gifts. Now I am much more protective of what I do with my time and vigilant about fulfilling my own wants and needs. That's how I got free.
- About this book: Fear of telling the truth is what held all the power over me. Keeping all the overweight photos of me hidden. Refusing to talk about all my struggles with weight. Not revealing the painful things that caused me so much shame for so long. Always keeping up some kind of facade and not

letting anyone know the real me. Telling my story was taking my power back. Honesty is what crushed the fear and set me free.

STAGE SIX
DEATH TO SELF

Definition: The hero completely surrenders her ego. She stops trying to destroy that which holds the power over her and instead she rises above and reclaims her own power. She is free of fear and her mind is finally able to be at peace. The world no longer guides the actions of the hero, and instead the hero guides her own actions in the world. The hero becomes more than who she once was.[10]

This step is about letting go. Sometimes letting go may feel like a little death: something over forever. In this step, you stop clinging. You let go of the limited belief of what you thought you would be. You open yourself up to possibility. You let go of the old way of doing things. You say *yes* to all the little callings, even (and especially) to the ones that are head fears. You let go of the past and what once was. You let go of some of the dreams you had for your life (or at least the way you may have pictured them in your head), which admittedly will feel a lot like little parts of you are dying. You let go of the way you used to see things and what you used to believe so that you can move forward and see/believe new things, things that serve you better.

You stop fighting against yourself, against the way things were and are, against what you were called to do. You accept that everything changes, including you. You accept a new reality and you choose never to go back to living the way you were before and to being the person you were before. You stop fighting against your gifts, talents, and passions and you just let them happen. You let go of who you used to be and what you thought you would be so that you can become who you are meant to be. And in so doing, you discover your purpose and just what it is you're supposed to be doing with your life. Then you move forward, with confidence and trust in yourself, in the direction you know you need to go.

Here, too, is where you unburden yourself of all the things that are weighing you down, and once you aren't carrying them anymore, you will see that your load is so much lighter. You'll be able to rest. You'll have peace. You'll find the joy and have the fulfillment you've been searching for. And you will finally understand that you are being supported and guided wherever you go.

My death to self:
- About getting rid of the excess weight: Letting go of the way I was eating before. Letting go of the restrictive diets, crazy exercise, bingeing, and purging. Letting go of the diet-go-round, gaining and losing and gaining and losing, over and over and over again, and never moving forward. Letting go

of what others said was the right way to lose weight and/or live my life. Taking my power back by choosing to create a way of living and eating that works for me.

- About being secure in my own self: Letting go of people. Letting go of goals that weren't mine to begin with and/or that didn't deeply matter to me. Letting go of how I used to react. Letting go of who I used to be. Letting go of things that are out of my control. Letting go of worry and instead believing that, in the end, everything really is going to be okay. Taking my power back by choosing to forge my own path.

- About this book: Letting go of the fear. Letting go of how it will be received. Letting go of any expectations for how it will do commercially. Taking my power back by choosing to write it to heal myself.

STAGE SEVEN
GOAL ACHIEVED

Definition: The hero achieves whatever it was she set out on her journey to get, usually something of great value to her. The hero breaks through the confines of any limits she has put on herself or others have put onto her. She becomes enlightened to all she is truly capable of achieving. The achievement of her goal moves her toward her ultimate destiny.[11]

Plain and simple, this one is where you reach what you set out to do. You hit whatever numbers/goals/targets you were aiming for. You reach your ideal life. But, and *here's the importance of the whole journey*, having gone through all the other steps and learned something about yourself and why you were abusing food to begin with, you'll now be able to keep the weight off and/or live in a body that feels true to you. That's the difference between being in the cycle of dieting (the diet-go-round), circling around and around and around, versus finally breaking free and moving on a forward and straight trajectory in your life. All the other steps prepared you so: 1. you will no longer live in fear of food or in shame about yourself, 2. food won't be your focus, and 3. what you actually want to have/be/do/say with your life will become your focus instead.

This is a transcendent step because you finally rise above the crazy-making dieting cycle and you blaze your own path, the path that you were actually meant to be on, a path that matters to you. If you've been doing the diet, get-skinny, gain-it-all-back-and-then-some, diet, get-skinny, gain-back, and on it goes for any length of time, you will reach this step and you will feel like you conquered a demon and/or slayed a dragon.

You will finally see that you no longer need to limit yourself for any reason. You will come to understand just how capable you truly are, and you'll firmly believe that you have it in you to reach any goal(s) that you set for yourself from now on. Keep in mind, too, that you may achieve your goal and then surpass it. It's entirely likely you may realize more than you ever believed possible.

My goal achieved:
- About getting rid of the excess weight: Blowing past my target goal of wearing a size 6 to wearing a size 0-2 (depending on the designer). But also, and even more importantly, changing how I thought and think about food. It's no longer the master of my life. It's no longer my focus. Food is fuel so I can get busy doing what I believe I'm supposed to be doing with my life.
- About being secure in my own self: I now know I'm whole and worthy and valuable as-is. I don't need anything else to complete me. No money. No people. No career. No matter what's happening around me or to me, no matter who is or is not in my life, no matter what anyone else thinks of me, no matter how close or far I am from reaching my goals, I am okay. I am whole right now.
- About this book: Typing the last sentence of the first draft and finishing it. Then rewriting and rewriting until it was done. So many times, I wanted to quit. It would've been easier to quit. But it was more important to me to heal myself by writing this book than it was to slide back into my comfort zone. This book was the hardest thing I've ever had to write up to this point in my life. And I finished it.

STAGE EIGHT
NOT WANTING TO COME BACK, MAKING A CAREFUL RETURN, AND SOME GUIDANCE FOR THE RETURN

Definition: For the story to be complete, the hero has a responsibility to come back to her normal life and share her newfound knowledge with others. But having found peace and happiness when she achieved her goal, the hero may refuse to return.[12] The hero may have to guard and protect her achieved goal, especially if it's something others have resentment/anger/jealousy about the hero having. Sometimes the return to normal life can be as much of an adventure (both exhilarating and perilous) as the initial quest.[13] Just like the hero received cosmic help when she finally said yes to her calling, she may need others to help her integrate into normal life once again as she returns. It also may happen that the hero doesn't want to return from her goal-achieved state of bliss; in which case, others may also need to help by retrieving the hero and facilitating her return to normal life.[14]

I've found that every hard thing in my life was in some way a gift. Mind you, it didn't ever seem like a gift at the time, but looking back I can see how I needed whatever happened to help me grow into the person I wanted to be. I've learned that finding meaning in the difficult things in life has been the key to making those things easier to accept and, more importantly, heal from so you can move on. Science backs me up on that with a process called post-traumatic growth. It's when someone goes through a period of intense suffering and then, as a result of struggling through the aftermath and adapting to a new reality, ends up having positive changes occur in their lives.[15]

I would argue that finding meaning is as easy as: 1. looking for the lesson in whatever is happening to you, even if it's hard to find, and 2. passing on that wisdom to hopefully spare someone else the hardship you went through. Here's something else I know to be true: it's the passing on of that wisdom that can be the most challenging because it requires you to be vulnerable, it requires you to share the difficulties and darkness that you went through, it requires that you be the one to light the path so others can also find a way out. And that's what this step, in my opinion, calls for.

So here you have two choices:

- Hang out in paradise by yourself (safe and secure, or so you tell yourself; but remember: there are still no guarantees even in paradise) and all the lessons learned stay with you.

OR

- Open yourself up and invite others into your life (risky with no idea of the outcome) and, in so doing, you have the opportunity to help them (whether they take that help or not) make their own little paradise, too.

If you go back to Maslow's hierarchy of needs from Chapter Two, you'll see that one of the foundational needs (which means you can't progress without it) of all human beings is a sense of belonging and connection. When you teach someone else and help them grow, you not only find meaning for yourself but you also foster a connection with that person (whether it's from face-to-face contact or writer to reader or speaker to listener). You get to see that you have valuable insights to offer. You also get to understand that you were never alone; there was always someone in the world who felt just the way you did. And finally, you get to experience a deeper way of being in the world than you ever experienced before. You'll probably be scared to share what you've learned. That's okay. Choose to do it anyway.

My not wanting to come back:
- About getting rid of the excess weight: Refusing to discuss any aspect whatsoever of my weight loss, even when people point-blank asked me about it.
- About being secure in myself: Refusing to talk about what I had to go through to finally get to the point where I trusted myself implicitly, even though I knew it would help others to do the same.

- About this book: Refusing to consider publishing it, even though I knew it could show others a way out of dieting craziness.

You do need to be discerning about when you're ready to return and share the wisdom you've gained. You may need to keep your newfound knowledge to yourself for a time. Opening yourself up to family, friends, co-workers, and/or the world before you're ready can have disastrous consequences for you. Why? Because of some of the things you may get hit with, including:

- Other people's negativity (sorry to say, there will be people who will cut you down simply because you reached your goal—mostly, I believe, because they themselves have not reached theirs).
- Being shoved into what feels like a spotlight with a lot more eyes on you and quite a bit more attention (this is especially hard if you are an introvert or have a history of avoiding being the center of attention).
- Hard questions coming at you fast (usually of a personal nature that people, even complete strangers, expect you to answer).
- People offering their unsolicited advice/criticism about how you're now living your life (you met your goal, it should be kudos to you, but you'll still find people telling you either: 1. how you could be doing better or 2. how you should limit yourself, which is really them putting their own limits on you. Honestly, I don't understand this, but that's what happens).
- People who don't like that you've changed and they just want everything to go back to the way it was, and so they give you a hard time (because, in my opinion, they are scared of pushing themselves and opening themselves up to a grander life; trust me, these people—even if you love them—are vampires, see Chapter Five).

If you return before you're ready and you're not mentally, physically, and spiritually prepared for whatever may get thrown at you, you could end up crashing and burning. All the progress and insights you gained, all the hard work you did, everything you strived to accomplish could go up in flames. If you're not careful about the timing, you might end up running back to whatever substances/behaviors you used to abuse to cope and numb, including abusing food.

An important note: after years of experience with this step (read: yo-yo dieting), I can tell you what's true: this is the step people don't treat with the seriousness it deserves. They get the weight off and then go running into the world to: 1. say *look at me* and/or 2. tell everyone how they did it. They aren't prepared for the pushback. It never occurred to them that some people (especially some that they love) wouldn't be happy for them. They get blindsided by the negativity coming at them and/or scared at the sudden onslaught of attention. Then they slide right back into old patterns because those old patterns are familiar and seem safer. Plus, those old patterns will make them the way they were before and, hence, more acceptable to those around them. The pushback will stop. They'll change back into the person they once were, who was unsatisfied and not living a purpose-filled life. I know this because I did this for decades. Yes, *decades*.

Honestly, there's no way of knowing everything you may encounter. That's why you need to be secure in yourself and your ability to handle life as it comes. With all that in mind, you take as much time as you need to prepare yourself; however, there's one caveat: don't drag out your return because of fear. You *do* need to return to share your wisdom. You *do* need to help where you can. You'll know when you're ready. This one's about trusting yourself, too.

My careful return:
- About getting rid of the excess weight: My weight was such a painful topic of discussion for me for so long (family/friends/strangers bringing it up, calling me out on it, demeaning/humiliating me about it, asking me questions) that I needed nearly four years after I got rid of all the weight to be able to talk about it without feeling shame.
- About being secure in myself: After the last person I had been using as a crutch was ripped away from me, it took a little over two years before I felt rock solid enough to share my story. A little over two years for me to really know in myself that *however* people reacted to me, I wouldn't be shaken or shattered or crushed, I wouldn't fall apart.
- About this book: In total, this one took about four years also. All those months of jotted notes. Two years after that to write and rewrite. Another six months for me to finally decide I was both ready to put it out into the world and strong enough to handle whatever reaction comes.

As I've been saying this entire book, I'm not a huge fan of expecting anyone else to come to the rescue. I don't think you should be either. I believe that mentality—that someone else is coming to fix it—keeps people waiting and waiting, in a holding pattern, while their lives pass them by.

With that said, I've often had people put in my path that helped me along the way. I look at those people as some guidance for the return: loved ones who believed in me and encouraged me to tell the truth, mentors who gave me advice or simply made me see things in a different light, colleagues who steered me away from making bad decisions or changed my thinking, friends who listened to my occasional ravings or helped me to alleviate some stress, and even strangers who told me the blunt truth because they had no vested interest in the outcome.

My point is this: on your way back once you've reached your goal, ask for what you need, keep moving forward, and be open to whatever form the guidance for the return will take. One caveat: just don't ever fall into the mindset of looking for someone to come fix it and/or do it for you (because as always: *no one is coming*).

My guidance for the return:

*   About getting rid of the excess weight: A photograph taken by someone else of me wearing a size 4. I saw for the first time how thin I really am because I still don't see it by just looking in a mirror. I nearly cried because: 1. of all the work I had to do to make it through, 2. it was worth it in the end, 3. I didn't have to live in fear of food anymore, and 4. I never had to go back and so I wasn't ever going to.
*   About being secure in myself: Now granted this one doesn't sound like a rescue but someone I respected rejected my work and added some personal comments that made it clear that this person also rejected me. It upset me for all of a couple of minutes. I sat with it. I felt it. I let it go. That was empowering. That was the moment I knew I was gonna be okay no matter what. It was proof to me that I was a different person (because before I would've gone running to abuse food to numb myself). Again, it also made me realize that I never had to go back to the way I used to be: going back was a choice.
*   About this book: A reader and friend, who told me that the book (in draft form) had already made a difference in her life. She also kept telling me that this book was my gift and purpose; that no matter how hard it might be to craft, it was the book I was meant to write. "You've healed yourself," she said, "now go heal the world." She gently pushed me to publish it.

STAGE NINE
RETURNING FROM THE UNKNOWN

Definition: The challenge when the hero gets back to her normal life is twofold: 1. to believe that the blissful state of her goal achieved was and is real (to bask in her accomplishment(s) and let it sink in), and 2. to remember everything she learned from her journey and to use that newfound wisdom not only to better her own life but also to share it so as to better the lives of others. The hero also realizes that her adventurous quest and her normal everyday life, which seemed before like two different worlds, are actually one world but just two ends of a single spectrum.[16]

This is the step, in my opinion, that a lot of people dismiss/discard. They reach the end of their quest, achieve their goal, and forget (it seems) everything they've learned. Yo-yo dieters do this all the time: hit their goal weight and celebrate by overeating and thinking now that they're thin they can eat whenever they want (not waiting to be hungry) and however much they want (eating way past full again) and believe that somehow (magically?) the fact that overeating-makes-you-overweight no longer applies to them. People who abuse any substance/behavior (including food) and finally free themselves do this too whenever they turn back to the substance/behavior, trying to achieve either some feeling or some lack of feeling and/or use that substance/behavior in a way for which it was never intended. Sigh, you're not alone, my hand is raised; I used to be one of those people. You may have been or may currently be one of those people, too. My suggestion to you: stop being one of them, it doesn't work.

You've been strong and determined and tenacious. You've thrown yourself out of your comfort zone. You've made difficult and uncomfortable choices. You've persevered. You've worked really hard throughout this entire book, I know you have. You're on your way to reaching your goal or maybe you've already reached it. Either way, from me to you, a big and hearty congratulations for: 1. not giving up and, 2. a job well done! Just know this: *it's not over*. First, you need to take a moment (or a lot of moments) to give yourself credit, bask in your achievement(s), acknowledge the awesome feat you accomplished, and give yourself some much-deserved recognition for the amazing person you are. Second, you still have to remember everything you learned. You still have to put all that knowledge into practice *daily*. You still have to take action and move forward in your life. Is it as challenging as the initial quest? Usually not. But you still can't rest on your laurels and forget everything you struggled to learn or go back to who you once were and to the way you did things before, not if you want to live in a body that feels true to you, not if you want to stop abusing food and have a different life and grow from the experience.

The best way I've found to know if you've truly learned something is to teach it to someone else. Teaching is remembering and integrating and deepening your understanding all at the same time. Only when you *know* what you're doing, only when you *fully* understand it, can you explain it to someone else. That's why teaching and passing on your wisdom is so important; you are not only helping others by showing them the way but also helping yourself by keeping the wisdom fresh in your memory.

My returning from the unknown:
- About getting rid of the excess weight: I live every day doing what I've taught you to do in this book. Yes, sometimes I still screw it up. *I just don't let my mistakes derail me anymore.* That, right there, is the secret to success. I simply take a deep breath and remember everything I've learned and I try again. I do that daily and as many times as it takes (unlimited tries, remember). It's either that or be overweight again. And I've already chosen: I'm not ever going back to who I used to be.
- About being secure in myself: I learned a lot of things about myself in the two years it took me to get all the weight off. I am strong, courageous, tenacious, and capable of achieving anything—and I do mean *anything*—that I decide I want to do. I know who I want to be in the world now. I have a purpose that wasn't quite clear to me before. I fully understand and live out my now-firm belief that

I don't need anything or anyone from without to be whole. I now know how to use my gifts, talents, and passions to bring meaning and fulfillment to my own life and to help heal others.

- About this book: I wrote it first and foremost to heal myself. Writing it helped keep all the stages/steps I went through fresh in my memory, reinforcing them so I wouldn't easily forget and reminding me of what I needed to do if I started to fall back into old patterns. Writing it also helped me see just how much I've changed my life, just how much progress I had made and how far I had already come. And lastly, I had the knowledge in my head; putting it down on paper was the best way for me as a writer to share it with the rest of the world.

STAGE TEN
FINDING BALANCE AND FREEING YOURSELF

Definition: The hero is comfortable and free to move from her normal day-to-day life to the blissful state of the goal achieved because she has completely surrendered resistance to becoming something new. This is where the hero insides match her outsides. The hero relaxes into life, knowing she is strong enough to handle whatever comes her way. The hero knows who she is as a person and moves comfortably and confidently through the world as herself.[17] The hero with all her hard-won wisdom becomes a master at living her own life. The hero realizes that no matter what happens in her life, she as an individual person is whole. She lives as she truly is instead of as a false persona. The hero detaches from the outcome and accepts change as inevitable, and so she is free to live without fear. The hero is free to live in the here-and-now, neither focusing on the past nor being anxious about the future.[18]

This step is what being whole is all about. It's about being comfortable and at ease with yourself and who you are as a person (inner world) so that you can move through your life with confidence and determination (outer world). This is the point where you fully understand that inner peace starts from within. You're no longer fighting yourself and letting head fear stop you; instead, you're healing the rift/hole inside yourself caused by incongruence (where you are one person in private and a different person in public) and taking action to move forward in the direction you know you need to go.

I'd argue too that this step is where you start truly believing that:

- all things really do work out for your good (so you take a deep breath and look for the lesson or the gift in whatever is happening to you, especially in the challenging stuff).
- life is rigged in your favor (and you realize that what's been limiting you all along is your own thinking).

- you are supported wherever you may go (so there's no need to waste your precious time and energy on worry).
- you will get everything you need right when you need it (because you're on a mission to find your purpose and come alive).
- no matter what is happening in your life, no matter how hard it might be to go through, everything is going to be okay (because, in the end, it will be).
- you are both strong enough and capable enough to handle anything that comes your way (because you're still here and you haven't given up).
- the only place you can change anything is in the present moment (and so you take action where you can and you let go where you can't).
- your life isn't about impressing anyone but is about becoming who you are meant to be (which is the only place where true freedom lies).
- creating a life that deeply matters to you is what will make you finally feel fulfilled (so you make and meet goals solely for yourself and you do what brings you joy).
- the only life you can truly save is your own (so your actions and your choices need to be about making yourself whole).

My finding balance:
- About getting rid of the excess weight: I am comfortable in my own skin for the first time in my life. I move through the world with a solid confidence and authority now. I don't need anyone else to approve of me; I approve of myself and that's enough. I no longer run to food to fix anything because I know *without a doubt* that food will never fix it.
- About being secure in myself: I know deep down in my core, where it matters most, that I'm strong enough to handle whatever situations come my way. I know who I am, who I want to be, and what deeply matters to me. I no longer need anyone else to prop me up. I feel head fear and I just take a deep breath and I keep on moving through it. I give myself permission to go after what I want for my life now, without waiting. I am now creating a life around things that bring me joy.
- About this book: I wrote it to heal myself and that's what happened. I told the truth. I put it out in the world. I don't feel shame, I feel free.

This step is also where you lose your fear of death, which in the end is what all fear (no matter how it shows up) comes down to—the death of something: your actual life, your pride, your fortune, your reputation, your relationships, your dreams, your set ways of thinking, your life as how you thought it would be, and the like. If you're afraid of dying or the death of something you cherish, you stay in your comfort zone, you build a kind of mental (or even physical) cocoon/wall around yourself and try to keep control, you do your best to keep things safe and risk free, you settle instead of striving for what you'd like to have in your life.

Again, fear is what slows you down, maybe to the point that it stops you in your tracks. Fear is what paralyzes you so that you don't even start. But once you lose your fear of death (in whatever form that death takes), then you're free and willing to let things that aren't serving you anymore fall away. You're free and willing to change and grow and do whatever you like with your life. You're free to become the person you most want to be. And, I know this from personal experience, you won't ever be truly victorious—meaning, there'll always been some lingering doubt, nervousness, anxiety, and the like inside you—until you're free from the confines and limitations of fear.

Like I've said before, the only place you are actually empowered to do anything is in the present moment. The past is over, can't fix it. The future hasn't happened yet, so can't fix it either. Right now, this moment, is the only place where you can enact any change or feel any emotions. In this step, you fully understand and embrace that all your efforts to live in the past and/or the future are for naught, that trying to be somewhere other than right now is just a waste of your time and energy. So you start where you are and you move forward from right now and you make different choices that will create a future for yourself that's better and brighter.

You trust that you'll get to where you need to be. You know that everything that happened in your past was to get you to where you are today and who you are today. You realize that regret is a waste of your time and serves only to drive you crazy with choices you made or didn't make but can no longer change. You relax into your life and you let go of trying to control. You stop worrying and you take life as it comes because you know you're strong enough to handle anything that gets thrown at you. And here, in this step too, you trust that all of life really is aimed at helping you grow into the person that you are meant to be.

My freeing myself:
- About getting rid of the excess weight: I don't live in fear that the weight will come back. I have no fear of that at all. I'm not afraid of food or the scale or if my jeans will button the next time I put them on or of tearing through the pantry/refrigerator in response to anything that comes my way. If the scale goes up, I don't freak out because: 1. I'm so much more than that number, and 2. I absolutely know what to do to fix it.
- About being secure in myself: I am no longer afraid to be swamped by shame by just being myself. I'm not afraid to let others see the real me because I finally believe I'm whole and complete as-is. I know who I am at the core—what I stand for, what I believe, what matters deeply to me—and I don't back down from that.
- About this book: The fear of telling the truth is gone. The shame of telling the truth is gone, too. I'm a human being. This is what I went through. This is what was done to me. This is what I did to myself.

These are the mistakes I made. There is no shame in that. None whatsoever. Not even a little bit. And the fear of how this book will be received (pushback or criticism or publicity or failure or success) is gone, too. I wrote this book to heal myself. That's what mattered to me, and I succeeded in that. If you're able to receive some help and healing and hope from it too, well, that's just an added bonus.

OH, SOME SCIENCE

We already talked about the difference between real fear and head fear back in Chapter Three. Real fear protects you from potentially life-threatening situations. Head fear is every other fear you feel. And long-simmering head fear, the kind that keeps you from stepping out of your comfort zone and/or doing something you want/need to do, can be detrimental to your health.

Biologists will tell you that fear (both real fear and head fear) quite literally changes your body at the cellular level. A sudden jolt of fear causes your body to secrete cortisol and adrenaline. That's a good thing because those two biochemicals get you ready to fight for your life or flee to protect yourself; one of those reactions is what your survival depends on during real fear. When the threat is over, the level of those biochemicals in your body decreases.[19]

The problem arises in your body with ongoing head fear. That low-grade, constant head fear—when you know that you want/need to be doing something and you're afraid to step out and do it, worry, panic, anxiety, perfectionism, comparison, having a not-enough-for-me mentality, and on the head-fear list goes—triggers *those same biochemicals* to be secreted in your body.[20] Cortisol and adrenaline levels rise and rise and rise. Left unchecked, those two biochemicals have been scientifically linked to high blood pressure, inflammation, migraine headaches, irritable bowel syndrome, and strokes, among many other illnesses. High levels of those biochemicals can also, according to science, decrease your immune function, which makes you more susceptible to disease in general.[21]

We also need to talk about what head fear does to you mentally. Thoughts and emotions, like we already discussed, are just electrical and biochemical reactions in your brain. According to medical science, every emotion you have releases a different kind of electromagnetic energy and biochemical response (by itself or in combination with other electrochemical reactions) in the brain.[22] According to Dr. Caroline Leaf, some thoughts and emotions, especially fear-based ones, release biochemicals in either such large quantities or in unfavorable combinations that they can have an enormously damaging impact on your mental well-being.[23] For example, cortisol, a biochemical released when you're in fear, washes over the nerve cells in the brain. In the short-term (real fear), the effect on the mind is minimal. But in the long-term (head fear gone unchecked), medical science has conclusively shown that this overload of cortisol affects your ability: 1. to remember and 2. to think both clearly and in creative ways.[24]

So if you still have any doubt that fear-based thoughts/feelings and your body are linked, here's one last piece of information for you: research has shown that nearly 90% of illnesses (many of them chronic) have some correlation to a person's thought-life.[25] The most toxic thoughts/emotions that produce the most damaging effects on one's body, research has shown, are those produced by unchecked thoughts and feelings of fear.[26]

THIS IS A PRACTICE AND A PROCESS

Well, it's that time again to remind you that there's no mistake-free living to be had. You've got a choice when it comes to head fear: 1. allow it to stop your forward progress and instead linger in your body, wreaking havoc or 2. take action and move forward through it. That choice, I say kindly, is always up to you, so choose wisely (hint: choose to be the hero of your own story no matter how many tries it takes to get it right). And remember: you strive for progress and not perfection. You do the best you can with the information you've gotten. You cherry pick what works for you then you do that. You forgive yourself quickly and as many times as it takes when you screw up (because you will; there's absolutely no doing this perfectly). You move on and do what you believe is the next right thing. And you always remember: every mistake is simply a brand new chance to do it better the next time.

EPILOGUE

DON'T QUIT

OR

**You just need
to push your
way through.**

Epilogue

**"Just when the caterpillar thought the world was over,
it became a butterfly."
—Proverb**

ON A SUMMER *evening in a campground with twinkling lights strung high from tree to tree, a pockmarked boy
and I dance through the gravel and the flattened grasses. Music pumps from the back of someone's pickup truck,
a country song that reminds me of a happy day when I was little, playing in the woods, shuffling between the
barren trees, the dried leaves crackling and bunching around my feet, Father squatting down, balancing on the
balls of his feet, swaying slightly, the camera between his hands.*

*"C'mon, Shelli. C'mon and smile. You can do it. Don't be afraid. The flash is just a light. It won't hurt you."
Then he hefted the camera a bit, his chin and mouth and nose vanishing, and eased a finger alongside the shutter
button. He cocked his head as he focused down the viewfinder. "Okay, Pumpkin. Give your Dad a big smile."*

*And just as the shutter clicked and the flash fired, I turned my head. Father huffed a hard breath out of
his nose. He said, "All right. Let's try one more. You don't even have to smile. Just stay still." And I posed stiffly,*

wadding my pink jumpsuit in my little fists, gritting my teeth, watching the little bulb on top of the camera, widening my eyes to keep them open, knowing the flash of light would hurt and, at least for a little bit, blind me.

I think about that as I press my palm to the boy's bony shoulder blade, while he holds me close and my cheek flattens against his chest and his breath washes warm over the crown of my head and his heart beats steady and comforting in my ear. I think about how happy I had been in that moment after the shutter clicked, the wide smile that split Father's face, and how he'd dropped the camera so it swung from a strap around his neck, and how the sunlight coming through the trees glinted along the dark edge of his big, round eyeglasses, and how he'd clapped his hands and called me very brave. And I think, too, about how patient he'd been, the failed attempts, the dozen or so shutter clicks then the slight whirring as the film advanced, while I turned away, watching the leaves drift down around me like confetti.

"Dad," I say softly.

"What?" the boy says.

"Nothing."

"You sure?"

"Yeah."

And I hold the boy tightly, feeling my rolls of flesh press against his rib cage, as we dance across the dirt road snaking between the campsites, stepping through the tall weeds at the edge, moving over shallow potholes, the lights winking on then off then on again above our heads. A handful of other teenagers gather near a cooler full of beers, silhouetted around the bonfire. Far off in the distance, warm yellow light spills from a farmhouse window and lands in long rectangle across the grass. I see two small faces framed in that window for a moment, watching then vanishing just as quick, the curtains swishing behind them.

I think of Father and how, when we were done taking pictures, I'd put my small hand in his large one, and we'd walked into the house that way. Father said, "You did really good today. I'm proud of you." I had nodded, my six-year-old head all wobbly on my neck, and held Father's hand and felt good for making him so happy. Father opened the freezer door, the cold air spilling out like a mist, and plucked out two Creamsicles, the orange ones with vanilla ice cream in the middle that I liked so much, and together we sat on the deck, overlooking the backyard, ice cream dribbling down the wooden sticks and onto our fingers.

I let my palm fall to the small of the boy's back. I trace the sharp nubs of his spine as we dance along the side of the road underneath the lights. My right ear is against his chest; my head rises and falls as he breathes. I feel the vibration as he hums along with the tune. It's August, the night warm and sticky, a sheen of sweat along my bare arms. Beyond the edge of the woods, the land opens up into acres of hayfield. The wind rustles through the long grasses, bending them low. Fireflies flick on and off, on and off. I dance through the gravel, grinding it underneath the toes of my sneakers as I twirl in slow circles, and I think about catching fireflies a long time ago. Father held the glass jelly jar filled with a few blades of grass and with holes poked through its lid. I cupped my hands around a tiny lit bug and held it close to my face, watching the light spill in a little circle on my palms.

That was years ago, I think then blink against the tears. Before . . . well before.

I hold the boy tighter. My eyeglasses skew and press into the bridge of my nose. He dips his chin, resting it on the crown of my head and murmurs a tiny thread of words, soft and tuneless, the lyrics to the song. For a long time, we dance slow as the darkness grows complete, the last of the sun slipping below the rim of the horizon.

"When can we go to your house, Shelli?"

And I think of a few weeks before in the den when my back was turned and Father shoved me hard enough that I stumbled, taking two wild steps to the right before I managed to catch my balance. Mother was there. She watched, waited. Father said to her, "Tell your daughter to stay out of my way." I had crossed my arms over my chest and hunched my shoulders far inward, trying to protect my front: the soft belly, the malleable mind, the tender heart. Well, I thought, tell Mother what else you need me to hear. But he didn't say anything. He didn't even look at me. He took the stairs two at a time, disappearing toward the kitchen. I stood with my face on fire and my skin too tight, trembling, sobbing silently on the inside where no one could see it and feeling the space just between my shoulder blades gone raw and hot, the skin with a red discoloration in the size and shape of his palm that would, in a little while, turn into a light purplish bruise.

I rise on my tiptoes and pull the shy and unpopular boy forward two steps then to the left then back. Bits of gravel plink against each other. My jeans make a soft swish, swish as my thighs rub together. I take in a long slow breath, pulling the smell of him—wood smoke and flowery laundry soap and fried chicken—deep into my lungs.

The boy brings his hand up to his face to swat away a mosquito. It's sudden, unexpected. I flinch. It's a tiny movement, just a quick flick of my chin, a ripple of my shoulders, barely noticeable had you been watching. But I know it. I know it all too well. My body always remembers. All the years of Father raising his right arm, the muscles bulging and rolling under the skin, the fingers sometimes curling into a fist. My own self flinching every single time, the shame in that, not only that Father hated me but also that I, myself, would do nothing to stop the beating that was coming.

The boy and I dance past the bonfire, which crackles as logs cave in on themselves, spitting a handful of sparks into the deep black night. And I think of how Father had always pinned me against things. Long ago, he had pinned me against my bedroom wall, our faces inches apart, one hand near my throat, the other balled into a fist, the arm cocked back, bits of spittle sailing between us, dotting my forehead. In that moment, Father's face had been a bright red, the color of a sunburn, as shocking as that. The boy gently touches my back as we twirl past an empty lawn chair, the blue nylon seat sagging low. I remember the way my spine had dug into the wall and my eyes darted toward the open and empty door. I remember how I felt powerless in that moment. Trapped. Helpless. And how I'd tried to cover the sensitive parts of me with my hands, how I'd tried to draw into myself in a desperate attempt to make myself small. How many times have I done that? Small, smaller, smallest. Small enough not to be noticed. Small enough that maybe I will disappear. I don't even know how many times. Too many, I think. Too damn many. And then, as the boy leads me onto the grass again and we trample a dozen buttercups, smashing them flat beneath our sneakers, I think about those words Father said, especially fat and ugly, and how they echo through my head, back then and now and forever. How he caused bruises that turned a deep purplish blue then faded to a putrid yellow, a reminder for all the weeks it took until they faded completely and were gone. How terrified I'd been of Father, how I'd lain huddled under the blankets late at night, praying with my hands cupped near my face, my breath warm on my palms, asking angels to help, asking God (are you there, where are you, where did you go, why won't you help me) to make Father stop.

We dance past someone's old hound dog, patches of fur missing around its muzzle, and it rises on its front legs, a rusted chain jangling, then it barks softly one time. The boy says, "Well, Shelli? When can I come over?"

I let out the breath I didn't even realize I was holding. What I think is: I don't know how Father will react. More stone cold silence? Or yelling? Or telling me, with bits of spittle flying from his mouth, how worthless I am? Maybe a fist to my back? Or both my wrists trapped in his meaty hand then pinned above my head? Who knows? I'm afraid for your comfort and safety. I'm afraid for my own.

We dance through our own campsite now, past the two tents, one of them leaning lopsided and lit by a flashlight from inside, then the boxy van with the dark windows and the badly-dented fender, then beyond the empty fire ring filled with clumps of old ashes and encircled by blackened rocks, as a mist rises from the warm ground, swirling around my ankles and climbing my shins. I hold him tight, this skinny boy who noticed me, who talked to me, who listened to me, who wanted to touch me gently, who liked me. I don't answer.

I am fifteen years old.

YES, YOU ARE GOING TO HAVE TO CHANGE

As you are aware by now, you're going to have to change. You're going to have to leave your old self behind. You're going to have to become someone new. So with that in mind, a few things about metamorphosis (using things I learned in science class about butterflies as an example):

Caterpillars can put off going into a chrysalis.

Caterpillars know by instinct that it's time to spin a chrysalis, and yet sometimes they don't do it. Instead, some of them choose to hang on to their larval bodies, refusing to transform, postponing their metamorphosis by weeks, months, a year, or sometimes more. This is known as a diapause.

You, too, can put off your transformation. You can avoid it for months or years or your whole life. You can fight against it and cling to your old life and live in fear of change. But know this, if you don't transform, you will: 1. live in frustration, unhappiness, unfulfillment, and numbing behavior, 2. never become what you could, want, and are meant to be, and 3. slowly deteriorate because just like caterpillars are meant to be butterflies, you are meant to be something different and greater than what you currently are.

Just so you know: I get that this is not necessarily easy (although it can be: easy as you want to make it, remember). It took me four years of fighting it before I let go and said *yes* and let the transformation happen. Four years of struggle that, now, seeing the amazing things on the other side, I surely wish I could do over and say *yes* sooner.

Caterpillars have to go through the struggle.

When a butterfly is struggling to emerge, you can help only a little. You can only widen the opening in the chrysalis just a small bit. If you try to help more than that, say by cutting off the bottom of the chrysalis so it has an easier time getting out, what you'll be doing instead is killing that particular insect.

When a butterfly emerges, it has a soft body and also soft wings. It needs to come out on its own, cling to the chrysalis, and hang with its head higher than its wings. Its wings are wet and withered at that moment and a butterfly needs gravity to help pump blood from its body into its wings, expanding them so they will function when it goes to fly. Its body is also soft and needs to harden. It takes a bit of time for all that to happen, anywhere from thirty minutes to a few hours before it can take flight.

If you snip off the end of the chrysalis, you will doom that butterfly. It will slip out and fall to the ground. It'll make it out, yes, but it will have a grossly swollen body and tiny withered wings. Its wings will dry out and harden without blood being forced into them to give them shape. That particular insect will be a butterfly that will never fly. And because it can't fly and nourish itself, that butterfly will soon wither away and die.

In your case, maybe you won't physically die but you may end up feeling dead inside. You see, whatever you're struggling with right now is just to help strengthen you for the good things (quite possibly even phenomenal, miraculous, life-changing things) about to come your way. So once you make it through (which you will, I have no doubt, if you'll just keep going), you'll be able not only to maintain all the targets you've set for yourself but also you'll come to find out that you're capable of soaring even higher. You may even come to find that what you defined as your ideal life is just the tip of the iceberg of the good things coming your way.

But if you try to skip this stage, which a lot of people do because they want to find an easier way out, it's: 1. unlikely that you'll maintain your weight loss and/or stop abusing food for very long and 2. very likely you'll end up at the weight you were before you started and/or feeling crazed about food once again. My point in a nutshell: 1. you must cultivate patience because it's going to take some time for your transformation to be fully complete and for you to acclimate to the changes, 2. other people can help you a little, but only a little, and 3. the vast majority of the work, you must do yourself.

Caterpillars can't rush their transformation.

A caterpillar has to stay in its chrysalis until its metamorphosis is complete. During its time in a chrysalis, a caterpillar's body mostly liquifies and rebuilds itself into a butterfly. If it emerges too early, it won't have the time needed to change. Its body and wings will not be fully formed. And so when it slips out of its chrysalis, that insect, if it isn't already dead, will be earthbound and destined to wither away and die.

You can't rush your transformation either. There's no date to circle on the calendar as to when your entire transformation will be over. It may take a short while or longer than you ever imagined or maybe even your entire life. It's going to take however long it takes. You're in your body for life remember, so cultivate patience (sigh, yes, that again) and carry on, one tiny target after another, moving in the direction of your ideal life. With every step you take, you'll be transforming yourself. And if you don't rush your changing, if you'll just take the pressure off yourself and keep taking (even small) action and let your transformation happen naturally, the results will be well worth the wait.

The only way a caterpillar can get wings and fly is to transform.

There's no way around this one either; the only way out is through. A butterfly will never get its wings without the changes that occur to the caterpillar when it's in a chrysalis.

You, too, will never get your metaphorical wings and fly free until you go into your own chrysalis, where you let go of the old you and how you used to do things, and instead make changes to your life that will help you grow and transform into the person you're meant to become.

Once a caterpillar transforms into a butterfly, it can never go back to the way it was before.

Once a butterfly's transformation is complete, the caterpillar is no more. Its body has been liquified and reformed into something brand new; the caterpillar is gone, forever. No matter how much a butterfly might want to go back into that larval form or into that chrysalis, it's no longer possible. The only choices left to a butterfly at that point are either to stay earthbound, lamenting its predicament, and die or to spread its wings, trusting this is what it was made to do, and fly.

That's true for you, too. Once you transform your life and start getting rid of those things that no longer serve you, you will never be able to go back to being an uninformed person who just didn't know better. Now you do know better. Now you know you're making a choice. Now you know you are responsible for how your life turns out. Now you know you no longer have to be confined by any limits put upon you by others or by yourself.

Once you transform, you have two choices also: either say *no* to the life before you then try to fit yourself back inside the life that once held you or say *yes* to the life before you and let go and trust that you'll rise to become who you want and are meant to be, then watch your life unfold (often gloriously) in front of you.

A FEW REMINDERS

You have to get rid of the weight and/or stop abusing food for you.

If you're going through the effort of getting rid of the weight and/or stopping the abuse of food for any reason other than for yourself, you're doing it for the wrong reason. Any other reason will eventually let you down, I assure you that's true. And then when you get let down by that other reason (be it a person, event, happening, and the like), you'll use that as an excuse to abuse food again. You need to check your motivation, always, and make *you and only you* the reason you want to be thinner and/or you want to stop abusing food.

You are reason enough and worth the effort, I assure you that you are.

Being thin will not fix all your problems.

You probably already know this, at least intellectually, but still somewhere you likely harbor a sprig of hope that being thin equals your life being perfect or at least a lot closer to perfection than it is now. Here's the truth: it won't be. You need to understand that deep down in your bones.

Life will still come at you, some days harder than others. Being thin won't protect you from hurt or disappointment or any of the things you fantasize that it will. Please hear me on this one because, if you don't, you will crash and burn and start abusing food again when reality hits.

Being thinner makes you a healthier person, not a better person.

You will run into people who think you are more worthy now that you're thinner. They are wrong. You're just as worthy thin as you were overweight. Period. That kind of thinking is a character flaw with them; it has nothing—I repeat, *nothing*—to do with you. You will also run into overweight people who don't like you because you are thin. They may think you are better than they are. They're wrong, too.

All this comparison, competition, us-against-them mentality will just drag you down. Don't buy into it. Stop abusing food. Be thinner. Be healthy. Be your true self. Shine your own light.

Your weight may fluctuate and that's okay.

First of all, remind yourself of the truth: you have so much more to offer than just a number on a scale. And second, don't freak out: weight fluctuations are perfectly normal *within boundaries*, say up to ten or fifteen pounds (or whatever number you choose). Just pay attention to your body; you'll know the weight or size where you feel your best.

If you see the scale creeping up more than the number you choose, you need to pay closer attention to waiting for hunger signals to eat, you need to pay closer attention to stopping when you're full. Chances are that you're eating when you're not hungry or eating beyond full or both. Just start paying attention again. You'll get back on track soon enough.

You're on a journey for the whole of your life, so no need to hurry.

Getting rid of the weight is going to take some time. Remember, you're in your body for life; you're already in this for the long haul. So be patient and learn some things about yourself in the meantime. Make the changes you need to make in your life, discover your gifts, talents, and passions, and enjoy your life while you wait.

Whatever you do, just don't go running back to the way(s) you used to do things, hoping that maybe, just maybe, it'll work this time. It won't. Because if it had, you wouldn't be reading this now, searching for something else to try. So be kind, gentle, and patient with yourself as you carry on. Feel the fear and keep going. Push through no matter what. Find what works for you. No worries, you've got your whole life to figure it out.

Stay humble.

Eating foods you really want, only when you're hungry, then stopping when you're comfortably full is how you're going to eat for the rest of your life. I assure you: the longer you live that way, the easier it will be. Eventually, you'll come to the point (yes, you will) where food is just fuel, where you don't even think about food unless you're hungry, and where you leave food uneaten once you're comfortably full.

When you get rid of all the weight you want and/or stop abusing food entirely (which you will, if you'll just keep going), do yourself a kindness and don't get cocky. Don't go bragging to everyone you know about your smaller size, pounds lost, and/or how you no longer abuse food, especially in hopes of getting praise, admiration, and the like. Whatever you do, don't try to convince yourself that you've got this thing licked so now you can go back to abusing food and/or eating whenever you want. You can't, not if you want to stay thin, not if you want to be healthy, not if you want to live in a body that feels true to who you are.

Practice being humble. You did all the work in this book for you. It matters to you. That was reason enough for you to embark on the journey, work through your issues, and conquer what was holding you back. You bask in the glory of your own achievements. You reward yourself. You carry on. What anyone else thinks about your weight loss and/or cessation of abusing food is irrelevant.

You only fail if you quit.

Honestly, it doesn't matter how many tries you've given it. It doesn't matter how long you've been at it. It doesn't matter how many times you've been knocked back down in the dirt. The *only* thing that matters is that you get back up and try again. If you want this for your life, if you want to be thinner, if you want to feel comfortable in your own body, if you want to no longer be crazed around and/or afraid of food, if you want a life that matters to and fulfills you, then you need to keep going until you find what works for you. Period.

Setbacks will happen, yes. You may overeat or abuse food again, you may gain weight, you may have a few horrible days, you may spiral out of control for weeks/months. But keep in mind: 1. defeat is optional, 2. you are in your body for the entirety of your life, and 2. life moves on with or without you. Sometimes you need time to regroup, to come back at something stronger and wiser, and that's okay *as long as you come back at it*. Sometimes, a lot of times, you'll have to hang in there longer than you ever thought you would.

Just so you know: it once took me six months to get rid of nine pounds. I had weeks where the scale went up and weeks where the scale didn't move and weeks where the scale moved down a quarter of a pound. Frustrating, yes. But what's the alternative? Chucking it all and saying: *The heck with this, it's not working, I quit*. Sure, that's an option. But keep in mind: that choice won't *ever* get you to where you want to be. So I just carried on and made some adjustments, trying to figure out what I was doing wrong. Turns out, I needed to learn some things—*really learn them and take them to heart*—mostly about letting go (of others, of the outcome, of control) and once I did that, the pounds came off within a few weeks.

Again, patience is your friend (sometimes an annoying jerk of a friend, but a friend nonetheless). If you stick with it, if you keep taking action and moving forward and figuring out what works for you, if you look for the lessons life is trying to teach you then learn them, if you refuse to back down or go running back to the way you used to do things, if you stop tying your self-worth to a number on a scale and you don't quit, eventually you *will* get to where you want to be. Oh yes, you will. Remember: *it truly doesn't matter how slowly you go as long as you don't stop.*

Remember this, too: you really are so much stronger and braver than you give yourself credit for. That is true because you are still here, breathing, even with everything you've already been through. You can and will overcome whatever gets thrown at you, one (tiny, if need be) step at a time. I know you have it in you. *I know you do.*

You don't have to be lost to yourself anymore. You can find yourself, and once you do, that knowledge of who you really are deep down in your core will remain with you always. You do know what you want. You do know what you need to do to get it. So don't you let anyone, including yourself, tell you that you can't have it. The life you most want, one that is true to you and fulfills you, really is attainable. You just have to have the courage to reach for it and the strength to push through whatever comes and the perseverance to keep going when it'd be easier to quit. And you have all of those things inside of you, I know that about you, too.

A NOTE ON CHERRY PICKING

I said this in the preface and I'm saying it here again as a reminder because it's that important: you need a weight-loss plan, lifestyle change, food schedule, or whatever term you want to use that works for *you*. Period.

Don't get trapped in other people's rules, dogma, and/or what works for them, and that includes mine because that will just get you stuck and keep you stuck. You take what works for *you* out of this book. You tailor a lifestyle that meets *your* particular wants and needs. That's the only way you're ever going to stick long-term with whatever it is you're doing, be it weight loss or something else, at least that's been my experience.

So you give yourself permission to cherry pick from the information you've gotten in this book, and you create a life for yourself that you love by doing those things that work best for you.

What Cherry Picking Looks Like In Real Life

I've been doing this for a long while. It took me several years to figure out what things work best for me. You can and need to do the same after (do yourself a kindness and make sure it's *after*) you've gotten the hang of listening to your body: eating only when you're hungry and stopping when you're comfortably full (or whatever way of eating you decide works best for you). Here's a partial list of things I currently (as of this writing) do:

- I tend to eat a lot of smaller meals throughout the day so I don't always reach comfortably full because that works better for my body.
- I tend not to eat after eight o'clock in the evening because I don't sleep well if I do. If I get hungry later than eight o'clock in the evening, then I eat something small (like a couple of crackers) to stop the hunger pangs because, again, a full stomach at bedtime doesn't agree with my body.
- I don't stick to any rigid food rules—*ever*. One day, I may do this. The next day, I might do that. I always listen to my body and let it be my guide.
- I still *temporarily* (that's key!) avoid/limit certain foods if I'm struggling to not abuse them.
- I tend to lean toward prepackaged portions of foods *temporarily* (that's key!) when I'm struggling emotionally because bingeing is how I abused food, and prepackaged portions of food make it more difficult to do that.
- Whenever I'm struggling with abusing food or wanting to abuse food, I always ask myself out loud in a kind voice: "*What's the matter, Shelli? What do you need?*" Then I take the time to find out what

triggered me and I take steps to meet my own needs. I still do that to this day and most likely always will.

- No matter how often I screw up with food, because sometimes I still do (just less frequently and consuming much less amounts of food—for instance, a binge of four cookies when before it would've been the entire package), I just forgive myself and wait until I'm hungry before I eat again.

I tell you all this so that you can give yourself permission, *right now and always*, to create a plan that works for you and also so you can feel free to change that plan whenever you need to. The most important thing you need to do is find out what works for you at any given moment and do that.

THIS IS A PRACTICE AND A PROCESS

Well, we've reached the end of our journey together. This is your last friendly reminder that there is no perfection in any of this. You strive for progress and you do the best you can. I assure you that you'll get to where you want to be faster and with a lot less suffering if you'll just show yourself compassion instead of tearing yourself down. Like I keep saying: self-compassion is what you most need to heal yourself. So be kind and gentle and patient with yourself always. Give yourself unlimited tries. Forgive yourself as many times as it takes because that's how you'll find peace. Encourage yourself and tell yourself whatever you most need to hear at any given moment to build yourself up. You will make mistakes, there's just no way around it. Don't ever use any mistake as a reason to give up on yourself (and keep in mind, abusing food and/or substances/behaviors is giving up on yourself). Just take a deep breath and start again, right where you are. And remember: *every mistake is simply a brand new chance to do it better the next time.*

What you want most out of your life really is within your grasp.

So don't you quit.

Go be happy.

Go create a life you love.

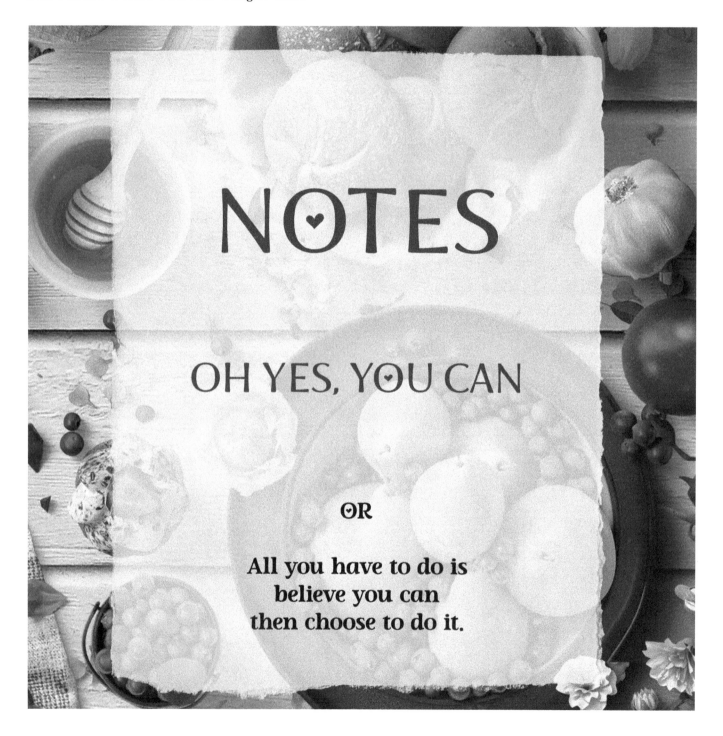

Notes

THOSE WHO ARE BRAVE ARE FREE

[1] Excerpt (also known as "The Man In The Arena") from the speech "Citizenship in a Republic" delivered at The Sorbonne in Paris, France on April 23, 1910.

PREFACE

THE REASON WHY

[1] Observed from a variety of different diet-pill advertisements found in magazines and online.
[2] Dozens of advertisements found in newspapers, magazines, online, and on television. Interviews with two family physicians, both of whom have been practicing medicine for over two decades.

[3] "Dove Self-Esteem Project." *Dove US*, 11 Jan. 2016, https://dove.com/us/en/dove-self-esteem-project.html. Accessed 20 May 2019.

[4] "Obesity and Overweight." *World Health Organization*, World Health Organization, https://who.int/news-room/fact-sheets/detail/obesity-and-overweight. Accessed 29 July 2019.

[5] Hales CM, et al. "Prevalence of Obesity Among Adults and Youth: United States, 2015–2016." NCHS data brief, no 288. Hyattsville, MD: National Center for Health Statistics. 2017. https://cdc.gov/nchs/data/databriefs/db288.pdf. Accessed 20 May 2019.

[6] "Data & Statistics | Overweight & Obesity | CDC." *Centers for Disease Control and Prevention,* Centers for Disease Control and Prevention, 13 Aug. 2018, https://cdc.gov/obesity/data. Accessed 20 May 2019. Accessed 20 May 2019.

[7] "Data & Statistics | Overweight & Obesity | CDC." *Centers for Disease Control and Prevention.* Accessed 20 May 2019.

[8] "Obesity and Overweight." *World Health Organization.* Accessed 29 July 2019.

[9] "Prevalence of Obesity." *World Obesity Federation*, https://worldobesity.org/about/about-obesity/prevalence-of-obesity. Accessed 29 July 2019.

[10] More than 20 different studies published by research companies, universities, governments, as well as interviews with two family physicians, both of whom have been practicing medicine for over two decades, and personal observation of dieters.

[11] "Clinical Guidelines On The Identification, Evaluation, And Treatment Of Overweight And Obesity In Adults." *U.S. Department Of Health And Human Services*, U.S. Department Of Health And Human Services, Sep. 1998, https://nhlbi.nih.gov/files/docs/guidelines/ob_gdlns.pdf. Accessed 20 May 2019.

[12] Larosa, John. "Outlook Is Strong For U.S. Weight Loss Market." *Marketdata Enterprises Inc*, 25 Sept. 2018, https://marketdataenterprises.com/outlook-is-strong-for-u-s-weight-loss-market. Accessed 20 May 2019.

[13] "Weight Cycling Is Associated with a Higher Risk of Death." *Weight Cycling Is Associated with a Higher Risk of Death | Endocrine Society*, 29 Nov. 2018, https://endocrine.org/news-room/2018/weight-cycling-is-associated-with-a-higher-risk-of-death. Accessed 20 May 2019.

[14] Snook KR, et al. "Change in Percentages of Adults With Overweight or Obesity Trying to Lose Weight," 1988-2014. JAMA. 2017; 317(9):971–973. doi:10.1001/jama.2016.20036. Accessed 20 May 2019.

[15] *Google Search*, Google, https://google.com/search?q=whole dictionary&oq=whole dictionary. Accessed 20 May 2019.

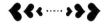

SOME GUIDANCE FOR THE JOURNEY

[1] Wikipedia contributors. "Reward System." *Wikipedia, The Free Encyclopedia*. Wikipedia, The Free Encyclopedia, 6 May 2019, https://en.wikipedia.org/wiki/Reward_system#Pleasure_centers. Accessed 21 May 2019.

CHAPTER ONE

[1] "AMA Declares Obesity a Disease." *Medscape*, 19 June 2013, https://medscape.com/viewarticle/806566. Accessed 24 Jul 2019.

[2] "Controlling the Global Obesity Epidemic." *World Health Organization*, World Health Organization, 6 Dec. 2013, https://who.int/nutrition/topics/obesity/en/. Accessed 24 Jul 2019.

[3] "About Obesity." *World Obesity Federation*, https://worldobesity.org/about/about-obesity. Accessed 24 Jul 2019.

[4] Maslow, A.H. (1943). "A theory of human motivation." *Psychological Review*, 50: 370–396.

[5] *Google Search*, Google, https://google.com/search?q=shame+definition&oq=shame. Accessed 21 May 2019.

[6] Leaf, Caroline. *Who Switched Off My Brain?: Controlling Toxic Thoughts and Emotions.* Switch On Your Brain, 2009, p. 3.

[7] "Neurons That Fire Together Wire Together." *Psychologist's Guide to Emotional Well Being*, 20 Aug. 2018, https://dailyshoring.com/neurons-that-fire-together-wire-together/. Accessed 22 Jul 2019.

[8] Wikipedia contributors. "Neuroplasticity." *Wikipedia, The Free Encyclopedia*. Wikipedia, The Free Encyclopedia, 18 May 2019, https://en.wikipedia.org/wiki/Neuroplasticity. Accessed 21 May 2019.

[9] Lally, Phillippa, et al. "How Are Habits Formed: Modelling Habit Formation In The Real World." *European Journal of Social Psychology*. 2010;40(6):998–1002. Published 2009 Jul 16. https://doi.org/10.1002/ejsp.674. Accessed 22 Jul 2019.

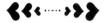

CHAPTER TWO

[1] Interviews with two family physicians, both of whom have been practicing medicine for over two decades.

[2] Maslow, A.H. (1943). "A theory of human motivation." *Psychological Review*, 50: 370–396.

[3] Wikipedia contributors. "Amygdala Hijack." *Wikipedia, The Free Encyclopedia*. Wikipedia, The Free Encyclopedia, 15 Apr. 2019, https://en.wikipedia.org/wiki/Amygdala_hijack#Positive_hijacks. Accessed 22 May 2019.

[4] Wittbrodt, Matthew, et al. "Dehydration Impairs Cognitive Performance: A Meta-Analysis." *Medicine & Science in Sports & Exercise*. 2018;50(11):2360–2368. Published 2018 Nov. doi: 10.1249/MSS.0000000000001682. Accessed 1 Aug. 2019.

[5] Wikipedia contributors. "Ghrelin." *Wikipedia, The Free Encyclopedia*. Wikipedia, The Free Encyclopedia, 9 Jul. 2019, https://en.wikipedia.org/w/index.php?title=Ghrelin&oldid=905437059. Accessed 21 Jul. 2019.

[6] Lindqvist, Andreas, et al. "Effects of Sucrose, Glucose and Fructose on Peripheral and Central Appetite Signals." *Regulatory Peptides*, U.S. National Library of Medicine, 9 Oct. 2008, www.ncbi.nlm.nih.gov/pubmed/18627777. Accessed 21 Jul. 2019.

[7] Yang, Qing. "Gain Weight by 'Going Diet?' Artificial Sweeteners and the Neurobiology of Sugar Cravings: Neuroscience 2010." *The Yale Journal of Biology and Medicine, YJBM*, vol. 83,2 (2010): 101-8. https://ncbi.nlm.nih.gov/pmc/articles/PMC2892765/. Accessed 22 May 2019.

[8] Basso, Julia, et al. "The Effects of Acute Exercise on Mood, Cognition, Neurophysiology, and Neurochemical Pathways: A Review." *Brain Plasticity*. 2017;2(2):127–152. Published 2017 Mar 28. doi:10.3233/BPL-160040. Accessed 21 Jul. 2019.

[9] "Physical Activity Basics | Physical Activity | CDC." *Centers for Disease Control and Prevention*, Centers for Disease Control and Prevention, www.cdc.gov/physicalactivity/basics/index.htm?CDC_AA_refVal=https://cdc.gov/physicalactivity/basics/pa-health/index.htm. Accessed 24 May 2019.

[10] Leaf, Caroline. *Who Switched Off My Brain?: Controlling Toxic Thoughts and Emotions*. Switch On Your Brain, 2009, pp. 80-81.

[11] Davidhizar, R. "The Pursuit of Illness for Secondary Gain." *The Health Care Supervisor*, U.S. National Library of Medicine, Sept. 1994, https://ncbi.nlm.nih.gov/pubmed/10172109. Accessed 24 May 2019.

[12] Taylor, Jill Bolte. *My Stroke of Insight a Brain Scientist's Personal Journey.* Viking, 2008, p. 146.

[13] Wikipedia contributors. "Leptin." *Wikipedia, The Free Encyclopedia.* Wikipedia, The Free Encyclopedia, 18 Jul. 2019. https://en.wikipedia.org/w/index.php?title=Leptin&oldid=906761560. Accessed 21 Jul. 2019.

[14] Leaf, Caroline. *Who Switched Off My Brain?*, pp. 130-131.

[15] Wikipedia contributors. "Hypothalamus." *Wikipedia, The Free Encyclopedia.* Wikipedia, The Free Encyclopedia, 25 Jun. 2019. https://en.wikipedia.org/w/index.php?title=Hypothalamus&oldid=903442289. Accessed 20 Jul. 2019.

[16] Wikipedia contributors. "Amygdala Hijack." *Wikipedia, The Free Encyclopedia.*

[17] Hamilton, Diane Musho. "Calming Your Brain During Conflict." *Harvard Business Review*, 16 Feb. 2016, https://hbr.org/2015/12/calming-your-brain-during-conflict. Accessed 24 May 2019.

[18] Harvard Health Publishing. "Understanding the Stress Response." *Harvard Health*, 1 May 2018, https://health.harvard.edu/staying-healthy/understanding-the-stress-response. Accessed 24 May 2019.

CHAPTER THREE

[1] *Google Search*, Google, https://google.com/search?q=shame+definition&oq=shame. Accessed 21 May 2019.

[2] Interview with a licensed independent social worker—clinical practice, who is founder and director of her own practice and holds dual Masters Degrees in Social Work and Public Health.

[3] Eisenberger, Naomi I, et al. "Does Rejection Hurt? An FMRI Study of Social Exclusion." *Science (New York, N.Y.)*, U.S. National Library of Medicine, 10 Oct. 2003, https://ncbi.nlm.nih.gov/pubmed/14551436. Accessed 29 May 2019.

[4] Leaf, Caroline. *Who Switched Off My Brain?: Controlling Toxic Thoughts and Emotions.* Switch On Your Brain, 2009, p. 3.

[5] Leaf, Caroline. *Who Switched Off My Brain?*, pp. 21-25.

[6] Leaf, Caroline. *Who Switched Off My Brain?*, p. 36.

[7] Leaf, Caroline. *Who Switched Off My Brain?*, p. 36.

CHAPTER FOUR

[1] Leaf, Caroline. *Who Switched Off My Brain?: Controlling Toxic Thoughts and Emotions.* Switch On Your Brain, 2009, pp. 37, 39.

[2] Leaf, Caroline. *Who Switched Off My Brain?*, pp. 57-61.

[3] Russo, Marc A et al. "The Physiological Effects of Slow Breathing in the Healthy Human." *Breathe (Sheffield, England)* vol. 13,4 (2017): 298-309. doi:10.1183/20734735.009817. Accessed 1 Jun. 2019.

[4] Russo, Marc A et al. "The Physiological Effects of Slow Breathing in the Healthy Human."

CHAPTER FIVE

[1] Interview with a family physician, who has been practicing medicine for over two decades.

[2] *Google Search*, Google, https://google.com/search?q=label+definition&oq=label. Accessed 19 Jun. 2019.

[3] *Google Search*, Google, https://google.com/search?q=judgment+definition&oq=judgment. Accessed 19 Jun. 2019.

[4] NIDA. "Drugs, Brains, and Behavior: The Science of Addiction." *National Institute on Drug Abuse*, 20 Jul. 2018, https://drugabuse.gov/publications/drugs-brains-behavior-science-addiction. Accessed 19 Jun. 2019.

[5] "Biology of Addiction." *National Institutes of Health,* U.S. Department of Health and Human Services, 8 Sept. 2017, https://newsinhealth.nih.gov/2015/10/biology-addiction. Accessed 19 Jun. 2019.

[6] "Biology of Addiction." *National Institutes of Health.*

[7] NIDA. "Drugs, Brains, and Behavior: The Science of Addiction."

[8] Leaf, Caroline. *Who Switched Off My Brain?: Controlling Toxic Thoughts and Emotions.* Switch On Your Brain, 2009, pp. 24-25.

[9] Leaf, Caroline. *Who Switched Off My Brain?*, pp. 21, 25.

[10] Leaf, Caroline. *Who Switched Off My Brain?*, pp. 56-68.

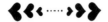

CHAPTER SIX

[1] Rosner, Zachary A et al. "The generation effect: activating broad neural circuits during memory encoding." *Cortex; A Journal Devoted to the Study of the Nervous System and Behavior* vol. 49,7 (2013): 1901-9. doi:10.1016/j.cortex.2012.09.009. Accessed 1 Jul. 2019.

[2] *Memory Encoding - Memory Processes - The Human Memory*, https://human-memory.net/processes_encoding.html. Accessed 1 Jul. 2019.

[3] Ehrsson, H Henrik, et al. "Imagery of Voluntary Movement of Fingers, Toes, and Tongue Activates Corresponding Body-Part-Specific Motor Representations." *Journal of Neurophysiology*, U.S. National Library of Medicine, Nov. 2003, https://ncbi.nlm.nih.gov/pubmed/14615433. Accessed 2 Jul. 2019.

[4] Leaf, Caroline. *Who Switched Off My Brain?: Controlling Toxic Thoughts and Emotions.* Switch On Your Brain, 2009, p. 116.

[5] Leaf, *Who Switched Off My Brain?*, p. 116.

[6] Leaf, *Who Switched Off My Brain?*, p. 116.

[7] Young, Simon N. "How To Increase Serotonin In The Human Brain Without Drugs." *Journal Of Psychiatry & Neuroscience*: JPN vol. 32,6 (2007): 394-9.

[8] Ward, Adrian F. "The Neuroscience of Everybody's Favorite Topic." *Scientific American*, 16 July 2013, https://scientificamerican.com/article/the-neuroscience-of-everybody-favorite-topic-themselves/. Accessed 10 Jul. 2019.

[9] Carmody, Dennis P, and Michael Lewis. "Brain Activation When Hearing One's Own and Others' Names." *Brain Research* vol. 1116,1 (2006): 153-8. doi:10.1016/j.brainres.2006.07.121. Accessed 10 Jul. 2019.

[10] Wikipedia contributors. "Reward System." *Wikipedia, The Free Encyclopedia*. Wikipedia, The Free Encyclopedia, 6 May 2019, https://en.wikipedia.org/wiki/Reward_system#Pleasure_centers. Accessed 9 Jul. 2019.

[11] Wikipedia contributors. "Reward System." *Wikipedia, The Free Encyclopedia*. Accessed 9 Jul. 2019.

[12] Wikipedia contributors. "Reward System." *Wikipedia, The Free Encyclopedia*. Accessed 9 Jul. 2019.

[13] Buckley, Christine. "UConn Researcher: Dopamine Not About Pleasure (Anymore)." *UConn Today*, University of Connecticut, 10 Dec. 2012, https://today.uconn.edu/2012/11/uconn-researcher-dopamine-not-about-pleasure-anymore/#. Accessed 11 Jul. 2019.

CHAPTER SEVEN

[1] Campbell, Joseph. *The Hero with a Thousand Faces.* Princeton University Press, 1973, p. 58.

[2] Campbell, Joseph. *The Hero with a Thousand Faces.* p. 59.

[3] Campbell, Joseph. *The Hero with a Thousand Faces.* pp. 70, 72.

[4] Campbell, Joseph. *The Hero with a Thousand Faces.* pp. 77, 79.

[5] Campbell, Joseph. *The Hero with a Thousand Faces.* pp. 90-91.

[6] Campbell, Joseph. *The Hero with a Thousand Faces.* pp. 97, 101, 109.

[7] Campbell, Joseph. *The Hero with a Thousand Faces.* pp. 111, 113-114.

[8] Campbell, Joseph. *The Hero with a Thousand Faces.* pp. 121-122.

[9] Campbell, Joseph. *The Hero with a Thousand Faces.* pp. 130-131, 136.

[10] Campbell, Joseph. *The Hero with a Thousand Faces.* pp. 151, 162.

[11] Campbell, Joseph. *The Hero with a Thousand Faces.* pp. 173, 181, 190.

[12] Campbell, Joseph. *The Hero with a Thousand Faces.* p. 193.

[13] Campbell, Joseph. *The Hero with a Thousand Faces.* pp. 196-197.

[14] Campbell, Joseph. *The Hero with a Thousand Faces.* p. 207.

[15] Wikipedia contributors. "Posttraumatic growth." *Wikipedia, The Free Encyclopedia.* Wikipedia, The Free Encyclopedia, 8 Jul. 2019, https://en.wikipedia.org/w/index.php?title=Posttraumatic_growth&oldid=905268474. Accessed 19 Jul. 2019.

[16] Campbell, Joseph. *The Hero with a Thousand Faces.* pp. 217-218, 223.

[17] Campbell, Joseph. *The Hero with a Thousand Faces.* pp. 229, 236.

[18] Campbell, Joseph. *The Hero with a Thousand Faces.* pp. 238-239, 243

[19] Leaf, Caroline. *Who Switched Off My Brain?: Controlling Toxic Thoughts and Emotions.* Switch On Your Brain, 2009, pp. 9, 57.

[20] Leaf, Caroline. *Who Switched Off My Brain?,* pp. 57-62.

[21] Leaf, Caroline. *Who Switched Off My Brain?*, pp. 67-74.

[22] Leaf, Caroline. *Who Switched Off My Brain?*, p. 21.

[23] Leaf, Caroline. *Who Switched Off My Brain?*, p. 49.

[24] Leaf, Caroline. *Who Switched Off My Brain?*, pp. 75-76.

[25] Leaf, Caroline. *Who Switched Off My Brain?*, p. 4.

[26] Leaf, Caroline. *Who Switched Off My Brain?*, pp. 20-21, 49.

Join the Community

Just imagine what we—all of us—could all be doing with our lives, following our own dreams and reaching our own goals, cultivating our own passions, making both our inner and outer worlds a more blissful and peaceful place, if we weren't running in circles on the diet-go-round, chasing a number on the scale, catching the goal weight, only to have it slip away so the chase begins again.

The diet-go-round is what I call it when you jump from one diet to the next to the next, hoping that this next one will finally be the answer. It rarely is, but there's always that sprig of hope that keeps you trying again and again. You could also be jumping from one food-abusing scenario to another—compulsive overeating, bingeing, purging, starving, and the like—so that you're still going around in circles in your life.

I spent decades trapped in that circle, around and around and around I went, never moving forward to create the life I really wanted. So if that's what you're looking for, to get out of that cycle now and start moving forward in a straight line toward your future, then I invite you to find out more about Start Where You Are Weight Loss and this community of people ready to feel at peace with food and at home in their own bodies so we can all go on to create a life we love.

Visit:
startwhereyouareweightloss.com

Join the Mailing List

Get a free copy of the Start Where You Are Weight Loss Manifesto

Sign up to receive emails filled with motivation, inspiration, encouragement, and occasional freebies to help you create a life you love. You'll also receive an email every time I create a new product. You'll get some freebies to choose from (including the manifesto) after you confirm your subscription. As always, there's no charge and no obligation.

Subscribe now:
shellijohnson.com/join

About the Author

Shelli Johnson is an award-winning journalist (sports reporting), novelist (grand prize winner), and blogger (shellijohnson.com/blog). She holds degrees in both journalism and fiction writing. She's also a truck owner, horse rider, dog lover, photographer, yoga enthusiast, Krav Maga devotee, and slow-cooker fan. Learn more at: shellijohnson.com/about

Find out about Shelli's other books at:
shellijohnson.com/books

Disclosures and Disclaimers

This book is published in print format. All trademarks and service marks are the properties of their respective owners. All references to these properties are made solely for editorial purposes. Except for marks actually owned by the Author or the Publisher, no commercial claims are made to their use, and neither the Author nor the Publisher is affiliated with such marks in any way.

Unless otherwise expressly noted, none of the individuals or business entities mentioned herein has endorsed the contents of this book.

Limits of Liability & Disclaimers of Warranties

Because this book is a general educational information product, it is not a substitute for professional advice on the topics discussed in it.

The materials in this book are provided "as is" and without warranties of any kind either express or implied. The Author and the Publisher disclaim all warranties, express or implied, including, but not limited to, implied warranties of merchantability and fitness for a particular purpose. The Author and the Publisher do not warrant that defects will be corrected. The Author does not warrant or make any representations regarding the use or the results of the use of the materials in this book in terms of their correctness, accuracy, reliability, or otherwise. Applicable law may not allow the exclusion of implied warranties, so the above exclusion may not apply to you.

Under no circumstances, including, but not limited to, negligence, shall the Author or the Publisher be liable for any special or consequential damages that result from the use of, or the inability to use this book, even if the Author, the Publisher, or an authorized representative has been advised of the possibility of such damages. Applicable law may not allow the limitation or exclusion of liability or incidental or consequential damages, so the above limitation or exclusion may not apply to you. In no event shall the Author or Publisher total liability to you for all damages, losses, and causes of action (whether in contract, tort, including but not limited to, negligence or otherwise) exceed the amount paid by you, if any, for this book.

You agree to hold the Author and the Publisher of this book, principals, agents, affiliates, and employees harmless from any and all liability for all claims for damages due to injuries, including attorney fees and costs, incurred by you or caused to third parties by you, arising out of the products, services, and activities discussed in this book, excepting only claims for gross negligence or intentional tort.

You agree that any and all claims for gross negligence or intentional tort shall be settled solely by confidential binding arbitration per the American Arbitration Association's commercial arbitration rules. Your claim cannot be aggregated with third party claims. All arbitration must occur in the municipality where the Author's principal place of business is located. Arbitration fees and costs shall be split equally, and you are solely responsible for your own lawyer fees.

Facts and information are believed to be accurate at the time they were placed in this book. All data provided in this book is to be used for information purposes only. The information contained within is not intended to provide specific legal, financial, tax, physical or mental health advice, or any other advice whatsoever, for any individual or company and should not be relied upon in that regard. The services described are only offered in jurisdictions where they may be legally offered. Information provided is not all-inclusive, and is limited to information that is made available and such information should not be relied upon as all-inclusive or accurate.

For more information about this policy, please contact the Author at the website address listed in the Copyright Notice at the front of this book.

IF YOU DO NOT AGREE WITH THESE TERMS AND EXPRESS CONDITIONS, DO NOT READ THIS BOOK. YOUR USE OF THIS BOOK, INCLUDING PRODUCTS, SERVICES, AND ANY PARTICIPATION IN ACTIVITIES MENTIONED IN THIS BOOK, MEAN THAT YOU ARE AGREEING TO BE LEGALLY BOUND BY THESE TERMS.

Affiliate Compensation & Material Connections Disclosure

This book may contain references to websites and information created and maintained by other individuals and organizations. The Author and the Publisher do not control or guarantee the accuracy, completeness, relevance, or timeliness of any information or privacy policies posted on these websites.

You should assume that all references to products and services in this book are made because material connections exist between the Author or Publisher and the providers of the mentioned products and services ("Provider"). You should also assume that all website links within this book are affiliate links for (a) the Author, (b) the Publisher, or (c) someone else who is an affiliate for the mentioned products and services (individually and collectively, the "Affiliate").

The Affiliate recommends products and services in this book based in part on a good faith belief that the purchase of such products or services will help readers in general.

The Affiliate has this good faith belief because (a) the Affiliate has tried the product or service mentioned prior to recommending it or (b) the Affiliate has researched the reputation of the Provider and has made the decision to recommend the Provider's products or services based on the Provider's history of providing these or other products or services.

The representations made by the Affiliate about products and services reflect the Affiliate's honest opinion based upon the facts known to the Affiliate at the time this book was published.

Because there is a material connection between the Affiliate and Providers of products or services mentioned in this book, you should always assume that the Affiliate may be biased because of the Affiliate's relationship with a Provider and/or because the Affiliate has received or will receive something of value from a Provider.

Perform your own due diligence before purchasing a product or service mentioned in this book.

The type of compensation received by the Affiliate may vary. In some instances, the Affiliate may receive complimentary products (such as a review copy), services, or money from a Provider prior to mentioning the Provider's products or services in this book.

In addition, the Affiliate may receive a monetary commission or non-monetary compensation when you take action by using a website link within in this book. This includes, but is not limited to, when you purchase a product or service from a Provider after going to a website link contained in this book.

Health Disclaimers

As an express condition to reading to this book, you understand and agree to the following terms.

This book is a general educational health-related information product. This book does not contain medical advice.

The book's content is not a substitute for direct, personal, professional medical care and diagnosis. None of the exercises or treatments (including products and services) mentioned in this book should be performed or otherwise used without prior approval from your physician or other qualified professional health care provider.

There may be risks associated with participating in activities or using products and services mentioned in this book for people in poor health or with pre-existing physical or mental health conditions.

Because these risks exist, you will not use such products or participate in such activities if you are in poor health or have a pre-existing mental or physical condition. If you choose to participate in these risks, you do so of your own free will and accord, knowingly and voluntarily assuming all risks associated with such activities.

Earnings & Income Disclaimers

No Earnings Projections, Promises or Representations

For purposes of these disclaimers, the term "Author" refers individually and collectively to the author of this book and to the affiliate (if any) whose affiliate hyperlinks are referenced in this book.

You recognize and agree that the Author and the Publisher have made no implications, warranties, promises, suggestions, projections, representations or guarantees whatsoever to you about future prospects or earnings, or that you will earn any money, with respect to your purchase of this book, and that the Author and the Publisher have not authorized any such projection, promise, or representation by others.

Any earnings or income statements, or any earnings or income examples, are only estimates of what you might earn. There is no assurance you will do as well as stated in any examples. If you rely upon any figures provided, you must accept the entire risk of not doing as well as the information provided. This applies whether the earnings or income examples are monetary in nature or pertain to advertising credits which may be earned (whether such credits are convertible to cash or not).

There is no assurance that any prior successes or past results as to earnings or income (whether monetary or advertising credits, whether convertible to cash or not) will apply, nor can any prior successes be used, as an indication of your future success or results from any of the information, content, or strategies. Any and all claims or representations as to income or earnings (whether monetary or advertising credits, whether convertible to cash or not) are not to be considered as "average earnings".

Testimonials & Examples

Testimonials and examples in this book are exceptional results, do not reflect the typical purchaser's experience, do not apply to the average person and are not intended to represent or guarantee that anyone will achieve the same or similar results. Where specific income or earnings (whether monetary or advertising credits, whether convertible to cash or not), figures are used and attributed to a specific individual or business, that individual or business has earned that amount. There is no assurance that you will do as well using the same information or strategies. If you rely on the specific income or earnings figures used, you must accept all the risk of not doing as well. The described experiences are atypical. Your financial results are likely to differ from those described in the testimonials.

The Economy

The economy, where you do business, on a national and even worldwide scale, creates additional uncertainty and economic risk. An economic recession or depression might negatively affect your results.

Your Success or Lack of It

Your success in using the information or strategies provided in this book depends on a variety of factors. The Author and the Publisher have no way of knowing how well you will do because they do not know you, your background, your work ethic, your dedication, your motivation, your desire, or your business skills or practices. Therefore, neither the Author nor the Publisher guarantees or implies that you will get rich, that you will do as well, or that you will have any earnings (whether monetary or advertising credits, whether convertible to cash or not), at all.

Businesses and earnings derived therefrom involve unknown risks and are not suitable for everyone. You may not rely on any information presented in this book or otherwise provided by the Author or the Publisher, unless you do so with the knowledge and understanding that you can experience significant losses (including, but not limited to, the loss of any monies paid to purchase this book and/or any monies spent setting up, operating, and/or marketing your business activities, and further, that you may have no earnings at all (whether monetary or advertising credits, whether convertible to cash or not).

Forward-Looking Statements

Materials in this book may contain information that includes or is based upon forward-looking statements within the meaning of the Securities Litigation Reform Act of 1995. Forward-looking statements give the Author's expectations or forecasts of future events. You can identify these statements by the fact that they do not relate strictly to historical or current facts. They use words such as "anticipate," "estimate," "expect," "project," "intend," "plan," "believe," and other words and terms of similar meaning in connection with a description of potential earnings or financial performance.

Any and all forward looking statements here or on any materials in this book are intended to express an opinion of earnings potential. Many factors will be important in determining your actual results and no guarantees are made that you will achieve results similar to the Author or anybody else. In fact, no guarantees are made that you will achieve any results from applying the Author's ideas, strategies, and tactics found in this book.

Purchase Price

Although the Publisher believes the price is fair for the value that you receive, you understand and agree that the purchase price for this book has been arbitrarily set by the Publisher or the vendor who sold you this book. This price bears no relationship to objective standards.

Due Diligence

You are advised to do your own due diligence when it comes to making any decisions. Use caution and seek the advice of qualified professionals before acting upon the contents of this book or any other information. You shall not consider any examples, documents, or other content in this book or otherwise provided by the Author or Publisher to be the equivalent of professional advice.

The Author and the Publisher assume no responsibility for any losses or damages resulting from your use of any link, information, or opportunity contained in this book or within any other information disclosed by the Author or the Publisher in any form whatsoever.

YOU SHOULD ALWAYS CONDUCT YOUR OWN INVESTIGATION (PERFORM DUE DILIGENCE) BEFORE BUYING PRODUCTS OR SERVICES FROM ANYONE. TIIIS INCLUDES PRODUCTS AND SERVICES SOLD VIA WEBSITE LINKS REFERENCED IN THIS BOOK.

Printed in the USA
CPSIA information can be obtained
at www.ICGtesting.com
LVHW082316070324
773895LV00037B/1421